Synopses of the British Fauna (New Series)

Edited by R. S. K. Barnes and J. H. Crothers

No. 51

MARINE AND BRACKISH WATER
HARPACTICOID COPEPODS

Part 1

Keys and notes for identification of the species

R. HUYS

Zoology Department, The Natural History Museum
Cromwell Road, London SW7 5BD

J. M. GEE

Plymouth Marine Laboratory, Prospect Place
The Hoe, Plymouth PL1 3DH

C. G. MOORE

Department of Biological Sciences, Heriot-Watt University
Riccarton, Edinburgh EH14 4AS

R. HAMOND

Scaldbeck House, Morston, Holt NR25 7BJ

1996
Published for
The Linnean Society of London
and
The Estuarine and Coastal Sciences Association
by
Field Studies Council
Shrewsbury

Synopses of the British Fauna (New Series)

Fellows of the Linnean Society of London, and members of the Estuarine and Coastal Sciences Association, may obtain copies at a discount by calling at the Linnean Society's rooms in Burlington House, Piccadilly. London

or, through the post, from
FSC Publications, Preston Montford, Montford Bridge, Shrewsbury SY4 1HW

non-members may order copies from :-

FSC Publications, Preston Montford, Montford Bridge, Shrewsbury SY4 1HW
or
Universal Book Services, Warmonderweg 80. 2341 KZ Oegstgeest. The Netherlands

ISBN 1 85153 256 0

Printed in Great Britain by Henry Ling Ltd at The Dorset Press, Dorchester.

Marine and Brackish Water Harpacticoid Copepods
Part 1

R. HUYS, J.M. GEE, C.G. MOORE and R. HAMOND

Contents

Foreword

"More than 750 British species, all less than 1mm long and all looking exactly the same. They're absolutely impossible to identify." So runs a widespread, but inaccurate, concept of the order Harpacticoida and one that the present team of authors plans to disprove emphatically. In reality, there are nearer 900 local species that show a range of form (as is evident from the cover illustrations) and they *can*, now, be identified, at least to genus.

As harpacticoids are usually the second most abundant group of animals (after nematodes) in marine benthic communities, often reaching between 100 and 1,000 per 10cm^2 (and occasionally up to 4,000. 10cm^{-2}), it is important that they be identified as accurately as possible in reputable faunal surveys. Few people, however, would dispute that this has been a 'difficult' group of animals; one that, hitherto, could only be identified by specialists.

For these, and many other, reasons we are delighted to publish the first coherent English language account of the Harpacticoida in North-western European Waters since Sars' (1911:1921) *Account of the Crustacea of Norway*.

The present *Synopsis* is the first of the three volumes planned to deal with the local fauna. It has taken seven years of dedicated collaborative work and we are very grateful to the team for their skills in making sense out of confusion and producing this scholarly account. We can only marvel at the detail and precision of the illustrations, which would have required an A3 format to give them full credit.

This is the third *Synopsis* volume to deal with copepods. Numbers 46 and 47, Gotto (1993) and Kabata (1993), described those commensal and parasitic forms which are associated with marine invertebrates (and whales) or fish, respectively. No local harpacticoids are known to be parasitic on fishes but some 23 species are included in Gotto (1993). Of these, some 10 are also to be found in this volume.

R. S. K. Barnes
Cambridge University
and
Estuarine & Coastal Sciences Association

J. H. Crothers
Field Studies Council
and
Linnean Society of London

Introduction

The Order Harpacticoida is one of ten orders of the sub-class Copepoda (Huys & Boxshall, 1991) which, along with six other sub-classes (Boxshall & Huys, 1989), make up the class Maxillopoda, one of the classes of the lower Crustacea (Bowman & Abele, 1982). At the moment, the order contains well over 3,000 species belonging to 460 genera contained in 50 families. Most species are free-swimming in marine and brackish water, although a few are ectoparasitic or commensal on corals, tunicates, crustaceans, cephalopods or baleen whales. Three families and 945 species are found exclusively in freshwater. Marine harpacticoids are primarily bottom-living copepods, although a few are exclusively planktonic, and are most abundant in soft sediments and on macro-algae. They are small, predominantly less than 1mm long, and are usually the second most abundant group of animals (after nematodes) in benthic meiofaunal communities.

The harpacticoid copepods considered here are from the area shown in Fig. 1, bounded on the south and east by the coast of Europe from Brest to Bergen (but excluding the Baltic Sea) and on the north and west by the 200m isobath which delineates the edge of the continental shelf[1]. Within this region, approximately 800 species belonging to over 190 genera have been recorded to date, mostly from littoral and nearshore sublittoral habitats. Offshore areas of the North Sea and Atlantic shelf region have not been sampled extensively and many more species are likely to be found in these areas (Huys et al., 1992). It has proved impractical, at the present time, to deal in detail with all the known species. Therefore, we have provided keys and detailed descriptions to enable the user to identify material down to the generic level. Whilst this avoids many of the taxonomic problems, which are mostly at the species level, it still allows the non-specialist to arrive at an ecologically useful taxon as recent research indicates that, in some ecological contexts such as pollution monitoring, analysis of meiofaunal communities at the generic level results in almost no loss of information when compared with analyses at the species level (Heip et al., 1988; Warwick, 1988). However, for most genera we have listed the recorded north-west European species, provided a species key and table of setal formulae (where taxonomically feasible), given details of their habitat and distribution and provided references to full descriptions against which species identifications should always be checked.

---

[1] Editors' note: We felt that this area could hardly be described as "Britain" even though any species known to occur therein might very well be found in British territorial waters. Accordingly, we have requested that the term "local" be used, in place of "British", when referring to species found in this area.

The taxonomy of harpacticoid copepods is in a constant state of flux and, since the last monographic treatment of the order by Lang (1948), many new genera have been described and some new families erected. We have attempted to incorporate as many of these changes as possible. A new familial key is provided and, under each family, a new or the latest published key to world genera. Other useful identification and reference works are the monographs of Sars (1911, 1921) and Lang (1948, 1965); the numerical key of Wells (1976) and its supplements (Wells 1978, 1979, 1981, 1983 & 1985) and the catalogue of marine species by Bodin (1988).

All the British genera cannot be accommodated in a single volume and, unfortunately, the classification of Harpacticoida does not reflect three major divisions which would fit neatly into the three volumes required. This present volume, therefore, embraces Lang's (1944) sub-order Polyarthra and fourteen families of the sub-order Oligoarthra (i.e., those treated first in Lang's (1948) monograph).

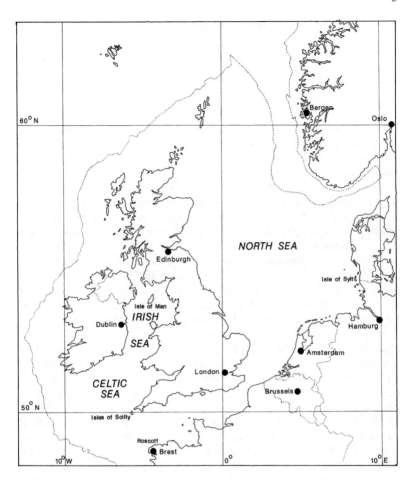

Fig. 1. Northwest Europe : Map of the sea area covered by this *Synopsis*. The dashed line denotes the 200m isobath.

General structure

The terminology relating to the external morphology of harpacticoids follows that adopted by Huys & Boxshall (1991). In the sub-class Copepoda, there are two basic plans of body organisation or **tagmosis**, gymnoplean and podoplean, differentiated by the position of the major body articulation. In the gymnoplean plan (found in Platycopioida and Calanoida), this is behind the fifth pedigerous **somite** whereas in the podoplean plan (as found in the Harpacticoida and all remaining orders of Copepoda) it is between the fourth and fifth pedigerous somites. The major articulation divides the body into an anterior **prosome** and a posterior **urosome** (Fig. 2). The prosome is further divided into two sub-regions. Anteriorly is the **cephalosome**, covered by a continuous **cephalic shield** formed by the fusion of the tergites of the somites bearing the five head appendages and the maxillipeds. However, in most harpacticoids, the somite bearing the first pair of swimming legs is also fused to the cephalosome to form the **cephalothorax**. Posterior to this are three **free prosomites** (sometimes called the free thoracic somites or metasome) bearing the second to fourth swimming legs (Fig. 3). However, in the Canuellidae, Phyllognathopodidae, Chappuisiidae and Cervinioidea the somite bearing the first pair of legs is not fused to the cephalosome and there are, therefore, four free prosomites (Fig. 2). The urosome comprises an anterior somite bearing the fifth pair of legs and five other somites (often referred to as the abdomen). In males, all the urosomites are separate but, in females, the second and third urosomites are usually fused to form the **genital double-somite** (Fig. 4). The last urosomite or **anal somite**, in which the median anus opens either terminally or dorsally, bears two posterior **caudal rami** (or furcal rami). Harpacticoids are typically linear in shape with the prosome slightly wider than the urosome and the whole body tapering posteriorly (Figs 2 and 3A).

Limbs and/or the body surface are ornamented with various structures. A **thorn** is a more or less pointed projection of the integument itself. A **seta**, which is flexible, and a **spine**, which is rigid, are similar in that each is inserted into a hole passing through the integument (Fig. 3D-F); each has a central, hollow, core and the position of each is constant for a species and sex. **Setules** and **spinules** (Fig. 3B-C) are borne on the outer surface of the integument and leave only a tiny scar, not a hole, when they fall off. Spines and setae may each have one or more rows of setules and/or spinules (**pinnules**) and therefore may be described as **unipinnate**, **bipinnate**, **tripinnate** or **multipinnate** (Fig. 3E). Setae with hair-like pinnules are commonly described as **plumose**. The body surface (except of the penultimate somite) is often covered with minute **sensilla**, fine hair-like filaments projecting through the cuticle (Fig. 3A), and other features such as **pores**, **microspinules** and **microsetules**. The somites and limb segments are flexibly hinged to one another by **arthrodial membranes** accompanied by somatic or

5

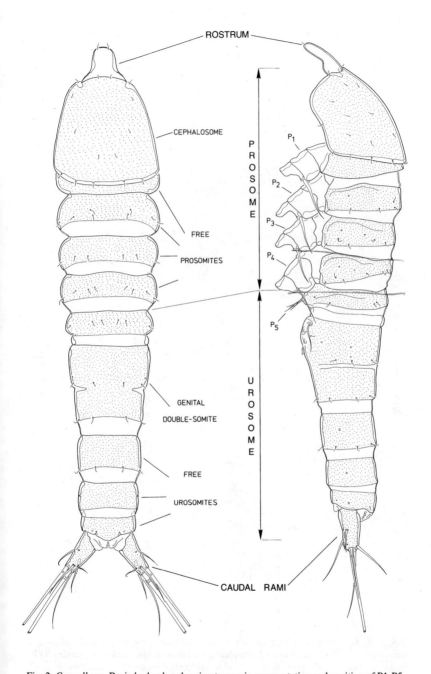

Fig. 2. *Canuella* sp. Basic body plan showing tagmosis, segmentation and position of P1-P5.

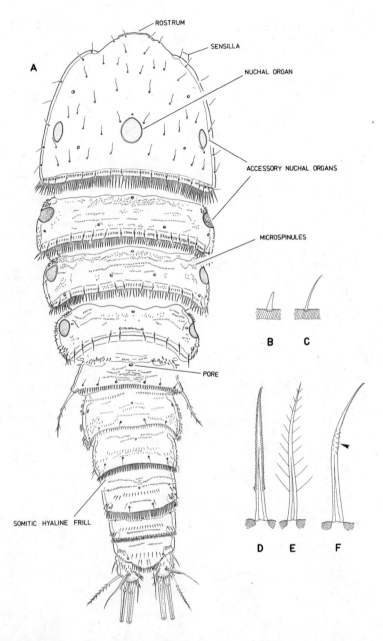

Fig. 3. A. *Microarthridion* sp.; dorsal view of body showing different kinds of surface ornamentation; B-C, integumental ornamentation elements (B, spinule; C, setule); D-F, armature elements (D, pinnate seta; E, plumose seta; F, geniculate seta, flexure point arrowed).

7

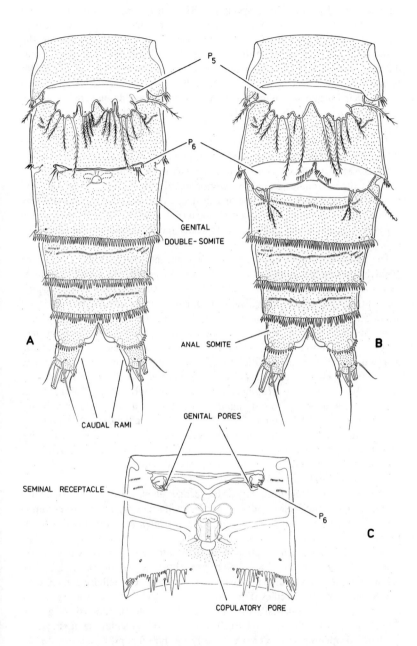

Fig. 4. A-B, basic structure of female (A) and male (B) urosome; C, genital double-somite (female); all shown in ventral aspect.

appendicular hyaline frills respectively. These frills, particularly the somatic hyaline frills (Fig. 13B) are of major taxonomic importance in some families (e.g. Ectinosomatidae) and should not be confused with rows of spinules on the posterior border of a somite (arrowed in Fig. 13D). Many harpacticoids, such as the freshwater Canthocamptidae and Parastenocarididae, the brackish water *Paronychocamptus nanus*, and some of the fully-marine *Heteropsyllus* spp, have a dorsal **nuchal organ** whose function is still uncertain. In addition to this structure, Tachidiidae also have paired lateral **accessory nuchal organs** on the cephalothorax and various free prosomites (Fig. 3A).

The cephalosome bears six (seven if it is a cephalothorax) pairs of appendages (Fig. 5): antennules (A1), antennae (A2), mandibles (Md), maxillules (Mxl), maxillae (Mx) and maxillipeds (Mxp). A **rostrum** (R) usually projects forward between the antennules from the anterior margin of the cephalic shield. The rostrum may be **defined** at the base by a distinct articulation (Figs 2; 6C) or it may be **undefined** and fused to the cephalic shield (Figs 3; 6D). The rostrum may vary considerably in size and shape but is typically furnished with two sensilla (Fig. 6C).

The **antennules** (sometimes called the first antennae) have a maximum of nine segments in females and fourteen in males. As a rule, the fourth and distal segments bear an **aesthetasc** (Fig. 6) which is a translucent, presumably sensory, filament. In Canuellidae, Longipediidae and some Peltidiidae, and in males of some oligoarthran families (e.g. Cerviniidae, Clytemnestridae, Tegastidae, Aegisthidae), additional aesthetascs may be present. Sometimes the aesthetasc position can be obscured by a secondary fusion of the antennulary segments. In males, the antennules are modified for grasping the female during mate guarding (see page 24). They are always geniculate, with one or several swollen segment(s) around the geniculation. **Haplocer** antennules are only weakly modified, the middle segments being at most slightly swollen and with a variable number of segments distal to the geniculation (Fig. 6B). In **subchirocer** antennules, the middle segments are more swollen and there are only two distal segments (Fig. 6D). **Chirocer** antennules are the most strongly modified, usually with one extremely swollen and thick-walled segment and only one distal segment (e.g. some Tachidiidae, Harpacticidae).

The **antennae** (sometimes called the second antennae) have a 2-segmented protopod (**coxa** and **basis**) and are biramous with an **exopod** and an **endopod** (Fig. 7). The coxa is usually small, unarmed and often absent or fused with the basis. The exopod has a maximum of eight segments (some Canuellidae, Longipediidae) but is usually no more than 4-segmented, is rarely as large as the endopod and in some species is completely absent (most Ancorabolidae). The endopod is 3-segmented in the Longipediidae and some Canuellidae and typically 2-segmented in other families (Fig. 7A). In many species, the basis and proximal endopod segment are partially or completely fused into an **allobasis** (Fig. 7B). The distal margin of the endopod usually bears several **geniculate setae** (Fig. 3F).

The **oral opening** is bordered anteriorly by the **labrum**, posteriorly by the paired **paragnaths** and laterally by the mandibles. The labrum is a posteroventrally directed outgrowth of the antennary somite, overlies the mouth

9

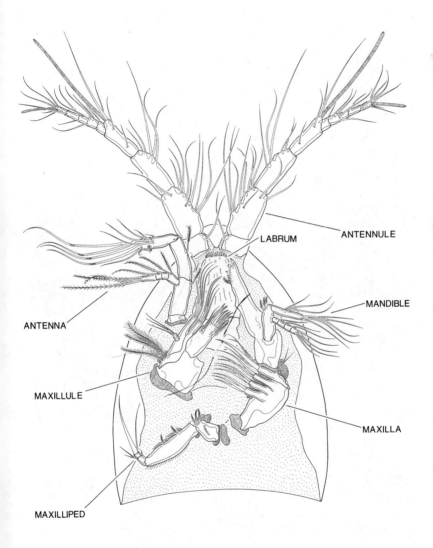

Fig. 5. Ventral view of cephalothorax to show the appendages. Note that, for clarity, whilst both antennules are shown, only the right antenna, maxillule and maxilliped; and only the left mandible and maxilla have been illustrated. P1 omitted.

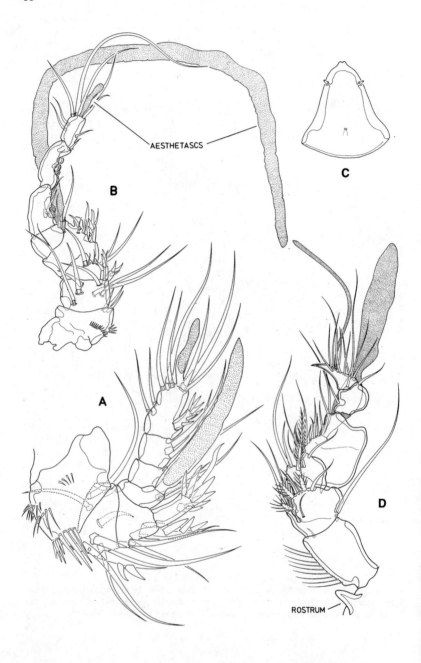

Fig. 6. *Bathycamptus eckmani* Huys & Thistle; A, female antennule; B, male antennule; C, rostrum; D *Paramesochra mielkei* Huys, male antennule.

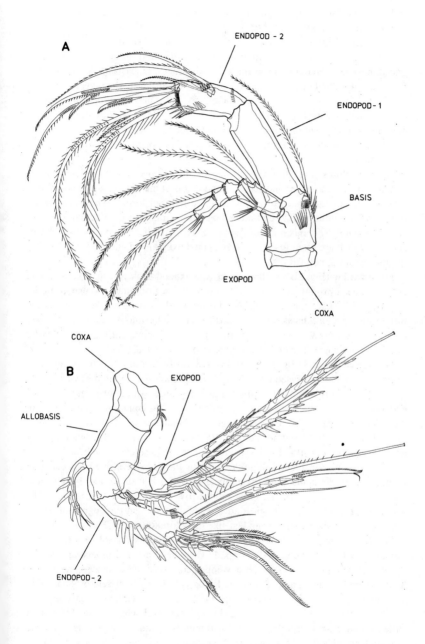

Fig. 7. Antenna of A, *Neobradya pectinifera* T. Scott; B, *Thompsonula hyaenae* (I. C. Thompson).

and acts as the ventral wall of the preoral chamber. In many species it is decorated with numerous spinules and/or setules or it may be bare (Fig. 8D).

The **mandibles** (Fig. 8A-C) also have a 2-segmented protopod and are biramous. The massive proximal coxa has a toothed, axial cutting edge or **gnathobase** with up to two setae at the dorsal corner. The basis has a maximum of four inner setae and bears an endopod and an exopod. The endopod is typically 1-segmented (rarely 2-segmented) and the exopod has a maximum of four segments (Fig. 8B). Reduction in both rami, but usually the exopod, can result in a uniramous, 1-segmented **mandibular palp** (Fig. 8A).

All post-mandibular limbs have a 3-segmented protopod, i.e., with a **praecoxa**, **coxa** and **basis**.

The **maxillules** (Fig. 9A) have a praecoxa developed into a medial **arthrite** armed with several spines and setae around its distal margin and usually with two setae on the anterior surface (absent in some reduced forms). The coxa bears a distinct **coxo-endite** and an **epipodite** (exite) which is incorporated into the coxa and represented by a maximum of five setae. The basis bears two closely set **baso-endites** (which are often fused), a 1-segmented exopod and endopod (the latter 2-segmented in Canuellidae).

The **maxillae** (Fig. 9B) are uniramous (the exopod is absent) and the praecoxa and coxa, each primitively bearing two **endites**, are fused into a **syncoxa**. In the majority of harpacticoids, the basis and proximal segment of the endopod are fused forming an **allobasis**. The allobasis has an endite which is often transformed into a curved claw. The number and setation of maxillary endites can be secondarily reduced. The endopod is at most 4- segmented.

The **maxillipeds** (Fig. 10) vary considerably throughout the order. The praecoxa and coxa are fused into a well-developed syncoxa. Both the syncoxa and the basis are furnished with spines and setae along their inner margin. The endopod is primitively 2-segmented (Fig. 10A) but this condition is only found in the Cerviniidae, Tisbidae, Chappuisiidae and Paramesochridae. In most families, the endopod is either 1-segmented (Fig. 10B) or reduced to a vestige with a strong endopodal claw (Fig. 10C-D). These are **subchelate** (also called prehensile) types because they are capable of a high degree of inward flexure at the basis-endopod joint. In Ectinosomatidae and Idyanthinae (*Zosime*, *Peresime*), the 3-segmented maxilliped is non-prehensile, long and narrow (**stenopodial** type - Fig. 62E) whilst in the Canuellidae, Longipediidae, Neobradyidae and Phyllognathopodidae it is non- prehensile but broad and leaf-like (**phyllopodial** type - Fig. 10E).

The first four pairs of swimming legs (**pereiopods P1-P4**) are basically biramous with an exopod and endopod. They have a small praecoxa (usually situated at the outer corner), a well-developed coxa (bearing an inner spine only in the Canuellidae and Longipediidae) and a basis with an outer seta or spine (Fig. 11A) and an inner spine on the P1 (Fig. 11B). The two members of each leg pair are united into a single functional unit by an **intercoxal sclerite** (Fig. 11C) often called coupler or interpodal bar. Each ramus is at most 3-segmented and the segments are identified by a number (1-3) starting with the proximal segment, so that **endopod-3** is the distal segment of the endopod. However, only in a few families (e.g. Tachidiidae, Ectinosomatidae, Neobradyidae) has the P1 retained

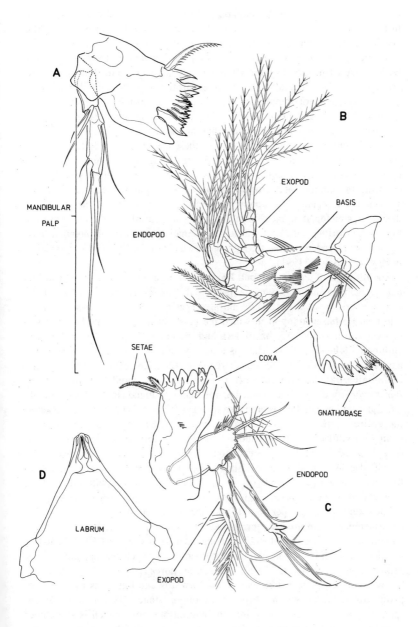

Fig. 8. Mandible of A, *Leptastacus corsicaensis* Huys; B, *Neobradya pectinifera* T. Scott; C, *Thompsonula hyaenae* (I. C. Thompson). D, labrum of *Tisbe* sp.

the basic form of a 3- segmented, non-prehensile, exopod and endopod as found in P2-P4. In many species, the endopod and/or exopod is extensively modified and for this reason the P1 is of great taxonomic importance.

The arrangement of setae and spines on the leg rami is the character most widely used for species identification and a **setal formula** denotes this arrangement. This indicates, in tabular form, the respective number of spines and/or setae (but not spinules or setules) on the constituent segments of each ramus of P1 (unless highly modified), P2, P3 and P4. The outer margin of the first and second segments almost always has one seta/spine in the exopod and is always devoid of them in the endopod so these are not included. Therefore, the setal formula is derived by starting at the proximal segment and counting the number of **inner** setae / spines on each segment and, on the distal segment, also counting the number of **terminal** and **outer** seta/spines, the counts for each segment being separated by a point or colon. This is done first for the exopod and then for the endopod of each limb. Thus the setal formula for the limb shown in Fig. 11A is written 1.1.223 1.1.321. An alternative setal formula notation, more suitable as a standard format throughout the whole of the Copepoda, is explained in Huys & Boxshall (1991).

The fifth pair of legs **(pereiopod P5)** are each basically biramous and leaf-like, but the endopod and basis remain separate only in a few species (e.g. *Longipedia*, some Neobradyidae, Fig. 12B). In all other species, the two elements have fused into a single **baseoendopod** in which the most abaxial part is prolonged into a process bearing the outer **basal seta** and the endopod is recognisable as the **endopodal lobe** (Fig. 12A). There is usually no trace of a coxa but some species have retained a minute intercoxal sclerite (Fig. 12A). The exopod is 1-segmented in females but in males of certain families (e.g. most Cerviniidae and *Parastenhelia*) a 2- or 3-segmented exopod is to be found (Fig. 12C). Often, the left and right baseoendopods are fused together forming a continuous plate across the entire ventral side of the urosome (Fig. 12E). In some families (e.g. Cylindropsyllidae), the baseoendopod and exopod form a non-segmented plate (Fig. 12D) whilst in others the endopodal lobe may be reduced completely (e.g. Cerviniidae, Aegisthidae, some Tisbidae, Fig. 12C). The setae are counted from the innermost on each ramus (as in P1-P4) and are written with those of the exopod first. The outer basal seta is not counted as it is always present (Fig. 12A).

The sixth pair of legs **(pereiopod P6)** is the last in both sexes (Fig. 4). In males, each member is primitively represented by a single plate with three setae, the outermost of which is homologous with the outer basal seta of P1-P5 (Fig. 4B). In females, the sixth leg is vestigial and incorporated in the closing apparatus of the genital antrum (Fig. 4A, C). The paired **genital pores** (gonopores) are closed off by the sixth leg plate which can swing forwards and outwards by means of promotor muscles when oviposition takes place. During copulation, spermatophores are introduced into the **copulatory pore** which is sometimes partially covered by a swelling of the ventral urosome wall. The complex structure of the, usually paired, **seminal receptacles** is visible through the transparent cuticle (Fig. 4C).

In most families, the anus is closed off in the anal somite by a distinct

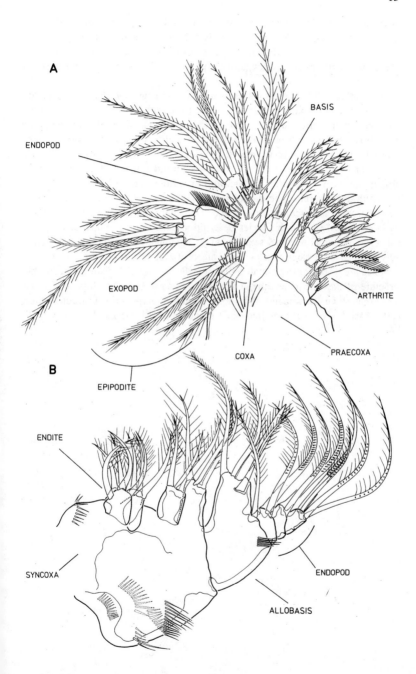

Fig. 9. *Neobradya pectinifera* T. Scott; A, maxillule; B, maxilla.

operculum, often armed with spinules or setules (Figs 2, 3A & 13B-C). However, species with a deeply cleft anal somite (e.g. Ectinosomatidae, Neobradyidae and Danielsseniidae) usually lack a true operculum but have developed a **pseudoperculum** as an outgrowth of the posterior edge of the penultimate somite (Fig. 13D).

Substantial modifications may be found in the structure and shape of the **caudal rami**. However, a basic pattern of seven (three lateral, one dorsal and three terminal) **ramal setae** can be recognised (Fig. 13A). The **anterolateral accessory seta** (I) is often reduced or absent and is frequently set close to the **anterolateral seta** (II). The **posterolateral seta** (III) stands at the outer sub-distal corner. The **outer terminal seta** (IV) and the **inner terminal seta** (V) typically have an articulation near the base. The **terminal accessory seta** (VI) is situated at the inner sub-distal corner. The **dorsal seta** (VII) is very characteristic because it is nearly always triarticulate at the base. The relative position of these setae is variable (Fig. 13A-C). In species descriptions, the inner terminal seta is often called the principal terminal seta but this is an ambiguous term as seta V can be very reduced at the same time as others are very well-developed (Fig. 13C).

Males are nearly always smaller than females but are also distinguished by the structure of the antennules, the genital somite and the P5 (which is smaller and less ornate than the female). Additional sexual dimorphism can occur in other parts of the body but is very frequently found on the P1 basis and the rami of P2-P4.

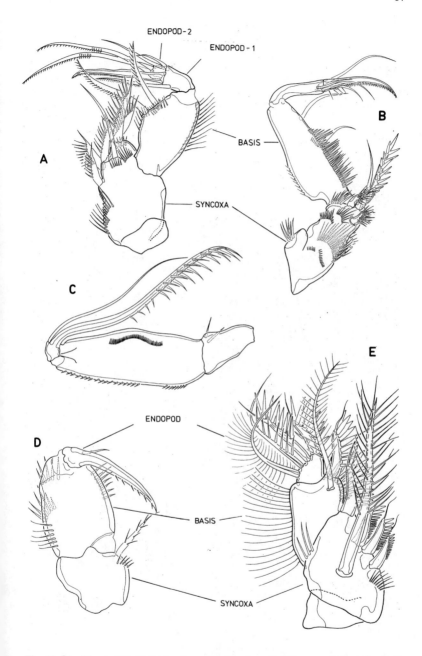

Fig. 10. Maxilliped of A, *Tachidiopsis cyclopoides* Sars; B, *Thompsonula hyaenae* (I. C. Thompson); C, *Leptastacus kwintei* Huys; D, *Bathycamptus eckmani* Huys & Thistle; E, *Marsteinia typica* Drzycimski.

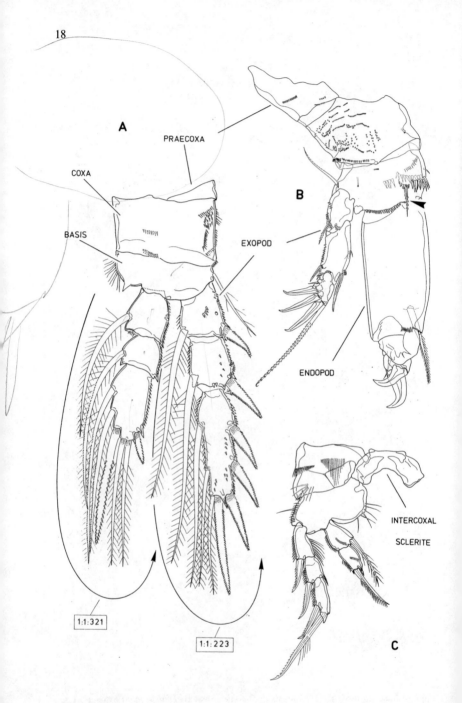

Fig. 11. A, basic structure of P2 - P4, showing setal formula; B, P1 of *Hamondia superba* Huys; C, P4 of *Paramesochra mielkei* Huys.

19

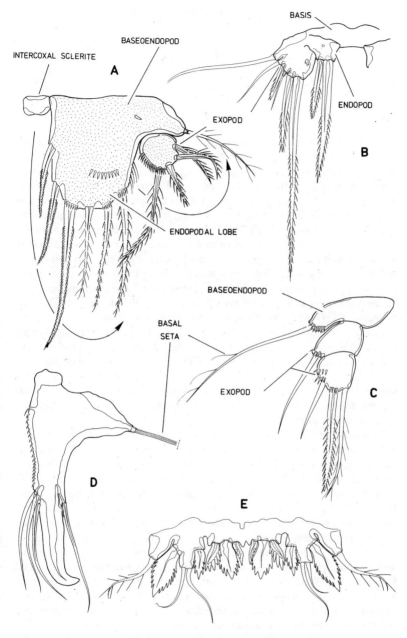

Fig. 12. A, basic structure of female P5, armature elements are counted as shown by the arrows; B, *Neobradya pectinifera* T. Scott, P5 male; C, *Superornatiremis* sp. P5 male; D, *Leptastacus corsicaensis* Huys, P5 female; E, *Arbutifera phyllosetosa* (Kunz), P5 female.

Biology

Ecology

Harpacticoid copepods are essentially free-living benthic organisms, although a few are planktonic (*Microsetella*, *Euterpina*, *Clytemnestra*, *Macrosetella*) or found in association with other organisms (e.g. *Sunaristes*, commensal on hermit crabs). In marine sediments, they are usually the second most abundant meiofaunal taxon after nematodes but tend to become the dominant taxon in coarse-grained sediments and on marine algae. Maximum densities of 100-1,000.$10cm^{-2}$ are usual in fully saline intertidal habitats but may occasionally reach as many as 4,000.$10cm^{-2}$ in clean sand. Generally, there is a reduction in abundance with increasing depth of water such that, in the deep ocean, densities of >10.$10cm^{-2}$ are the norm. Harpacticoids can be found living in sediment particle interstices (mesopsammic), burrowing in the sediment (endopsammic) or living on the sediment surface (epipsammic). Small, vermiform, interstitial species (e.g. *Arenosetella*, Cylindropsyllidae and Paramesochridae) and broad, slightly flattened, epibenthic species (e.g. *Tachidius*) dominate in sandy sediments but the former disappear from the community when the silt/clay content of the sediment exceeds about 10%. Thus, muddy sand and mud habitats are dominated by burrowing and epibenthic species. Phytal habitats are typically occupied by species with a strongly prehensile P1 and either a long slender body (some Laophontidae) or a broad, strongly flattened body (Porcellidiidae, Peltidiidae, Tegastidae, Tisbidae).

In addition to species assemblages being associated with particular substrata, there is both horizontal and vertical zonation of species within the sediment. Harpacticoids in general are known to be intolerant of anaerobic conditions and are therefore confined to the oxygenated layers of the sediment, usually the top 1cm in muddy sediments but as much as the top 50-100cm on high-energy sand beaches. Within these depths, different species are known to occupy distinct horizons with respect to each other, although the whole or part of the community may migrate vertically on both a tidal and seasonal basis in response to changes in environmental parameters such as temperature, oxygen and pore water content and/or biological factors such as competition and reproductive requirements. Similarly, assemblages or even congeneric species exhibit horizontal zonation across beaches or along salinity gradients in estuaries. The number of species in a community and the distribution of individuals amongst those species (diversity) tends to be fairly constant, worldwide, for any particular habitat, although, of course, the actual species present will be different in different regions. In intertidal sediments, the community typically comprises about 30 species with the majority of individuals belonging to three to five of those species (dominants). In phytal

21

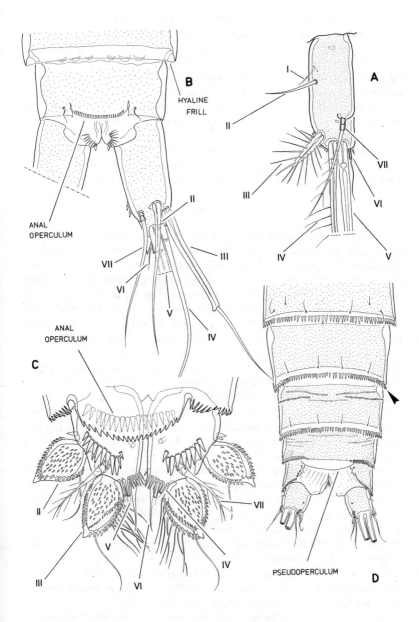

Fig. 13. A, *Paramesochra mielkei* Huys, left caudal ramus, dorsal; B, *Leptastacus corsicaensis* Huys, anal somite and right caudal ramus, dorsal; C, *Arbutifera phyllosetosa* (Kunz), anal operculum and caudal rami, dorsal; D, *Marsteinia typica* Drzycimski, abdominal somites, dorsal.

communities diversity may be somewhat higher and the highest diversity is found in those habitats where both phytal and sediment harpacticoids are present, such as *Laminaria* (kelp) holdfasts. Whilst the overall abundance of harpacticoids decreases with depth, the number of species increases (typically around 60-70 on the continental shelf) and the individuals are spread more evenly among the species (i.e., dominance decreases) so that, in the deep sea, each species may be represented by only one or two individuals. Conversely, as one progresses from the marine intertidal into low salinity regions there is a decrease in the number of species and increasing dominance by one species. Similar changes are also associated with certain kinds of pollution such as organic (e.g. sewage) enrichment. In addition to spatial and temporal niche fractionation, species diversity may also be maintained by partitioning of the available food resources.

Feeding

Potential food sources of harpacticoids are organic matter and detritus (or more probably the decomposer organisms, such as bacteria, associated with detritus), other small autotrophic and heterotrophic organisms such as microalgae and ciliates, dissolved organic matter and specialised energy sources such as mucus and other extracellular polymer secretions. Direct carnivory of metazoan organisms is relatively unknown amongst harpacticoids but utilisation of any particular food source is difficult to deduce from the morphology of the feeding apparatus, except for filter feeding in Longipediidae and Canuellidae and mucus trap feeding in the Leptasticidae. Most other harpacticoids are regarded as surface feeders and it has been suggested that, amongst these, food resources may be partitioned by adaptations for feeding on different types and shapes of surfaces: (a) selective epistrate feeders, with small mouth parts which feed at a particular point on large surfaces; (b) edge scrapers that embrace rectilinear edges and cylinders with prehensile P1s and move along the edge collecting food particles with tiny hooks and claws of their mouthparts; (c) plane-sweepers and sand-filers which sweep food into their mouths with the antennae from large planar surfaces of organic material or scrape food from faults and depressions in sandgrains; (d) solid feeders who either crush prey with prehensile maxillae, rotate spheres of organic floccules in their mouths and clean prey from the surface, or clean food off organic debris which is then passed back through the arch of the swimming legs. In addition, some harpacticoids are known to be able to cultivate or concentrate suitable food organisms either by producing mucus which acts as a growth substrate for bacteria (*Diarthrodes nobilis*) or through commensal associations with other organisms such as molluscs and Crustacea. A few harpacticoids have very specialised food sources, such as the medullary tissue of red algae utilised by frond-mining species in the Thalestridae.

It was thought that most harpacticoids were non-specific in their choice of prey items. However, whilst many harpacticoids are able to utilise a wide variety of food sources (e.g. *Nitokra*) and can switch from one source to another either seasonally or at different stages of the tide (e.g. *Microarthridion*), evidence is accumulating from experimental studies to suggest that many harpacticoids are

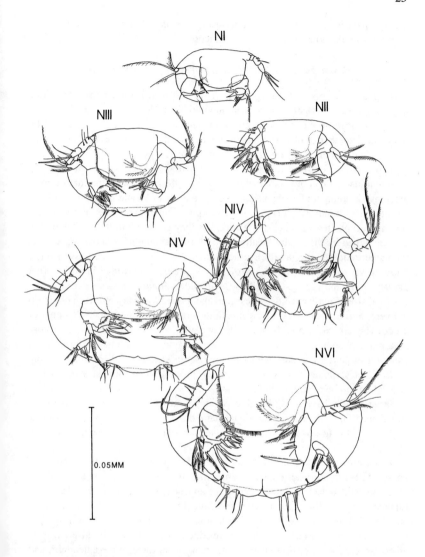

Fig. 14. Naupliar stages of *Paramphiascella fulvofasciata* Rosenfield & Coull with only one of each pair of appendages drawn. After Dahms (1990a).

highly specific in their choice of food organisms either for survival or as a required stimulus to growth and/or reproduction.

Reproduction and post-embryonic development

Harpacticoid copepods are gonochoristic and fertilisation is by copulation involving the attachment of a spermatophore by the male to the copulatory pore of the female. Prior to this, the male grasps the female with his prehensile antennules in one of a number of places; by the terminal caudal setae (e.g. Ectinosomatidae), by the caudal rami themselves (e.g. some Canuellidae), by the postero-lateral margin of the cephalothorax (e.g. Tachidiidae) or by the P3 or P4 (e.g. Laophontidae). Precopulatory mate guarding is the norm with the mature male grasping an immature female, usually copepodite IV or V, and remaining with her until the final moult, when copulation takes place. Sperm are stored in the female seminal receptacles, the eggs are fertilised as they emerge into the genital antrum and are united by their outer membranes to form a single or a double egg-sac. As the name indicates, the family Diosaccidae is characterised by the possession of two egg-sacs which is otherwise of only sporadic occurrence in some other harpacticoid families (e.g. Canuellidae, Miraciidae, *Huntemannia*).

Brood size of harpacticoids varies from about three (in many interstitial species) to over 100 (in some phytal species) with the norm in the range of 15-30 eggs per brood. The number of broods per single copulation varies from 2-15 (in laboratory cultured species) and some species produce broods throughout the year (most common in phytal habitats) whilst others have a well defined breeding season. Thus either seasonally or continuously, the proportion of immature stages in a population can be relatively high.

Harpacticoids have direct benthic development (other than in Longipediidae and Canuellidae where the nauplii are planktonic) and pass through six naupliar stages (Fig. 14) followed by six copepodite stages (Fig. 16), copepodite VI being the adult.

On hatching from the egg, nauplius I already possesses three pairs of appendages, namely antennules, antennae and mandibles and the body is unsegmented. At each successive moult the appendages develop by the addition of further setae and/or segments. In addition, further appendages (maxillules, maxillae, maxillipeds and P1) develop in more or less rudimentary form. Nauplii of the Canuellidae (Fig. 15A) and Longipediidae are significantly different from other harpacticoids having four segments rather than three in the antennules and simple setae on antennae and mandibles rather than the well-developed masticatory cutting processes, hooks and other specialised features in other harpacticoids. Whilst most harpacticoid nauplii are circular or pear-shaped and somewhat flattened, those of *Stenhelia* (Fig. 15B) are "crab-like", with an unusually well-developed mandibular exopod. The nauplii of algal mining harpacticoids are characterised by the reduction of antennules and mandibles and the development of an exceptionally powerful masticatory process on the antennae.

At moult to copepodite I (Fig. 16) the body gains the characteristic harpacticoid

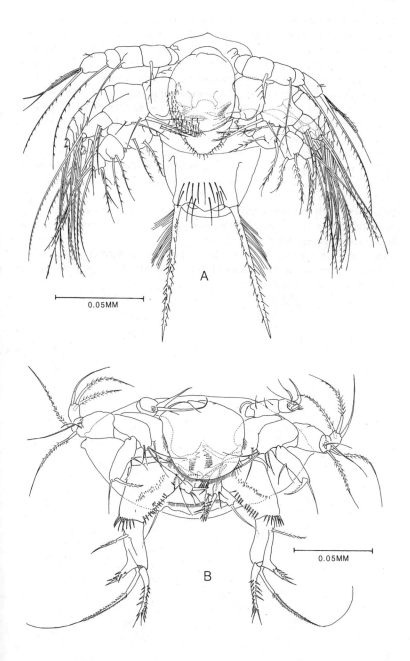

Fig. 15. A, Nauplius I of *Canuella perplexa* T. & A. Scott; B, Nauplius II of *Stenhelia (Delavalia) palustris* (Brady). After Dahms (1990a).

shape. Except for those forms in which the P1 bearing somite is not fused with the head, CI has five somites, counting the cephalothorax as one. In addition to the antennules, antennae and mouthparts, the cephalothorax bears the P1s which have 1-segmented rami. The first free prosomite bears P2 at a similar stage of development and the second free prosomite bears the primordia of P3. These prosomites are followed by two urosomites plus the caudal rami. At each successive moult a further somite is added and the developing P1-P5 become increasingly elaborated. By CV, there are, thus, nine somites and all six pairs of legs are present. The sexes become distinguishable at CIV, the sexual dimorphism of the antennules being the most noticeable feature.

At the final moult, one more urosomite is added, giving a total of ten somites (although the second and third urosomites are usually fused in the female), and genital complex and legs attain their full development. It is important to distinguish clearly between copepodite V and adult, since there are instances in the literature of new species, and even new genera, being erroneously based on descriptions of copepodite V.

These and other aspects of the biology and ecology of harpacticoid copepods are comprehensively reviewed by Hicks and Coull (1983) who should be consulted for more detailed information.

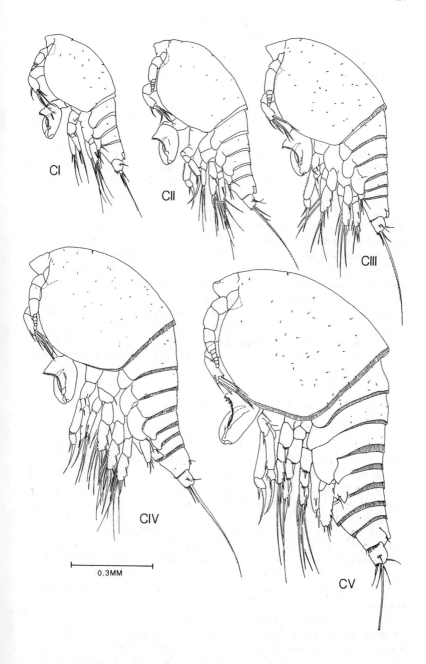

Fig. 16. Copepodite stages I-V of *Thalestris longimana* Claus. After Dahms (1990b).

Methodology

Collection

Quantitative samples of harpacticoids are best collected from sediments by hand coring. A core diameter of 20-60mm is generally suitable; however, core length is dependent upon sediment type and location as harpacticoids penetrate sediments to different depths (page 20). Sawn-off disposable syringes are ideal samplers for fine sediments. Good quantitative samples of copepods from sublittoral sediments can also be collected using certain remote corers, especially the Craib and multicorer (Fleeger *et al.*, 1988). Qualitative samples from these sediments may be collected by epibenthic sledge or macrobenthic grab (McIntyre & Warwick, 1984), the contents of which are discharged into a bin and allowed to stand for several hours, during which time, most of the copepods move to the sediment surface. Stirring of the supernatant water raises the copepods into suspension, allowing them to be netted with a 63μm mesh net. Copepods living on seaweeds can be collected by placing a plastic bag over the weed fronds and removing the whole frond from the rock.

Copepod samples are most conveniently fixed and preserved in 5% buffered formalin.

Extraction

The extraction of copepods from sediment samples can be simply achieved by decantation. The sample is vigorously agitated in water in a one litre stoppered measuring cylinder or other suitable container. This is left to stand for a few seconds allowing the sand particles to settle, after which time the supernatant is poured off through a 63μm mesh sieve. This procedure should be repeated a number of times. An anaesthetic, such as 10% $MgCl_2$ in seawater, increases the extraction efficiency for live material. This simple method can provide excellent copepod samples from sandy sediments but muddy sediments may give rise to samples contaminated with much detritus. Such samples can be further cleaned by flotation in colloidal silica (trade name LUDOX) or sugar. Details of this method and of other suitable extraction techniques for copepods are given by Pfannkuche & Thiel (1988). *NOTE* **that when using colloidal silica, rubber gloves should be worn.**

Copepods on seaweeds and epifauna can be separated from these substrates by shaking them in water followed by decantation. Again, extraction efficiency is increased by the addition of an anaesthetic, a small quantity of formalin or by using tapwater instead of seawater. Mucus produced by larger algae such as fucoids and laminarians can hinder the collection of clean material. However, copepods are generally more abundant on the smaller filamentous and tufty seaweeds which produce little or no mucus.

Even the best extraction methods fail to remove all the detritus and for efficient sorting and identification of copepod collections the samples must be free from detritus and other meiobenthic taxa. This can be accomplished only by placing the sample in a gridded petri dish or Borogov tray and systematically scanning the dish under a stereo microscope, picking out all the copepods and transferring them into a solid watch glass. This can be done using a Pasteur pipette or a needle made from tungsten wire with the end bent into a small loop.

Sorting

With a little experience, it will be found that much of the copepod collection can be sorted to family under the stereo microscope, using a magnification of at least x40. This is the most efficient method of preliminary sorting through large collections. The family descriptions (p116 onwards) include relevant information for this process. However, in the absence of an experienced teacher, complete beginners are advised to sort only small samples, separating the adult specimens into groups of putative species that look the same. Important features to examine at this stage include body size and shape, colour, length of antennules, size and shape of rostrum and caudal rami and the presence of any conspicuous swimming legs, such as a prehensile P1. Even under the stereo microscope, several sexually dimorphic features will be apparent; in particular, the males will almost always be smaller, the antennules will differ in shape (page 8) and, with a little experience, the complete separation of urosomites-2 and -3 can be discerned. The unequivocal identification of copepodites to species is hardly ever possible and so they are best ignored by beginners.

For species identification, one specimen of each putative species should be selected for dissection and, if possible, this should be a female. Following dissection and identification (see below), any other similar specimens must be checked for conspecificity using a compound microscope. This can usually be achieved by mounting several specimens in lactic acid. Crushing of the material can be avoided by supporting two sides of the coverslip on other coverslips. The specimens can be rolled over, as appropriate, by movement of the coverslip. Large numbers of whole specimens on a slide can be checked, and misidentified ones removed after dispensing with the coverslip. If the lactic acid drop is spread out, excellent optical quality can be achieved for dry objectives up to x40. Whole mounts may sometimes be all that is needed for identification to species, especially when the fauna of a site is already well-known; however, the beginner is strongly advised to undertake dissection.

Dissection

Dissection is performed using two needles made from 0.35mm diameter tungsten wire projecting about 20mm from a pin vice. The tip of a needle can be sharpened by electrolysis where the needle and a metal or carbon electrode are immersed in a saturated solution of potassium, or sodium, hydroxide and connected by wires with crocodile clips to the poles of a six volt ac supply (a stereo microscope lamp transformer is suitable). A fine point is produced by gently moving the needle up and down in the electrolyte. An alternative method of dipping the tungsten wire into molten anhydrous sodium nitrite is not recommended as it can be extremely dangerous.

For the permanent mounting of a dissection, the following four mountants are most widely used: Reyne's (Reyne, 1950), Hoyer's (Stitt *et al.*, 1948), polyvinyl lactophenol, and lactophenol (coverslips ringed with BIOSEAL). The first two are aqueous based and the specimen is therefore dissected in water whereas, for the other two, the dissection is done in lactic acid. For routine identification, polyvinyl lactophenol is the most convenient medium but for taxonomic research work the others are recommended.

Prior to dissection, ensure that the specimen is free of detritus. This can be achieved either by repeatedly sucking up and discharging the specimen into a specimen-tube half filled with water using a Pasteur pipette or by holding the specimen with a nylon bristle (from a hairbrush and held in a pin vice) and cautiously brushing the specimen in an antero- posterior direction with another bristle.

For dissection, transfer the specimen on a needle point to a drop of lactic acid in one corner of a microscope slide. Then, using a coarse needle point, make a very thin streak of polyvinyl lactophenol near the centre of the slide. Dissection is carried out under maximum magnification on a stereo microscope (at least x40) and entails using one needle to hold the specimen steady on its side, while using the other needle to cut laterally through the body somites. First, hold the prosome and cut away the urosome (i.e., cut between P4 and P5) then, moving anteriorly separate each of the free prosomites in turn, together with their respective appendages, and finally cut the P1 from the cephalothorax. As each element is separated, it should be transferred on the point of a dissecting needle to its equivalent position (urosome, P4, P3, P2, P1, cephalothorax) in the mountant streak, making sure that each is correctly orientated (i.e., both the cephalothorax and urosome should be ventral face up) before the medium stiffens after about 20 minutes. After this time, a cross of medium is placed on a coverslip which is gently lowered onto the mountant streak. The drop of lactic acid is then removed from the corner of the slide by wiping with alcohol and the positions of the dissected pieces are recorded on a stick-on label. The slide can be used with care immediately, although the mountant will take several days to harden. An alternative method (in which there is no risk of mixing the limbs up but which is nowhere near as convenient for viewing) is to mount each element in one of six drops of polyvinyl lactophenol, placed within a 15 x 15mm area in the centre of the slide, cover all the drops with a coverslip and then mark the position of each element by ringing and labelling them C, 1, 2, 3, 4 and U on the underside of the slide with a fine, indelible pen.

This procedure is generally quite adequate for routine identification work but, for detailed taxonomic studies, it is necessary to dissect out all the cephalic appendages, to separate P5 from the urosome, to ensure that the legs are mounted anterior face upwards, and to put each appendage under a separate coverslip. Alternative dissection strategies are described by Hamond (1969) and Coull (1977).

Classification

Lang (1944) divided the Harpacticoida into two sub-orders ("Sektionen"), the Polyarthra, containing the families Longipediidae and Canuellidae, and the Oligoarthra containing all the other families. The names Polyarthra and Oligoarthra refer to the number of segments in the exopod of the antenna (six to eight in the former and four or fewer in the latter). The Polyarthra is a monophyletic, taxonomically valid group. The Oligoarthra, however, are polyphyletic and the term has no strict taxonomic significance but, at the moment, is the only one available to cover the remaining families.

Within the Oligoarthra, Lang (1944) created a number of superfamilies but these have not been adopted generally by subsequent workers because of their doubtful taxonomic and phylogenetic validity. Therefore, although Huys (1988, 1990a, 1993) has recently redefined and diagnosed two superfamilies, the Cervinioidea (which includes the Aegisthidae, Cerviniidae, Rotundiclipeidae and Styracothoracidae) and the Laophontoidea (which includes the Laophontidae, Adenopleurellidae, Cristacoxidae, Orthopsyllidae and Laophontopsidae), we have omitted superfamilial taxa in the classification given below and the oligoarthran families are listed in alphabetical order. However, the families dealt with in this volume *do* follow the sequence given in Lang (1948).

At present, the familial classification of the Harpacticoida is also in a state of flux and many changes are likely to occur in the near future. It is recognised that many of the Langian families such as the Tisbidae, Canthocamptidae and Diosaccidae are not natural families. Recently, Por (1986) proposed a number of new families within the Langian family Cletodidae. Hicks (1988) removed the Donsiellinae from the Laophontidae to the Thalestridae and Huys (1990b) removed some species from the Thalestridae into two new families, the Hamondiidae and Ambunguipedidae. Similarly Huys (1995a) and Huys & Gee (1990) have extensively revised the Langian family Tachidiidae and transferred many of the genera to the family Paranannopidae, now re-named Danielsseniidae (Huys & Gee, 1996). Fiers (1990) established the Cancrincolidae; Huys & Willems (1989) have created new families from the Laophontidae and Huys (1992) raised the sub-family Leptastacinae (former Cylindropsyllidae) to familial status. Finally, Huys (1993) established the new deep-sea family Styracothoracidae. These changes are incorporated below.

Three families, the Chappuisiidae, Phyllognathopodidae and Parastenocarididae contain only freshwater forms and eight families with marine genera do not have any representatives in north-west Europe. Whilst these are included in the classification and in the key to families, they are not considered further. The genera listed here are those which have been recorded so far from British and adjacent waters up to 200m depth. A full list of known genera of marine harpacticoids up to 1988 is to be found in the excellent catalogue of Bodin (1988). The families marked with an asterisk are contained in this volume.

Phylum CRUSTACEA

Class MAXILLOPODA
Sub-class COPEPODA

Order HARPACTICOIDA
Sub-order POLYARTHRA

Family Longipediidae*
>> *Longipedia* Claus, 1863

Family Canuellidae*
>> *Sunaristes* Hesse, 1867
>> *Canuella* T. & A. Scott, 1893
>> *Brianola* Monard, 1927
>> *Canuellopsis* Lang, 1936

[Sub-order OLIGOARTHRA]

Family Adenopleurellidae
>> *Sarsocletodes* C. B. Wilson, 1924

Family Aegisthidae

Family Ambunguipedidae
>> *Ambunguipes* Huys, 1990

Family Ameiridae
>> Sub-family Ameirinae
>>>> *Ameira* Boeck, 1865
>>>> *Nitokra* Boeck, 1865
>>>> *Psyllocamptus* T. Scott, 1899
>>>>>> sub-genus *Psyllocamptus* T. Scott, 1899
>>>> *Ameiropsis* Sars, 1907
>>>> *Pseudameira* Sars, 1911
>>>> *Leptomesochra* Sars, 1911
>>>> *Sarsameira* C. B. Wilson, 1924
>>>> *Proameira* Lang, 1944
>>>> *Sicameira* Klie, 1950
>>>> *Parapseudoleptomesochra* Lang, 1965
>>>> *Pseudoleptomesochrella* Lang, 1965
>>>> *Interleptomesochra* Lang, 1965
>>>> *Parevansula* Guille & Soyer, 1966

Sub-family Stenocopiinae
> *Stenocopia* Sars, 1907
> *Malacopsyllus* Sars, 1911
> *Anoplosoma* Sars, 1911

Family Ancorabolidae
Sub-family Laophontodinae
> *Laophontodes* T. Scott, 1894

Sub-family Ancorabolinae
> *Ancorabolus* Norman, 1903
> *Echinopsyllus* Sars, 1909
> *Ceratonotus* Sars, 1909
> *Arthropsyllus* Sars, 1909
> *Dorsiceratus* Drzycimski, 1967

Family Arenopontiidae
> *Arenopontia* Kunz, 1937
>> sub-genus *Arenopontia* Kunz, 1937
> *Pararenopontia* Bodiou & Colomines, 1986

Family Argestidae
> *Fultonia* T. Scott, 1902
> *Mesocletodes* Sars, 1909
> *Eurycletodes* Sars, 1909
>> sub-genus *Eurycletodes* Sars, 1909
>> sub-genus *Oligocletodes* Lang, 1944
> *Argestes* Sars, 1910
> *Leptocletodes* Sars, 1920
> *Argestigens* Willey, 1935
> *Parargestes* Lang, 1944
> *Neoargestes* Drzycimski, 1967

Family Balaenophilidae
> *Balaenophilus* Aurivillius, 1879

Family Cancrincolidae (associates on gills of intertidal and semi-terrestrial crabs)

Family Canthocamptidae
> *Mesochra* Boeck, 1865
> *Heteropsyllus* T. Scott, 1894
> *Itunella* Brady, 1896
> *Hemimesochra* Sars, 1920
> *Nannomesochra* Gurney, 1932
> *Mesopsyllus* Por, 1960
> *Psammocamptus* Mielke, 1975
> *Bathycamptus* Huys & Thistle, 1989
> *Boreolimella* Huys & Thistle, 1989
> *Pusillargillus* Huys & Thistle, 1989
>
> Incertae Sedis (after Por 1986)
> *Cletocamptus* Shmankevich, 1875

Family Cerviniidae*
> *Cervinia* Norman, in Brady (1878)
> *Eucanuella* T. Scott, 1900
> *Cerviniopsis* Sars, 1909
> *Hemicervinia* Lang, 1935

Family Chappuisiidae (found only in freshwater)

Family Cletodidae
> *Cletodes* Brady, 1872
> *Enhydrosoma* Boeck, 1872
> *Stylicletodes* Lang, 1936
> *Acrenhydrosoma* Lang, 1944

Family Clytemnestridae*
> *Clytemnestra* Dana, 1848

Family Cristacoxidae

Family Cylindropsyllidae
> *Cylindropsyllus* Brady, 1880
> *Evansula* T. Scott, 1906
> *Stenocaris* Sars, 1909
> *Boreopontia* Willems, 1981
> *Stenocaropsis* Apostolov, 1982
> *Willemsia* Huys & Conroy-Dalton, 1993

Family Danielsseniidae*
>> *Danielssenia* Boeck, 1872
>> *Jonesiella* Brady, 1880
>> *Psammis* Sars, 1910
>> *Paradanielssenia* Soyer, 1970
>> *Micropsammis* Mielke, 1975
>> *Fladenia* Gee & Huys, 1990
>> *Telopsammis* Gee & Huys, 1991
>> *Paranannopus* Huys & Gee, 1996

Family Darcythompsoniidae*
>> *Leptocaris* T. Scott, 1899
>> *Darcythompsonia* T. Scott, 1906

Family Diosaccidae
>> *Stenhelia* Boeck, 1865
>>> sub-genus *Stenhelia* Boeck, 1865
>>> sub-genus *Delavalia* Brady, 1868
>> *Diosaccus* Boeck, 1872
>> *Robertsonia* Brady, 1880
>> *Pseudomesochra* T. Scott, 1902
>> *Amphiascus* Sars, 1905
>> *Schizopera* Sars, 1905
>>> sub-genus *Schizopera* Sars, 1905
>>> sub-genus *Neoschizopera* Apostolov, 1982
>> *Pseudodiosaccus* T. Scott, 1906
>> *Amphiascopsis* Gurney, 1927
>> *Amphiascoides* Nicholls, 1941
>> *Psammotopa* Pennak, 1942
>> *Amonardia* Lang, 1944
>> *Pseudamphiascopsis* Lang, 1944
>> *Paramphiascopsis* Lang, 1944
>> *Bulbamphiascus* Lang, 1944
>> *Robertgurneya* Lang, 1944
>> *Typhlamphiascus* Lang, 1944
>> *Rhyncholagena* Lang, 1944
>> *Paramphiascella* Lang, 1944
>> *Pararobertsonia* Lang, 1944
>> *Haloschizopera* Lang, 1944
>> *Protopsammotopa* Geddes, 1968
>> *Eoschizopera* Wells & Rao, 1976
>>> sub-genus *Eoschizopera* Wells & Rao, 1976

Family Ectinosomatidae*
>*Ectinosoma* Boeck, 1865
>*Bradya* Boeck, 1872
>>sub-genus *Bradya* Boeck, 1872
>>sub-genus *Parabradya* Lang, 1944
>*Microsetella* Brady & Robertson, 1873
>*Sigmatidium* Giesbrecht, 1881
>*Pseudobradya* Sars, 1904
>*Ectinosomella* Sars, 1910
>*Halophytophilus* Brian, 1917
>*Arenosetella* C. B. Wilson, 1932
>*Hastigerella* Nicholls, 1935
>*Pseudectinosoma* Kunz, 1935
>*Halectinosoma* Lang, 1944
>*Noodtiella* Wells, 1965
>*Lineosoma* Wells, 1965
>*Klieosoma* Hicks & Schriever, 1984

Family Euterpinidae*
>*Euterpina* Norman, 1903

Family Hamondiidae

Family Harpacticidae*
>*Harpacticus* Milne-Edwards, 1840
>*Zaus* Goodsir, 1845
>*Tigriopus* Norman, 1868
>*Perissocope* Brady, 1910

Family Huntemanniidae
>*Nannopus* Brady, 1880
>*Huntemannia* Poppe, 1884
>*Pseudocletodes* T. & A. Scott, 1893
>*Pontopolites* T. Scott, 1894
>*Metahuntemannia* Smirnov, 1946

Family Laophontidae

Laophonte Philippi, 1840
Asellopsis Brady & Robertson, 1873
Platychelipus Brady, 1880
Esola Edwards, 1891
Pseudolaophonte A. Scott, 1896
Onychocamptus Daday, 1903
Laophontina Norman & T. Scott, 1905
Harrietella T. Scott, 1906
Hemilaophonte Jakubisiak, 1932
Echinolaophonte Nicholls, 1941
Pseudonychocamptus Lang, 1944
Heterolaophonte Lang, 1944
Paronychocamptus Lang, 1944
Paralaophonte Lang, 1944
Pilifera Noodt, 1952
Klieonychocamptus Noodt, 1958
Quinquelaophonte Wells, Hicks & Coull, 1982

Family Laophontopsidae

Laophontopsis Sars, 1908

Family Latiremidae

Family Leptastacidae

Leptastacus T. Scott, 1906
Paraleptastacus C. B. Wilson, 1932
Psammastacus Nicholls, 1935
Arenocaris Nicholls, 1935
Schizothrix Huys, 1992

Family Leptopontiidae

Leptopontia T. Scott, 1902
Syrticola Willems & Claeys, 1982

Family Louriniidae

Family Metidae

Metis Philippi, 1843

Family Miraciidae*

Macrosetella Dana, 1847

Family Neobradyidae*

Neobradya T. Scott, 1892
Marsteinia Drzycimski, 1968

Family Normanellidae

Normanella Brady, 1880

Family Orthopsyllidae

Orthopsyllus Brady & Robertson, 1873

Family Paramesochridae
    Sub-family Paramesochrinae

Paramesochra T. Scott, 1892
Leptopsyllus T. Scott, 1894
    sub-genus *Leptopsyllus* T. Scott, 1894
Remanea Klie, 1929
Apodopsyllus Kunz, 1962
Kliopsyllus Kunz, 1962
Scottopsyllus Kunz, 1962
    sub-genus *Scottopsyllus* Kunz, 1962
    sub-genus *Intermedopsyllus* Kunz, 1962
    sub-genus *Wellsopsyllus* Kunz, 1981

    Sub-family Diarthrodellinae

Diarthrodella Klie, 1949

Family Parastenheliidae

Parastenhelia Thompson & A. Scott, 1903

Family Parastenocarididae (found only in freshwater)

Family Peltidiidae*

Peltidium Philippi, 1839
Alteutha Baird, 1845
Eupelte Claus, 1860

Family Phyllognathopodidae (found only in freshwater)

Family Porcellidiidae*

Porcellidium Claus, 1860

Family Rhizothricidae

Rhizothrix Sars, 1909
Tryphoema Monard, 1926

Family Rotundiclipeidae

Family Styracothoracidae

Family Superornatiremidae

Family Tachidiidae*
>> *Tachidius* Lilljeborg, 1853
>>> sub-genus *Tachidius* Lilljeborg, 1853
>> *Microarthridion* Lang, 1944
>> *Geeopsis* Huys, 1996

Family Tegastidae*
>> *Tegastes* Norman, 1903
>> *Parategastes* Sars, 1904

Family Tetragonicipitidae
>> *Tetragoniceps* Brady, 1880
>> *Phyllopodopsyllus* T. Scott, 1906
>> *Pteropsyllus* T. Scott, 1906
>> *Paraschizopera* Wells, 1981
>> *Aigondiceps* Fiers, 1995

Family Thalestridae
> Sub-family Thalestrinae
>> *Thalestris* Claus, 1863
>> *Amenophia* Boeck, 1865
>> *Parathalestris* Brady & Robertson, 1873
>> *Phyllothalestris* Sars, 1905

> Sub-family Rhynchothalestrinae
>> *Rhynchothalestris* Sars, 1905

> Sub-family Dactylopusiinae
>> *Diarthrodes* Thomson, 1882
>> *Dactylopusia* Norman, 1903 (= *Dactylopodia* Lang, 1936)
>> *Dactylopodopsis* Sars, 1911
>> *Dactylopusioides* Brian, 1928
>> *Paradactylopodia* Lang, 1944

> Sub-family Pseudotachidiinae
>> *Idomene* Philippi, 1843
>> *Pseudotachidius* T. Scott, 1897
>> *Dactylopodella* Sars, 1905

> Sub-family Donsiellinae
>> *Donsiella* Stephensen, 1936

Family Thompsonulidae*
>   *Thompsonula* T. Scott, 1905

Family Tisbidae
>   Sub-family Tisbinae
>>   *Tisbe* Lilljeborg, 1853
>>   *Scutellidium* Claus, 1866
>>   *Sacodiscus* C. B. Wilson, 1924

>   Sub-family Cholidyinae
>>   *Cholidya* Farran, 1914

>   Sub-family Idyanthinae
>>   *Zosime* Boeck, 1872
>>   *Idyella* Sars, 1906
>>   *Idyanthe* Sars, 1909
>>   *Tachidiella* Sars, 1909
>>   *Tachidiopsis* Sars, 1911

Systematic Part

Sub-class COPEPODA

Recognising a copepod as such is fairly straightforward but Huys & Boxshall (1991) have pointed out that giving a rigorous diagnosis of the sub-class is much more difficult. However, all copepods at some stage in their life-cycle

(a) possess at least two pairs of swimming legs with the members connected by an intercoxal sclerite;

(b) have a cephalosome into which the somite bearing the maxillipeds is incorporated.

Other reasonably reliable characters are

(c) the presence of uniramous antennules of up to 27 segments, although in many copepods (e.g. harpacticoids) the antennules are secondarily reduced; and

(d) the possession of egg-sacs, though some important groups lack true egg-sacs and they are secondarily lost in some highly derived parasitic forms.

Key to Orders of Copepoda

1. Body showing gymnoplean tagmosis, with prosome-urosome boundary located between fifth pedigerous and genital somites.
   2

   Body showing podoplean tagmosis, with prosome-urosome boundary located between fourth and fifth pedigerous somites.
   3

2. P2-P3 exopod-1 with two spines on outer margin; maxillule with lobate baso-exite bearing two setae; genital and first abdominal somites separate in female.
   ....**PLATYCOPIOIDA** Fosshagen in Fosshagen & Iliffe (1985)

   P2-P3 exopod-1 with at most one outer spine; maxillule baso-exite represented by at most one seta; genital and first abdominal somite fused into genital double-somite in female.
   ....**CALANOIDA** Sars, 1903

3. Cephalothorax without antennae, mandibles, maxillules, maxillae or maxillipeds; antennules at most 5-segmented in both sexes; adult female carrying eggs on long, ovigerous spines associated with median ventral genital aperture.
   ....**MONSTRILLOIDA** Sars, 1901

   Antennae to maxillipeds present, or when entirely absent antennules at least 15-segmented; adult female without ovigerous spines, eggs carried in paired (or a single) egg-sacs.
  4

4. Exopod of antenna 9-segmented in male, 8-segmented in female with setal formula [2.1.1.1.1.1.1.3].
   ....**MORMONILLOIDA** Boxshall, 1979

   Exopod of antenna at most 8-segmented in either sex, with maximum setation of [1.1.1.1.1.1.1.4].
   5

5. P1-P3 lacking intercoxal sclerites but with coxae fused in midline; P5 absent.
    ....**GELYELLOIDA** Huys, 1988

    P1-P3 with intercoxal sclerites, or with these legs absent; P5 present or absent.
    .... **6**

6. Exopod of antenna usually with two or more segments, rarely 1-segmented or absent, in which case baseoendopod of P5 with two or more setae.
    .... **7**

    Exopod of antenna at most 1-segmented, P5 baseoendopod represented by at most one seta.
    .... **8**

7. Antennule at least 16-segmented.
    ....**MISOPHRIOIDA** Gurney, 1933

    Antennule at most 14-segmented in male and 9-segmented in female.
    ....**HARPACTICOIDA** Sars, 1903

8. Oral cone present, formed by labrum and labium (derived by medial fusion of paragnaths); mandible with stylet-like coxal gnathobase passing medially into oral cone.
    ....**SIPHONOSTOMATOIDA** Thorell, 1859

    Oral cone absent, paragnaths separate; mandibular gnathobase not stylet-like.
    .... **9**

9. Male antennules typically geniculate; female antennules up to 26-segmented; maxillipeds usually similar in both sexes; female genital somite with single midventral copulatory pore (except in Oithonidae).
    ....**CYCLOPOIDA** Burmeister, 1834

    Male antennules non-geniculate; female antennules at most 7-segmented; maxillipeds always sexually dimorphic; female genital somite with copulatory pores located within dorso-lateral genital apertures (except in Erebonasteridae).
    ....**POECILOSTOMATOIDA** Thorell, 1859

Order **HARPACTICOIDA**

Harpacticoids can be recognised by their podoplean body plan; the presence of short antennules with at most 9 segments in females and 14 in males; the fusion of the endopod and basis into a baseoendopod on the fifth leg of both sexes of most species, those with a separate endopod having a maximum of two setae on it (e.g. Longipediidae).

Key to Families of Harpacticoida

This key is a practical aid for identification to family of any species worldwide, including those that are known to occur exclusively in freshwater and inland saline-water bodies (underlined in the footnotes). Several families, as presently constituted, are composite taxa (notably the Canthocamptidae and the families of the "cletodid complex") and are currently under study or await thorough revision. Waiting for these revisions would inevitably have delayed publication and failed to meet the current needs of ecologists and non-taxonomists. Modifications to this key will need to be made in future and these will be incorporated in the subsequent volumes on harpacticoids.

It has proved impossible to construct a purely pictorial key that would enable the non-taxonomist to identify harpacticoids without dissection. However, this illustrated dichotomous key has been designed to permit identification with as little dissection as possible. It relies on morphological features which are well exposed on the copepod body (in particular the rostrum, antennule, maxilliped, P1) and drawings or semi-diagrammatic illustrations are provided for any key characters. Figures cited in the couplets on the left-hand page are found on the facing, or a near-by, right-hand page and particular attention should be paid to the arrowed structures.

Each couplet is applicable to females and males since it contains either (i) characters valid for both sexes, or (ii) characters referring to males or females only, or (iii) a combination of both. **It is absolutely vital that every character is verified for a given sex, should a couplet contain a combination of characters, and that any identification made with the key is checked against the relevant descriptions.** Pointers to where these can be followed up in the literature are given in the morphological section of each genus.

The heterogeneity (either natural or artificial) of certain families is expressed in the key by their frequency of appearance in the couplets. For those families that key out more than once, the genera relevant to each couplet are listed in a corresponding footnote. In many cases this approach will speed up the process of identification and enable the reader to continue without using the respective generic keys.

Genera underlined in the footnotes have not been recorded in marine or brackish water. Those marine and brackish water forms printed in **bold type** *have* been recorded from the *Synopsis* area (Fig. 1). Although we do not intend to correct every misinterpretation that has appeared in the literature, some reinterpretations of erroneous observations that would lead to misidentification in this key are given in the footnotes. A few taxonomic and nomenclatural changes are also included. Families represented in the *Synopsis* area are indicated by their part number.

Readers are reminded that they should study the text and figures on general structure (pages 3-21) before attempting to use the key.

The dichotomous key is based on 29 figures (Figs 17-45) illustrating the 147 couplets. Figs 17-26 combine taxa which exhibit particular characters that are easy to observe and offer the possibility to short-cut the key. If none of the eight "short cut characters" is present, the user should go direct to couplet 35 which splits the main key into two sections according to whether the endopods of P2-P4 have two or less segments (couplets 36-98) or at least one of these rami (except male P3 endopod) is 3-segmented (couplets 99-147).

Short-cut characters

It is essential that these characters be checked in the following sequence.

1. Body laterally compressed (amphipod-like) or dorsoventrally depressed (shield-shaped) ....**couplet 1**

2. P1 as in Fig. 19 ....**couplet 5**

3. P1 coxa with inner spine or seta and antennary exopod 6- to 8-segmented ....**couplet 10**

4. P1 exopod-1 with inner seta or exopod a single segment with 7-10 setae / spines ....**couplet 12**

5. P1 exopod 1-segmented or absent ....**couplet 14**

6. First pedigerous somite free ....**couplet 21**

7. Maxilliped phyllopodial or stenopodial ....**couplet 23**

8. P1 endopod with total of 6-10 well-developed setae / spines ....**couplet 29**

9. None of the above characters present ....**couplet 35**

READ THREE ALTERNATIVES

1. Body laterally compressed, amphipod-like (Figs 17A, B); cephalothorax deeply produced ventrolaterally; male genital somite (or complex if different urosomites are fused) with ventrally expanded spermatophore reservoir (Fig. 17C); P1 with elongate protopod and 1-segmented rami (Fig. 17D).

    ....**Tegastidae** (Part 1: p. 288)

    Body dorsoventrally compressed, ovoid, shield-shaped (Figs 17E, H-K).

    ....**2**

    Body of a different shape.

    ....**5**

2. Epimeral plates of third free prosomite (P4-bearing somite) rudimentary in female (stippled in Fig. 17E); P5 laterally located, embracing urosome and lamelliform caudal rami (Figs 17E, F); urosome 3-segmented, consisting of short P5-bearing somite, genital somite (male: Fig. 17F) or double-somite (female : Fig. 17E), and one postgenital somite; P1 as in Fig. 17G.

    ....**Porcellidiidae** (Part 1: p. 304) [2]

    Epimeral plates of third free prosomite well-developed in both sexes (stippled in Figs 17H-K); P5 ventrally located (Figs 17H-J) or when lateral not embracing urosome and caudal rami (Fig. 17K); P1 of a different shape.

    ....**3**

---

[2] **Caution**: *Neopeltopsis* (Peltidiidae; Fig. 17J) shows the same urosome segmentation as the Porcellidiidae.

49

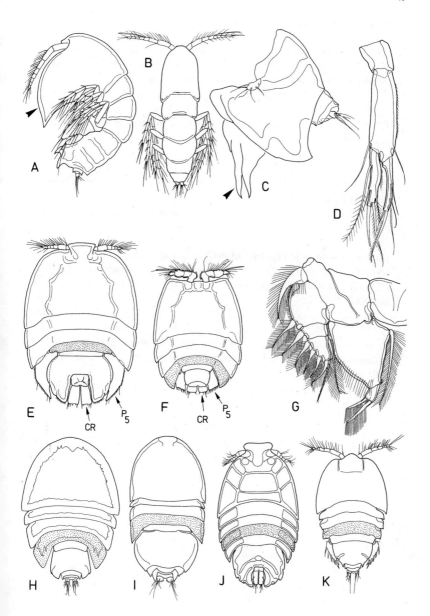

Fig. 17. Key to families of Harpacticoida. Couplets 1-2.

50

READ THREE ALTERNATIVES

3. P1 endopod not prehensile and shorter than or at most as long as exopod (Figs 18C, D); body as in Figs 18A, B; integument strongly chitinised (sometimes with pattern of anastomosing struts: Fig. 18B).
....**Peltidiidae** (Part 1: p. 310)

   P1 endopod prehensile and longer than exopod; integument never strongly chitinised.
   ....**4**

   P1 endopod prehensile and shorter than exopod (as in Fig. 19B); body typically as in Fig. 19A.
   ....**Harpacticidae** [3] (Part 1: p. 262)

4. Body of female as in Fig. 18E, of male as in Fig. 18F; free prosomites of about the same width in female; P1 endopod relatively slender (Fig. 18G); P2 endopod male 2-segmented (Fig. 18H); P3 endopod male not modified.
   ....**Thalestridae** [4]

   Body of female as in Fig. 18I; free prosomites tapering posteriorly; P1 endopod massive (Fig. 18J); P2 endopod male 3-segmented; P3 endopod male modified (Fig. 18K).
   ....**Hamondiidae** [5]

---

[3] *Zaus* (part.), *Zausodes* (part.)
[4] *Paramenophia*
[5] Monotypic. Marine. Description given by Huys (1990b).

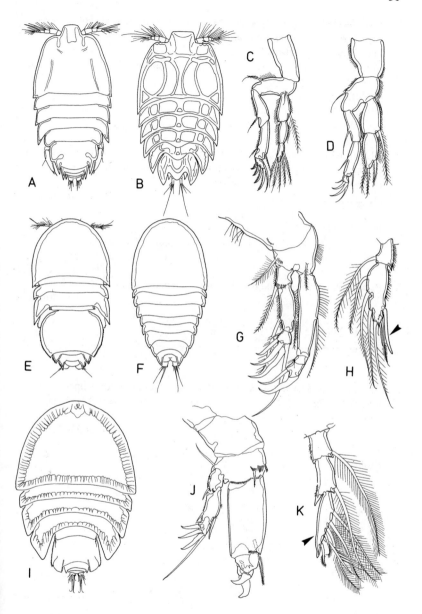

Fig. 18. Key to families of Harpacticoida. Couplets 3-4.

5. P1 as in Figs 19B-D (exopod of 2 elongate segments, rudiment of exopod-3 embedded in exopod-2 and armed with 5 claws; endopod much shorter than exopod and prehensile).

....**Harpacticidae** [6] (Part 1: p. 262)

P1 different.

....**6**

6. P1 as in Figs 19E, F (endopod 2-segmented, endopod-1 elongate, endopod-2 with 2 curved claws); protopod either longitudinally (Fig. 19E) or transversely (Fig. 19F) prolonged.

....**Thalestridae** [7] (Part 2)

P1 different.

....**7**

7. P1 as in Fig. 19G (exopod bent inwards; endopod 2-segmented).

....**Argestidae** [8]

P1 different.

....**8**

8. P1 as in Figs 19H-K (females: endopod strongly reduced; exopod bent inwards) or Figs 19L-M (males: endopod a strong spine or exopod-1 and -2 fused).

....**Huntemanniidae** [9] (Part 3)

P1 different.

....**9**

---

[6] *Discoharpacticus, Harpacticella,* **Harpacticus***, Paratigriopus,* **Perissocope***,* **Tigriopus***, **Zaus** (part.), Zausodes, Zausopsis*
[7] Donsiellinae: *Donsiella, Apodonsiella, Xylora, Oligoxylora*
[8] *Hypalocletodes*
[9] *Beckeria,* **Metahuntemannia** *(part.), Talpina*

53

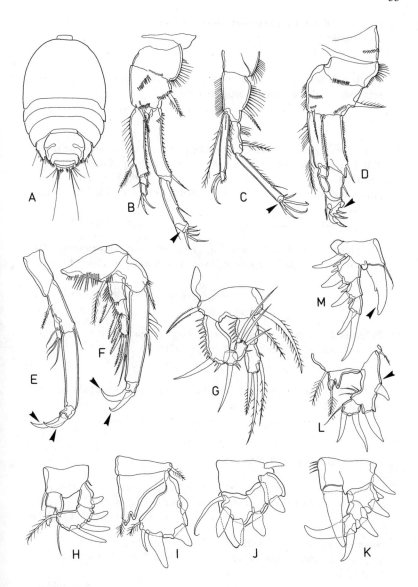

Fig. 19. Key to families of Harpacticoida. Couplets 5-8.

9. P1 coxa with inner spine or seta (Fig. 20A); antennary exopod at least 6-segmented.
....**10**

P1 coxa without inner spine or seta; antennary exopod at most 4-segmented or entire antenna vestigial or absent
....**11**

10. P2 endopod extremely elongated, reaching to distal end of urosome (Fig. 20B); P1 exopod-1 with inner seta; P5 well-developed and with free endopod in both sexes (female: Fig. 20C; male: Fig. 20D); anal operculum with large median and smaller lateral teeth (Fig. 20E); one egg-sac.
....**Longipediidae** (Part 1: p. 116)

P2 endopod not extremely elongated, P1 exopod-1 without inner seta; P5 strongly reduced and incorporated in somite in both sexes (Fig. 20F); two egg-sacs (Fig. 20 G).
....**Canuellidae** (Part 1: p. 122)

11. P1 exopod-1 with inner seta [10], or P1 exopod represented by a single segment with 7-10 setae / spines (Fig. 20H, 22H).
....**12**

P1 exopod-1 without inner seta, or when P1 exopod 1-segmented with 6 setae at most.
....**13**

READ THREE ALTERNATIVES

12. Antennary exopod 4-segmented (Fig. 20I); mandibular palp strongly-developed, biramous; caudal rami at most twice as long as body.
....**Cerviniidae** (Part 1: p. 138)

Antennary exopod small, indistinctly 2-segmented (Fig. 20J); mandibular palp rudimentary or absent; caudal rami about 5 to 7 times the body length (Fig. 20K).
....**Aegisthidae** [11]

These characters not combined
....**19**

---

[10] Records of this inner seta in some Argestidae are erroneous.
[11] Contains only the genus *Aegisthus*. Found exclusively in the plankton. Redescriptions are given by Boxshall (1979) and Huys (1988b).

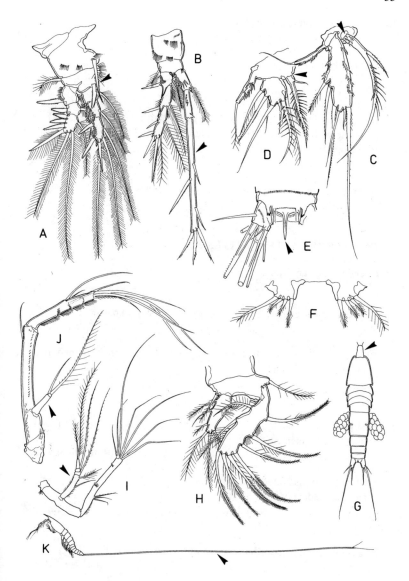

Fig. 20. Key to families of Harpacticoida. Couplets 9-12.

13. P1 exopod 1-segmented or absent.
....**14**

P1 exopod 2- or 3-segmented.
....**20**

14. P1 exopod represented by small segment with 1 seta (Fig. 21A) or completely absent (Fig. 21B); P1 endopod 2-segmented, prehensile; P2-P4 endopods 1-segmented.
....**Leptopontiidae** [12]

P1 exopod 1-segmented with at least 3 setae / spines.
....**15**

READ THREE ALTERNATIVES

15. P1 endopod 1-segmented.
....**16**

P1 endopod 2-segmented; P2-P4 endopods 1- to 2-segmented.
....**18**

P1 endopod 3-segmented; P2-P4 endopods 3-segmented (P2 endopod male 2- or 3-segmented).
....**19**

16. First pedigerous somite free; P1 as in Fig. 21C; P2 as in Fig. 21D; P2-P4 endopods 2-segmented.
....**Rotundiclipeidae** [13]

First pedigerous somite fused with cephalosome; P2-P4 bases transversely prolonged, endopods 1-segmented or vestigial.
....**17**

17. P1 as in Fig. 21E, endopodal segment with setae; P2 as in Fig. 21F.
....**Ameiridae** [14] (Part 2)

P1 as in Fig. 21G, endopod an asetose stump; P2 as in Fig. 21H
....**Paramesochridae** [15]

---

[12] Psammopsyllinae: *Ichnusella, Parasewellina, Prosewellina, Psammopsyllus, Sewellina*
[13] Monotypic. Anchialine caves. Description given by Huys (1988b).
[14] *Anoplosoma*
[15] *Kunzia* (part.)

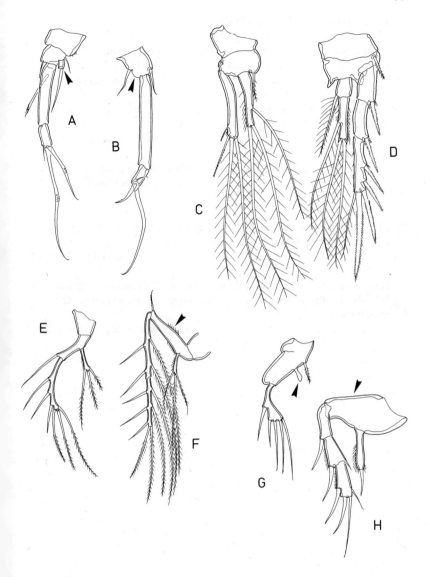

57

Fig. 21. Key to families of Harpacticoida. Couplets 13-17.

READ THREE ALTERNATIVES

18. P1 endopod prehensile, endopod-1 without inner seta, endopod-2 with claw and 1 minute setule (Fig. 22A); maxilliped as in Fig. 22B.
....**Laophontidae** [16] (Part 3)

P1 endopod prehensile, endopod-2 with 2 curved claws or 2 geniculate setae (Figs 22C, D); maxilliped as in Fig. 22E.
....**Paramesochridae** [17]

P1 endopod not prehensile (Fig. 22F); maxilliped as in Fig. 22G.
....**Leptastacidae** [18] (Part 3)

19. P1 endopod prehensile (Fig. 22H); P2 endopod of male 2-segmented (Fig. 22I); P5 with free exopod in both sexes.
....**Thalestridae** [19] (Part 2)

Body as in Fig. 22J; P1 endopod not prehensile, 3-segmented (Fig. 22L); P2 endopod of male 3-segmented; P5 uniramous in both sexes (Fig. 22K); planktonic.
....**Clytemnestridae** (Part 1: p. 300)

---

[16] *Afrolaophonte, Amerolaophontina,* **Echinolaophonte** (part.), *Galapalaophonte, Klieonychocamptoides,* **Laophonte** (part.), **Laophontina**, *Mexicolaophonte, Microlaophonte* (part.), *Namakosiramia, Novolaophonte, Tapholeon* (part.), *Wellsiphontina,* Xanthilaophonte (part.)
[17] *Caligopsyllus.* Records (Krishnaswamy, 1957; Rao & Ganapati, 1969) of a 1-segmented P1 exopod in some species of *Apodopsyllus, Kliopsyllus* and *Paramesochra* are doubtful.
[18] *Afroleptastacus, Arenotopa, Membranastacus,* **Minervella**, *Neopsammastacus,* **Psammastacus**
[19] **Diarthrodes** (part.)

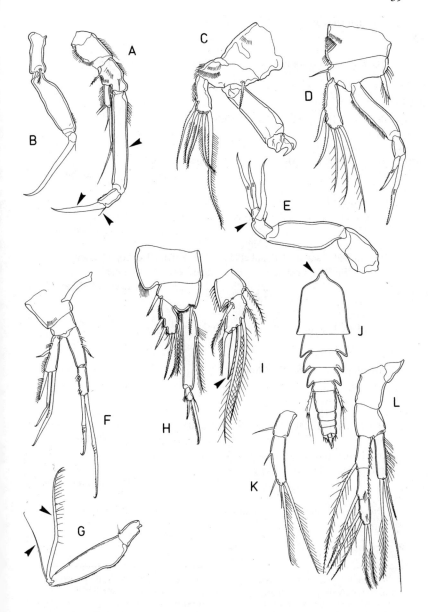

Fig. 22. Key to families of Harpacticoida. Couplets 18-19.

20. First pedigerous somite (bearing the P1) free. [20]

....**21**

First pedigerous somite (bearing the P1) fused with cephalosome.

....**22**

READ THREE ALTERNATIVES

21. Maxilliped 4-segmented, stenopodial (Fig. 23A); P1 endopod 2-segmented (Fig. 23B); P2-P4 endopod 1-segmented.

....**Chappuisiidae** [21]

Maxilliped lamelliform (Fig. 23C); P1 endopod 3-segmented (Fig. 23D); P2 endopod 3-, P3 endopod 2- or 3-, P4 endopod 1- or 2-segmented.

....**Phyllognathopodidae** [22]

Maxilliped 3-segmented, subchelate (Fig. 23E); P1 endopod 2-segmented (Fig. 23F); P2-P3 endopod 3-, P4 endopod 2- or 3-segmented.

....**Latiremidae** [23]

22. Maxilliped phyllopodial or stenopodial. [24]

....**23**

Maxilliped subchelate, vestigial or absent.

....**28**

23. Body as in Fig. 23G; mandibular endopod elongated, twisted over exopod and with long setae (Fig. 23H), visible in lateral aspect (Fig. 23I); maxilliped phyllopodial (Fig. 23J); P5 exopod laterally displaced (as in cyclopoids: Fig. 23K); 2 egg-sacs (Fig. 23G).

....**Diosaccidae** [25] (Part 2)

One egg-sac, attached mid-ventrally; other characters not combined.

....**24**

---

[20] The record of a free first pedigerous somite in *Horsiella* (= *Leptocaris*) is erroneous.

[21] Contains only the genus *Chappuisius*. Subterranean. Descriptions given by Glatzel (1989).

[22] Freshwater and anchialine caves. Contains the genera *Phyllognathopus*, *Allophyllognathopus* and *Parbatocamptus*. Useful descriptions are provided by Gurney (1932), Lang (1948), Kiefer (1967) and Dumont & Maas (1988).

[23] Arbutifera

[24] **Caution**: The prehensile maxilla of the Ectinosomatidae may be mistaken for the maxilliped which is often less well-developed and not subchelate (compare Figs 24G-I and 24J-M).

[25] *Stenhelia* (*Delavalia*) (part.).

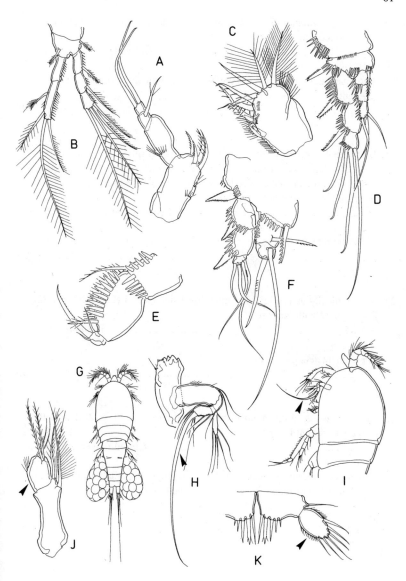

Fig. 23. Key to families of Harpacticoida. Couplets 20-23.

24. Exopod of antenna (Fig. 24A) and mandible 4-segmented; maxilliped phyllopodial (Fig. 24B).
....**Neobradyidae** (Part 1: p. 198)

Antennary exopod at most 3-segmented; mandibular exopod at most 1-segmented.
....**25**

25. Body fusiform (Figs 24C, D) or cylindrical (Fig. 24E), rarely dorso-ventrally depressed (Fig. 24F); maxilla characteristic, basis elongate, endopod with geniculate setae (Figs 24G-I); maxilliped semi-phyllopodial (Fig. 24J) or stenopodial (Figs 24K-M).
....**Ectinosomatidae** (Part 1: p. 155)

Body and maxilla different.
....**26**

26. Body typically as in Fig. 24N; maxilliped stenopodial (Figs 24O, P); P2-P4 exopod-1 with inner seta.
....**Tisbidae** [26] (Part 2)

These characters not combined.
....**27**

27. Body as in Fig. 24Q; maxilliped semi-phyllopodial (Fig. 24R); P2-P4 exopod-1 without inner seta.
....**Cletodidae** *incertae sedis* [27]

Maxilliped strongly reduced, not chelate, with phyllopodial or stenopodial appearance but different from types described in couplets 23 - 27.
....**35**

---

[26] *Peresime, Pseudozosime,* ***Zosime***
[27] *Actinocletodes*

63

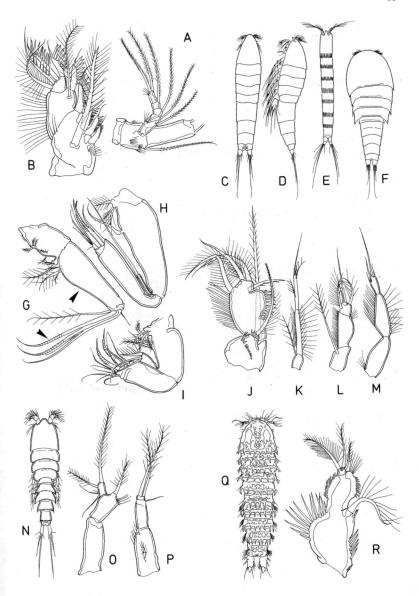

Fig. 24. Key to families of Harpacticoida. Couplets 24-27.

28. P1 endopod with at least 6 well-developed setae / spines in total. Figs 25A-C, E; 26B, E-I; but **not** as in Fig. 25D.

....**29**

P1 endopod with at most 5 well-developed setae / spines in total.

....**35**

29. P1 exopod 3-segmented, exopod-1 with 3 outer spines, exopod-2 with 2 outer spines, endopod-2 with 1-2 outer setae (Fig. 25A).

....**Superornatiremidae** [28]

P1 exopod 2- or 3-segmented; when 3-segmented with at most 1 outer spine on exopod-1 and exopod-2; endopod-2 without outer setae

....**30**

30. P1 rami 2-segmented (Fig. 25B), modified in the male (Fig. 25C).

....**Euterpinidae** (Part 1: p. 216)

P1 exopod 3-segmented; P1 endopod 2- or 3-segmented.

....**31**

31. P1 exopod-3 with 4 setae / spines (Fig. 25E).

....**Thompsonulidae** (Part 1: p.230)

P1 exopod-3 with 5-6 setae / spines.

....**32**

---

[28] Anchialine caves. Contains only the genera *Superornatiremis* and *Neoechinophora*. Descriptions are given in Huys (1995).

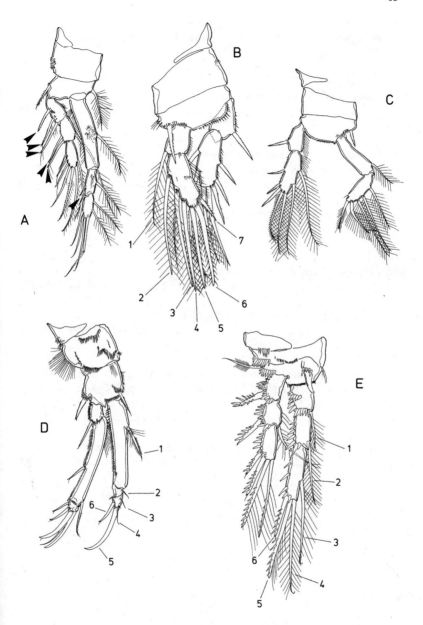

Fig. 25. Key to families of Harpacticoida. Couplets 28-31.

32. Prosome clearly demarcated from urosome (Fig. 26A); P1 endopod with penicillate brush setae (Fig. 26B); maxillule with enlarged exopod (Fig. 26C).
....**Tisbidae** [29] (Part 2)

These characters not combined.
....**33**

33. Cephalothorax and thoracic somites with paired accessory nuchal organs (Fig. 26D); P1 rami 3-segmented, not modified (Fig. 26E).
....**Tachidiidae** (Part 1: p. 220)

These characters not combined.
....**34**

34. P1 exopod-3 with 6 setae / spines (Figs 26F-H).
....**Tisbidae** [30] (Part 2)

P1 exopod-3 with 5 setae / spines (Fig. 26I).
....**Thalestridae** [31] (Part 2)

35. P2-P4 endopods (except male P3 endopod) at most 2-segmented in both sexes; if male P3 endopod 3-segmented, then endopod-2 with spinous apophysis (Figs 27A-D).
....**36**

At least one of these rami 3-segmented (except male P3 endopod)
....**99**

---

29 *Scutellidium*, *Sacodiscus*
30 *Idyanthe*, *Idyella*, *Tachidiopsis*
31 *Idomene* (part.), *Idomenella*, Pseudotachidius (part.)

67

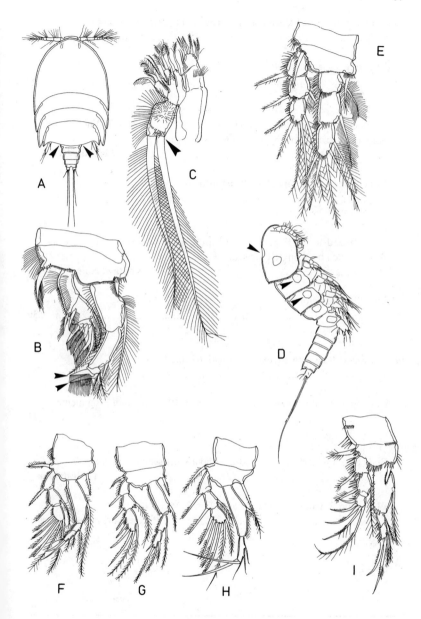

Fig. 26. Key to families of Harpacticoida. Couplets 32-34.

36. Commensal on the baleen plates of whales; Fig. 27E; P1 as in Fig. 27F.
....**Balaenophilidae** (Part 2)

Not commensal on whales.
....**37**

37. Commensal on cephalopods; body as in Figs 27G, H; P1 as in Fig. 27I; **or**,
body irregularly bean-shaped and wrinkled, with P3-P5 absent.
....**Tisbidae** [32] (Part 2)

Not commensal on cephalopods; P1 different.
....**38**

38. Maxilliped as in Fig. 27J (endopod with pinnate sigmoid claw
accompanied by a single long seta).
....**Leptastacidae** [33] (Part 3)

Maxilliped different.
....**39**

39. P1 exopod 3-segmented, exopod-3 with 6 setae / spines.
....**40**

P1 exopod-3 with at most 5 setae / spines, or P1 exopod not 3-segmented.
....**41**

40. Body as in Fig. 27K; P1 exopod-2 without inner seta; P1 as in Fig. 27L.
....**Thalestridae** [34]

P1 exopod-2 with inner seta; P1 as in Fig. 27M.
....**Paramesochridae** [35] (Part 2)

---

[32] Cholidyinae: *Avdeevia, Cholidya, Cholidyella, Tripartisoma*
[33] *Archileptastacus,* **Arenocaris***, Belemnopontia, Cerconeotes,* **Leptastacus***,*
Paraleptastacus*, Psamathea, Schizothrix, Sextonis*
[34] *Dactylopia*: this genus also keys out in couplet 105 because of the variable segmentation
of P2-P4 endopods (cf. couplet 35)
[35] **Remanea**

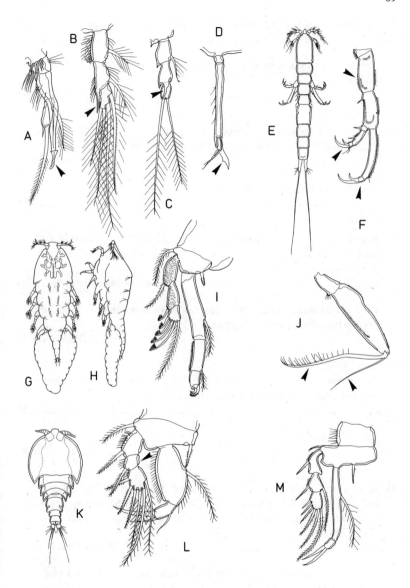

Fig. 27. Key to families of Harpacticoida. Couplets 35-41.

41. Antennary exopod 3-segmented; P1 endopod invariably 2-segmented.
   ....**42**

   Antennary exopod at most 2-segmented; P1 endopod absent, or 1- to 3-segmented.
   ....**44**

42. P1 exopod-1 longer than exopod-2 and exopod-3 combined (Fig. 28A); P1 endopod-2 with 4 setae / spines; P5 with fused rami (Fig. 28B).
   ....**Diosaccidae** [36]

   These characters not combined.
   ....**43**

43. Rostrum large, usually almost quadrate (Figs 28C, D); antennule with pinnate spines; antennary exopod as in Fig. 28E; P5 exopod not laterally displaced; 1 egg-sac.
   ....**Danielsseniidae** [37] (Part 1: p. 236)

   Rostrum triangular (Fig. 28F); antennule without pinnate spines; P5 exopod laterally displaced; 2 egg-sacs.
   ....**Diosaccidae** [38]

44. Female antennule 4- or 5-segmented; P1 with 2 brush setae on exopod-3 and 1 or 2 brush setae on endopod-2 (Figs 28H, J).
   ....**45**

   These characters not combined
   ....**46**

45. Antennules with outer thorn-like process on 2nd segment (Fig. 28G); P1 endopod-2 with 1 brush seta (Fig. 28H); P2-P4 with blunt spines on exopodal segments (Fig. 28I); male P3 endopod with strong apophysis (Fig. 27A).
   ....**Orthopsyllidae** (Part 3)

   Antennules without thorn-like process on 2nd segment; P1 endopod-2 with 2 brush setae (Fig. 28J); P2-P4 with pinnate setae or spines on exopodal segments (Figs 28K, L); male P3 endopod not modified
   ....**Rhizothricidae** (Part 3)

---

[36] *Pseudomesochra* (part.)
[37] *Paranannopus* (part.). Note that males may have 3-segmented P2-P4 endopods and therefore key out in couplet 111.
[38] *Onychostenhelia, Pseudostenhelia*

71

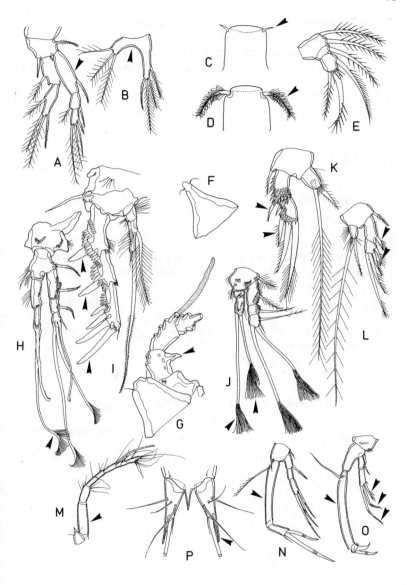

Fig. 28. Key to families of Harpacticoida. Couplets 42-46.

46. First antennulary segment much longer than second one (Fig. 28M); P1 endopod prehensile, distal exopodal segment with 3 setae (Figs 28N, 28O); caudal rami acutely produced posteriorly (Fig. 28P).
....**Leptopontiidae** [39] (Part 3)

These characters not combined.
....**47**

47. P1 exopod 3-segmented, exopod-2 without outer spine.
....**48**

P1 exopod-2 with outer spine **or** P1 exopod with less than 3 segments.
....**51**

48. P1 as in Fig. 29A; P2-P4 endopods 1-segmented; P3 exopod male transformed (Fig. 29B); urosomites with dorsal membranous areas (fenestrae) (Fig. 29C).
....**Parastenocarididae** [40]

P2-P4 endopods with different segmentation; P3 exopod male not transformed; urosomal fenestrae absent.
....**49**

49. P1 endopod 3-segmented or P1 as in Fig. 29D; P2-P4 exopod-2 with inner seta.
....**Ameiridae** [41] (Part 2)

P1 endopod 2-segmented; P2-P4 exopod-2 without inner seta.
....**50**

---

[39] Leptopontiinae: *Leptopontia*, *Notopontia*, *Syrticola*
[40] Almost exclusively freshwater with only 2 species, *Parastenocaris phyllura* and *P. vicesima* recorded from brackish water (descriptions in Lang, 1948: 1236, 1246). Jakobi's (1972) division of the genus *Parastenocaris* into 24 new genera has not been followed by most workers (Dussart & Defaye, 1990). At present, only the genera *Parastenocaris*, *Forficatocaris*, *Paraforficatocaris*, *Potamocaris* and *Murunducaris* are regarded as valid.
[41] *Leptomesochra* (part.), *Psammonitocrella*

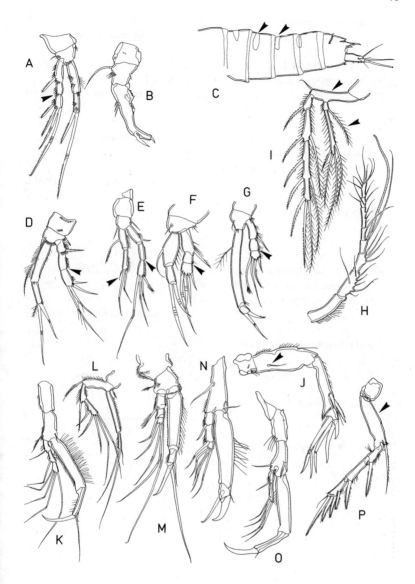

Fig. 29. Key to families of Harpacticoida. Couplets 47-52.

50. P1 endopod-2 with 3 setae (Fig. 29E); P2 endopod-1 with inner seta.
....**Cylindropsyllidae** [42] (Part 3)

P1 endopod-2 with 2 setae (Figs 29F, G); P2 endopod 1-segmented, or when 2-segmented without inner seta on endopod-1
....**Arenopontiidae** [43] (Part 3)

51. Antennule 8-segmented in both sexes (Fig. 29H), haplocer in male; P1 endopod distinctly longer than exopod; P2-P4 basis strongly prolonged transversely, endopod-1 with inner seta (Fig. 29I).
....**Ameiridae** [44] (Part 2)

These characters not combined.
....**52**

52. Antennary exopod absent or represented by a seta (Fig. 29J); P1 endopod-1 longer than exopod (Figs 29K-O); P2-P4 basis transversely prolonged (Fig. 29P) or endopod of P2 and P4 absent.
....**Ancorabolidae** [45] (Part 3)

These characters not combined.
....**53**

53. P1 endopod absent, 1- or 2-segmented.
....**54**

P1 endopod 3-segmented.
....**97**

---

[42] Cylindropsyllinae: *Boreopontia*
[43] *Arenopontia*
[44] *Malacopsyllus*
[45] *Algensiella*, *Ancorabolus*, *Laophontodes*, *Paralaophontodes*, *Probosciphontodes*, *Tapholaophontodes* (part.). **Note** that shape and armature of P1 endopod in *Paralaophontodes* (Fig. 29O) are reminiscent of the Laophontidae (Figs 30D-F), however the antennary exopod in the latter is a distinct segment with 2-4 setae.

54. P5 absent in both sexes; body as in Fig. 30A; maxilliped with elongate basis (Fig. 30B); P1 as in Fig. 30C.

....**Canthocamptidae** [46]

P5 present in both sexes; other characters not combined.

....**55**

55. P1 as in Figs 30D-F (endopod prehensile, endopod-1 usually without inner seta; endopod-2 with claw and small accessory seta); antennary exopod 1-segmented, with 1-4 setae.

....**Laophontidae** [47] (Part 3)

These characters not combined.

....**56**

56. P1 as in Fig. 30G (exopod and endopod may be 2-segmented); P2-P4 exopod 2-segmented (Fig. 30H); caudal ramus with spinous process (Fig. 30I).

....**Huntemanniidae** [48] (Part 3)

These characters not combined.

....**57**

57. P1 exopod 1- or 2-segmented.

....**58**

P1 exopod 3-segmented.

....**64**

---

[46] _Stygepactophanes_
[47] _Archilaophonte, Arenolaophonte,_ **_Asellopsis_**_, Chilaophonte, Coullia,_ **_Echinolaophonte_** (part.)_, Elapholaophonte,_ **_Esola_**_, Folioquinpes,_ **_Harrietella, Hemilaophonte, Heterolaophonte_**_, Hoplolaophonte, Indolaophonte,_ **_Klieonychocamptus_**_, Langia,_ **_Laophonte_** (part.)_, Lipomelum, Lobitella, Loureirophonte, Maiquilaophonte, Microlaophonte_ (part.)_, Mictyricola, Mourephonte,_ **_Onychocamptus, Paralaophonte, Paronychocamptus, Phycolaophonte,_** **_Pilifera, Platychelipus_**_, Platylaophonte, Psammolaophonte,_ **_Pseudolaophonte, Pseudonychocamptus, Quinquelaophonte,_** _Robustunguis, Stygolaophonte, Tapholeon_ (part.)_, Xanthilaophonte_ (part.)
[48] **_Huntemannia_**_, Rosacletodes_

76

58. P5 female leaf-like (Fig. 30L); exopod segments of P2-P4 with long outer spines (Fig. 30K); body as in Fig. 30J.

....**Tetragonicipitidae** [49]

P5 female not leaf-like; exopod segments of P2-P4 with short outer spines
....**59**

59. Antennary exopod absent; P1 often, P2-P4 always with transversely prolonged basis (Figs 31A, B); P5 basis with long cylindrical setophore (Figs 31C, D).

....**Ancorabolidae** [50] (Part 3)

Antennary exopod 1-segmented with 2-5 setae; P1-P4 basis not transversely prolonged; P5 basis with short, never cylindrical, setophore
....**60**

60. Antennule with outer spinous process on segment 2, 4-segmented in female (Fig. 31E); cephalothorax and body somites (except P4-bearing one) with lateral globular glands (Fig. 31F).

....**Adenopleurellidae** (Part 3)

Antennule without outer spinous process on segment 2 (but sometimes on segment 1), at least 6-segmented in female; lateral globular glands absent.

....**61**

61. P1 endopod represented by an asetose stump (Fig. 31G) or completely absent; maxilliped as in Fig. 31L .

....**Paramesochridae** [51]

These characters not combined.

....**62**

---

[49] *Oniscopsis*
[50] ***Arthropsyllus, Ceratonotus****, Dorsiceratus* (part.), *Patagoniaella*
[51] *Kunzia* (part.), *Meiopsyllus*

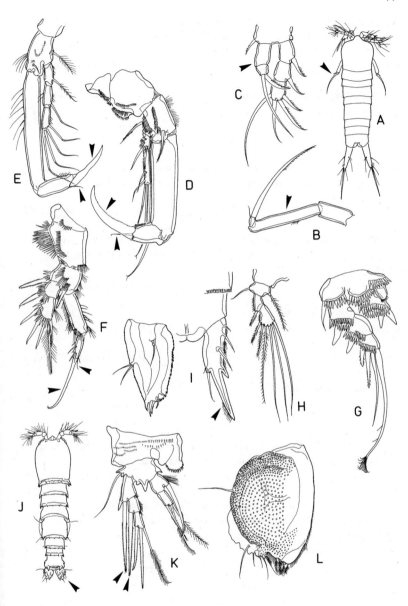

Fig. 30. Key to families of Harpacticoida. Couplets 52-58.

62. Cephalothorax usually with dorsal nuchal organ; P1 endopod-2 with 3 setae / spines (Fig. 31H); P3 endopod male with sigmoid apophysis (Fig. 31I); freshwater.

....**Canthocamptidae** [52]

Nuchal organ absent; P3 without sexual dimorphism; P1 endopod-2 with 1 or 2 spines/setae.

....**63**

63. P1 endopod-1 without inner seta, more than twice the length of endopod-2 (Figs 31J, K); male antennule subchirocer-chirocer; maxilliped as in Fig. 31L.

....**Paramesochridae** [53] (Part 2)

P1 endopod-1 with inner seta, less than twice the length of endopod-2 (Fig. 31N); male antennule haplocer (Fig. 31M); maxilliped as in Fig. 31O.

....**Arenopontiidae** [54] (Part 3).

64. Body cylindrical (Fig. 32A); P4 as in Fig. 32B; P5 a single plate (Figs 32C, D).

....**Cylindropsyllidae** [55] (Part 3)

These characters not combined.

....**65**

65. P1 endopod-1 elongate, longer than endopod-2 **and** at least reaching to distal margin of exopod-2; endopod often prehensile.

....**66**

P1 endopod absent, 1-segmented, or if 2-segmented then endopod-1 shorter than endopod-2 **and/or** endopod-1 not reaching to distal margin of exopod-2.

....**77**

---

[52] _Hypocamptus_, _Maraenobiotus_
[53] _**Apodopsyllus**_ (part.), _Biuncus_, _**Intermedopsyllus**_, _**Kliopsyllus**_ (part.), _**Leptopsyllus**_, _Paraleptopsyllus_, _**Paramesochra**_ (part.), _**Scottopsyllus**_, _**Wellsopsyllus**_
[54] _**Pararenopontia**_
[55] _**Cylindropsyllus**_, _Cylinula_, _**Evansula**_, _**Stenocaris**_, _Stenocaropsis_

79

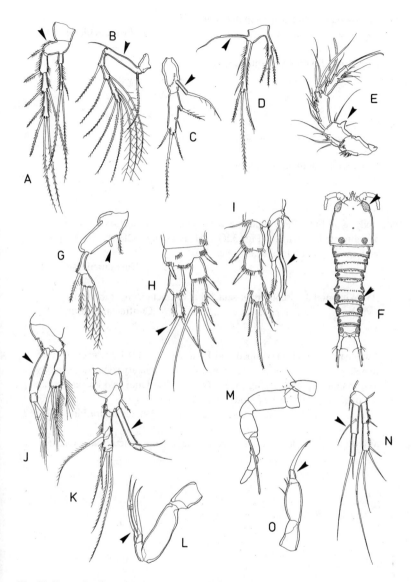

Fig. 31. Key to families of Harpacticoida. Couplets 59-63.

66. P1 exopod-3 with 5 setae / spines (Fig. 32E).
....**Normanellidae** [56] (Part 3)

P1 exopod-3 with 3 or 4 setae / spines.
....**67**

67. P1 exopod-2 with inner seta.
....**68**

P1 exopod-2 without inner seta.
....**69**

68. Body as in Fig. 32F; Antennule with cylindrical processes on segment 2, 4-segmented in female (Fig. 32G); P1 as in Fig. 32H; P3-P4 exopod-1 with inner seta, P5 female as in Fig. 32I.
....**Normanellidae** [57] (Part 3)

P3-P4 exopod-1 without inner seta; other characters not combined.
....**Canthocamptidae** [58] (Part 3)

69. Antennary exopod, maxilliped and P1 as in Figs 32J-L, respectively; P5 female often modified (Fig. 32N), and first antennulary segment distinctly longer than segment 2 (Fig. 32M) (when these latter two characters are not present, then P2-P4 exopod-2 with inner seta).
....**Tetragonicipitidae** [59] (Part 2)

Maxilliped and antennary exopod different; other characters not present.
....**70**

---

[56] Normanellinae: *Normanella*

[57] Cletopsyllinae: *Cletopsyllus*, *Pseudocletopsyllus*

[58] *Afrocamptus*, *Amphibiperita*, *Antarctobiotus* (part.), *Bryocamptus* (part.), *Cletocamptus* (part.), *Elaphoidella* (part.), *Fibulacamptus* (part.), *Mesochra* (part.), *Pholetiscus* (part.), *Thermomesochra*

[59] *Aigondiceps*, *Diagoniceps*, *Godianiceps*, *Laophontella*, *Odaginiceps*, *Phyllopodopsyllus*, *Protogoniceps*, *Tetragoniceps*

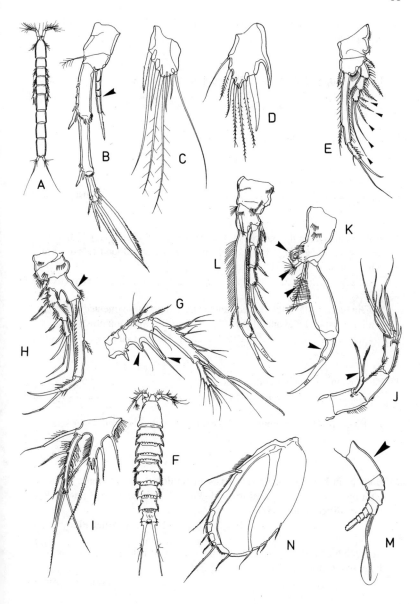

Fig. 32. Key to families of Harpacticoida. Couplets 64-69.

70. P3-P4 endopod absent or 1-segmented (P3 endopod male usually 3-segmented).

....**71**

P3-P4 endopod 2-segmented (P3 endopod male sometimes 3-segmented).

....**73**

71. P1 endopod-1 at least as long as exopod.

....**72**

P1 endopod-1 distinctly shorter than exopod (Fig. 33A).

....**Canthocamptidae** [60]

72. Antennule female 4-segmented; antennary exopod absent (Fig. 33B); P1 coxa with cristae (Fig. 33C); P5 exopod and baseoendopod female (Fig. 33D) and male (Fig. 33E) fused.

....**Cristacoxidae** [61]

Antennule female 6-segmented; antennary exopod 1-segmented; P1 coxa without cristae; P5 exopod female free (Fig. 33F). Male unknown.

....**Normanellidae** *incertae sedis* [62]

73. P2-P4 exopod-2 without inner seta.

....**74**

P2-P3 exopod-2 with inner seta, P4 exopod-2 with or without inner seta.

....**75**

74. Body as in Fig. 33G; cephalothorax without dorsal nuchal organ; antenna with basis and 2-segmented exopod (Fig. 33H); inner basal spine of P1 male modified (Fig. 33I).

....**Ameiridae** [63] (Part 2)

Cephalothorax usually with dorsal nuchal organ; antenna with allobasis; inner basal spine of P1 male not modified

....**Canthocamptidae** [64]

---

[60] *Parepactophanes* (part.)
[61] Marine. Contains the genera *Cristacoxa*, *Cubanocleta* and *Noodtorthopsyllus*. A revision of the family is given by Huys (1990a).
[62] *Pseudocleta*
[63] **Parevansula**
[64] *Antarctobiotus* (part.), *Gulcamptus*, *Moraria* (part.)

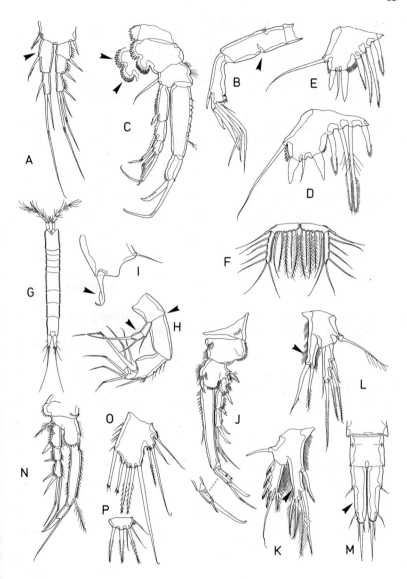

Fig. 33. Key to families of Harpacticoida. Couplets 70-75.

READ THREE ALTERNATIVES

75. Antennule 4-segmented in female, chirocer in male; P1 as in Fig. 33J; P5 rami always separate and with cylindrical endopodal lobe in both sexes (Figs 33K, L); caudal rami lamelliform, with reduced setae (Fig. 33M).
....**Laophontopsidae** (Part 3)

Antennule 5-segmented in female, chirocer in male; P1 as in Fig. 33N; P5 rami fused or, if separate, without such cylindrical endopodal lobe in both sexes (Figs 33O, P); caudal rami different from above.
....**Laophontidae** *incertae sedis* [65]

Antennule 6- to 9-segmented in female, haplocer in male.
....**76**

76. Antennule 9-segmented in female; P3 endopod male 2-segmented, without apophysis; antenna with basis.
....**Ameiridae** [66] (Part 2)

Antennule 6- to 8-segmented in female; P3 endopod male 3-segmented, with spinous apophysis (Fig. 34A); antenna with allobasis
....**Canthocamptidae** [67] (Part 3)

77. Cephalothorax and at least first three free prosomites with paired dorsal processes (Figs 34B, C); P1-P4 basis strongly prolonged transversely (Fig. 34D).
....**Ancorabolidae** [68] (Part 3)

P1-P4 basis at most slightly prolonged transversely.
....**78**

---

[65] *Apolethon*
[66] ***Leptomesochra*** (part.)
[67] *Antarctobiotus* (part.), ***Mesochra*** (part.), *Paracamptus*, *Pholetiscus* (part.)
[68] *Dorsiceratus* (part.), ***Echinopsyllus***

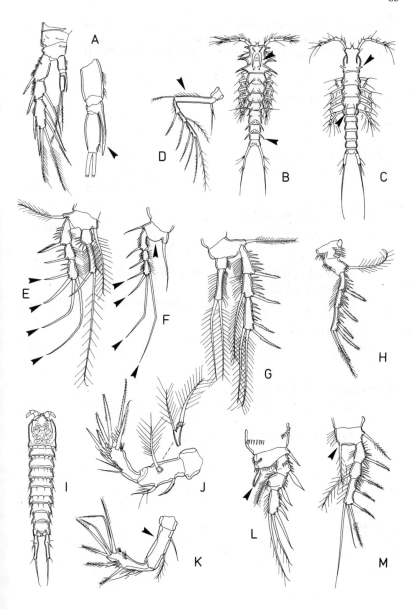

Fig. 34. Key to families of Harpacticoida. Couplets 76-81.

78. Antennule female 4- or 5-segmented; P1 as in Fig. 34E (exopod-2 without inner seta, exopod-3 with 4 setae / spines, endopod sometimes absent, cf. Fig. 34F); P2 exopod-3 with armature formula 022 (Figs 34G, H).
....**79**

These characters not combined.
....**80**

79. Body often as in Fig. 34I; antennary exopod present, represented by small segment with 1 or 2 setae (Fig. 34J).
....**Cletodidae** [69] (Part 3)

Antennary exopod absent (Fig. 34K).
....**Ancorabolidae** [70]

80. P1 endopod completely absent (Caution: inner basal spine might be present; arrowed in Figs 34L, M).
....**Cletodidae** *incertae sedis* [71] (Part 3)

P1 endopod present.
....**81**

81. P1 exopod-3 with 5 setae / spines.
....**82**

P1 exopod-3 with 3 or 4 setae / spines.
....**83**

---

[69] *Acrenhydrosoma*, *Australonannopus*, *Cletodes*, *Enhydrosoma*, *Enhydrosomella*, *Intercletodes*, *Monocletodes*, *Kollerua*, *Stylicletodes*
[70] *Echinocletodes* (this genus shows strong affinity with the Cletodidae and might eventually be transferred to it)
[71] *Scintis*, *Pseudocletodes*

87

82. P5 baseoendopod female with 5 setae (Fig. 35B); P3 endopod male 3-segmented with apophysis on middle segment (Fig. 35A); anal operculum with long spinules (Fig. 35C).
....**Canthocamptidae** [72]

P5 baseoendopod female with at most 4 setae (Fig. 35D); P3 endopod male 2-segmented or rudimentary, not modified; body as in Fig. 35E.
....**Argestidae** [73] (Part 3)

83. P2-P3 exopod-1 with inner seta.
....**Argestidae** [74] (Part 3)

P2-P3 exopod-1 without inner seta.
....**84**

84. P1 exopod-2 without inner seta; P4 endopod present.
....**85**

P1 exopod-2 with inner seta and/or P4 endopod absent.
....**95**

---

[72] *Ophirion*
[73] *Austrocletodes*, *Corallicletodes*, **Eurycletodes** (part.), *Hemicletodes*, *Megistocletodes*, **Mesocletodes** (part.)
[74] **Eurycletodes** (part.), *Leptocletodes* (part.)

READ FOUR ALTERNATIVES

85. Maxilliped absent; fifth pair of legs fused into a single plate (Figs 35F-I); P3 endopod male not modified; body cylindrical (Fig. 35J)
    ....**Darcythompsoniidae** [75] (Part 1: p. 206)

    Maxilliped as in Fig. 35K; P5 baseoendopods fused in both sexes, with numerous setae (Figs 35M, N); P3 endopod male with apophysis (Fig. 35L); caudal rami with a well-developed seta (Fig, 35O)
    ....**Louriniidae**

    Maxilliped as in Fig. 35P; male with dorsal fan-shaped structure on second abdominal somite (Fig. 35R); P5 a single plate with 4 setae at most, not fused medially (Fig. 35Q); P3 endopod male not modified; body cylindrical (Fig. 35S).
    ....**Darcythompsoniidae** [76] (Part 1: p. 206)

    Maxilliped of typical subchelate type (Figs 10B-D); other characters not combined.
    ....**86**

86. P5 exopod subcircular in shape or incorporated into baseoendopod (male); P2-P4 endopod-2 with 5-6 setae / spines.
    ....**87**

    These characters not combined.
    ....**88**

87. Rostrum very large (Figs 36A, B); antennary exopod 2-segmented; P1 endopod-1 without inner seta (Fig. 36C); P5 female with fused baseoendopod and exopod (Figs 36D, E).
    ....**Diosaccidae** [77] (Part 2)

    Rostrum of moderate size; antennary exopod 1-segmented; P1 endopod-1 with inner seta; P5 exopod female free (Figs 36F, G).
    ....**Canthocamptidae** [78] (Part 3)

---

[75] *Leptocaris*
[76] *Darcythompsonia*
[77] *Pseudomesochra* (part.)
[78] *Dahlakia*, *Hemimesochra*

89

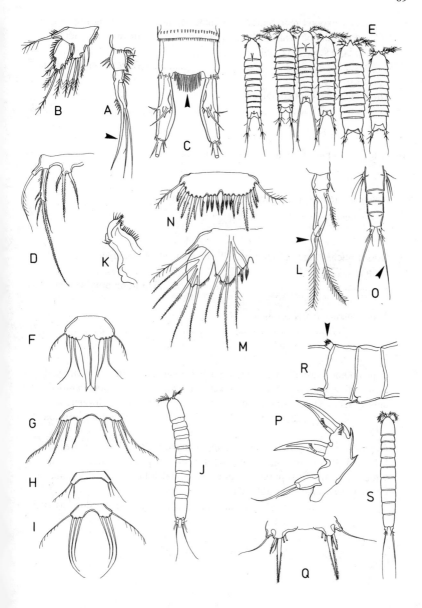

Fig. 35. Key to families of Harpacticoida. Couplets 82-85.

88. Antennary exopod represented by minute segment with a long seta (Fig. 36H); P3 endopod male without apophysis; P5 a minute plate with 3-4 setae in both sexes (Fig. 36I)
....**Darcythompsoniidae** [79]

These characters not combined.
....**89**

89. Antennule female 6- to 8-segmented, haplocer in male.
....**90**

Antennule female 4- to 5-segmented, short and (sub)chirocer in male.
....**92**

90. Dorsal nuchal organ absent; maxilliped reduced; P3 endopod male with apophysis (Fig. 36J)
....**Huntemanniidae** [80] (Part 3)

These characters not combined.
....**91**

91. Cephalothorax usually with dorsal nuchal organ (Fig. 36K); P3 endopod male with apophysis; P5 of both sexes with exopods and endopodal lobes closely set together or fused; anal opening of normal size; freshwater.
....**Canthocamptidae** [81]

Cephalothorax without dorsal nuchal organ; P3 endopod male not modified; P5 of both sexes with fused baseoendopods and free exopods which are widely separated from endopodal lobes (Fig. 36N); anal opening very large (Figs 36L, M).
....**Argestidae** [82] (Part 3)

---

[79] *Kristensenia*
[80] ***Metahuntemannia*** (male part.)
[81] *Attheyella* (part.), *Bryocamptus* (part.), *Ceuthonectes*, *Elaphoidella* (part.), *Epactophanes*, *Loefflerella*, *Moraria* (part.), *Morariopsis*
[82] *Leptocletodes* (part.), ***Mesocletodes*** (part.)

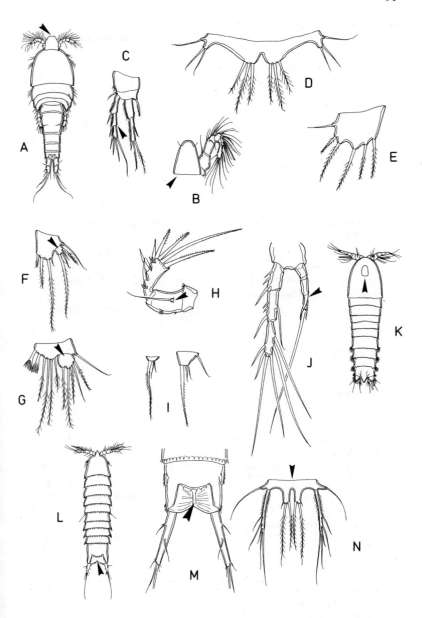

Fig. 36. Key to families of Harpacticoida. Couplets 86-91.

92. P4 endopod 1-segmented.
....**Huntemanniidae** [83] (Part 3)

P4 endopod 2-segmented.
....**93**

93. P1 exopod 2-segmented, exopod-2 with 6 setae / spines (Fig. 37A).
....**Paramesochridae** [84] (Part 2)

P1 exopod 3-segmented.
....**94**

94. Rostrum fused with cephalothorax; P5 exopod female a free segment (Figs 37B-D).
....**Cletodidae** *incertae sedis* [85]

Rostrum large, bell-shaped, defined at base (Fig. 37E); P5 female with fused exopod and baseoendopod (Fig. 37F).
....**Danielsseniidae** *incertae sedis* [86]

95. P2 exopod-2 without inner seta.
....**Cletodidae** *incertae sedis* [87]

P2 exopod-2 with inner seta.
....**96**

96. Antennule female 5-segmented (Fig. 37G); P1 endopod-1 without inner seta (Fig. 37H); P4 endopod a minute segment with 1 short and 1 long seta (Fig. 37 I), not modified in male.
....**Huntemanniidae** [88] (Part 3)

These characters not combined.
....**Canthocamptidae** [89] (Part 3)

---

[83] *Nannopus* (part.), ***Pontopolites***
[84] ***Diarthrodella*** (male part.)
[85] *Limnocletodes, Nannopodella*
[86] *Carolinicola*
[87] *Pontocletodes*
[88] *Nannopus* (part.)
[89] *Barbaracletodes*, ***Boreolimella***, *Bryocamptus* (part.), ***Cletocamptus*** (part.), *Echinocamptus* (part.), *Elaphoidella* (part.), *Fibulacamptus* (part.), ***Itunella***, *Leimia*, ***Mesopsyllus*** (part.), *Perucamptus*, ***Pusillargillus***, *Pyrocletodes*

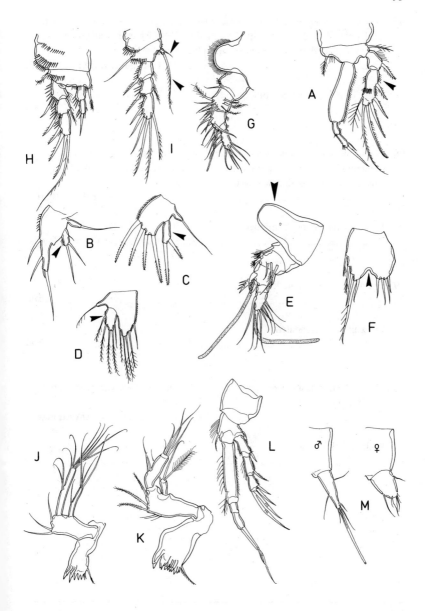

Fig. 37. Key to families of Harpacticoida. Couplets 92-97.

97. Rostrum prominent, defined at base; mandibular palp with well-developed rami (Figs 37J, K); maxilliped as in Fig. 32K; P1 endopod prehensile (Fig. 37L); caudal rami sexually dimorphic (Fig. 37M).
....**Tetragonicipitidae** [90] (Part 2)

These characters not combined.
....**98**

98. Cephalothorax without dorsal nuchal organ; antennule female 8- to 9-segmented; antenna with basis; P1 inner basal spine male modified (Figs 38A, B); P3 endopod male without apophysis.
....**Ameiridae** [91] (Part 2)

These characters not combined.
....**Canthocamptidae** [92] (Part 3)

99. P1 exopod 2-segmented.
....**100**

P1 exopod 3-segmented.
....**104**

100. Cephalothorax and free-prosomites with paired backwardly-directed horn-like processes.
....**Styracothoracidae** [93]

Such processes absent
....**101**

---

[90] *Pteropsyllus*, *Paraschizopera*
[91] *Leptomesochra* (part.), *Nitocrella*, *Pseudoleptomesochrella*, *Stygonitocrella*
[92] *Antrocamptus*, *Attheyella* (part.), **Bathycamptus**, *Bryocamptus* (part.), *Canthocamptus* (part.), *Echinocamptus* (part.), *Elaphoidella* (part.), *Epactophanoides*, **Heteropsyllus**, **Mesochra** (part.), **Mesopsyllus** (part.), **Nannomesochra,** *Parepactophanes* (part.), **Psammocamptus**, *Spelaeocamptus*, *Stygelaphoidella*
[93] Monotypic. Marine, deep-sea. Description given by Huys (1993).

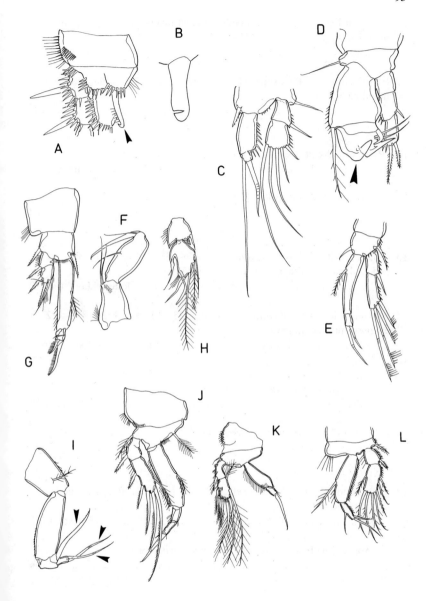

Fig. 38. Key to families of Harpacticoida. Couplets 98-104.

101. P1 as in Fig. 38C; P2-P4 exopod-1 without inner seta; P4 exopod male modified (Fig. 38D).

....**Latiremidae** [94]

P1 different; P2-P4 exopod-1 with inner seta; P4 exopod male not modified.

....**102**

102. P1 exopod-2 with 4 setae / spines (Fig. 38E).

....**Ameiridae** [95]

P1 exopod-2 with 5-8 setae / spines.

....**103**

103. Antenna with allobasis; maxilliped as in Fig. 38F; P1 as in Fig. 38G; P2 endopod male modified, 2-segmented (Fig. 38H).

....**Thalestridae** [96] (Part 2)

Antenna with basis; maxilliped as in Fig. 38I; P1 as in Figs 38J-L; P2 endopod male not modified.

....**Paramesochridae** [97] (Part 2)

104. P1 exopod-3 with 6-7 setae / spines.

....**105**

P1 exopod-3 with, at most, 5 setae / spines.

....**107**

105. P1 exopod-2 without inner seta; P1 as in Fig. 27L; P2-P4 exopod-1 without inner seta.

....**Thalestridae** [98]

P1 exopod-2 with inner seta; P2-P4 exopod-1 with inner seta

....**106**

---

[94] *Delamarella*
[95] *Paraleptomesochra*
[96] ***Diarthrodes*** (part.)
[97] ***Diarthrodella***, *Rossopsyllus*, *Tisbisoma*
[98] *Dactylopia*: this genus also keys out in couplet 40 because of the variable segmentation of P2-P4 endopods (cf. couplet 35).

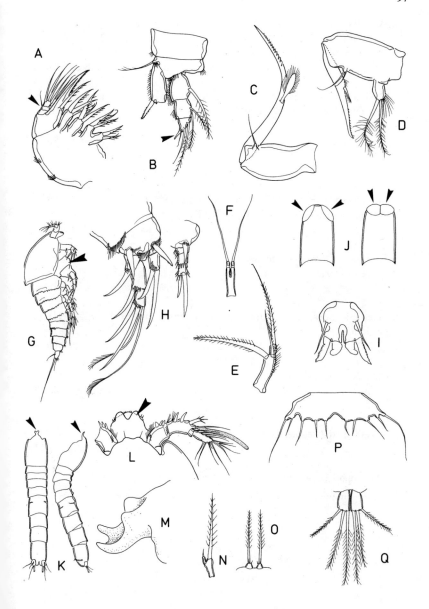

Fig. 39. Key to families of Harpacticoida. Couplets 105-111.

106. Maxilla with 3 closely-set endites on syncoxa and with well-developed
endopod (Fig. 39A); P3-P4 endopod-2 with 1 inner seta: P2 endopod-3
male with distal apophysis (Fig. 39B).
....**Tisbidae** [99] (Part 2)

Maxilla with at most 2 widely separated endites, endopod absent (Figs
39C, D); P3-P4 endopod-2 with 2 inner setae; P2 endopod-3 male without
distal apophysis
....**Tisbidae** [100] (Part 2)

107. Mandible, maxillule and maxilla reduced; maxillipeds as in Figs 39E-F;
P1 with robust protopod (Fig. 39G), as in Fig. 39H; P5 fused in both sexes
to form a small midventral plate (Fig. 39I).
....**Metidae** (Part 2)

These characters not combined.
....**108**

108. Cephalothorax with paired cuticular lenses anteriorly (Fig. 39J);
planktonic.
....**Miraciidae** [101]

Cuticular lenses absent.
....**109**

109. P4 endopod 2-segmented.
....**110**

P4 endopod 3-segmented.
....**116**

[99] *Idyellopsis, Tachidiella*
[100] *Bathyidya, Neotisbella, Octopinella, Paraidya, **Tisbe**, Tisbella, Tisbintra, Volkmannia, Yunona*
[101] *Miracia, Oculosetella, Distioculus*

110. Labrum with bifid anteriorly-directed process (Figs 39K-M); maxilliped as in Figs 39N, O.
....**Huntemanniidae** [102]

Labrum and maxilliped different.
....**111**

111. Rostrum as Figs 28C, D; P1 endopod 2-segmented, not prehensile; P5 with fused exopod and baseoendopod (Figs 39P, Q).
....**Danielsseniidae** [103] (Part 1 p. 236)

Rostrum different; other characters not combined.
....**112**

112. P1 endopod 2-segmented, endopod-1 shorter than endopod-2 (Fig. 40A); P2-P4 exopod-1 with inner seta.
....**Argestidae** [104]

These characters not combined.
....**113**

113. P1 exopod-3 with 5 setae / spines; P1 exopod-2 with inner seta (Fig. 40B).
....**Ameiridae** [105]

P1 exopod-3 with 4 setae / spines.
....**114**

114. P2-P4 exopod-1 with inner seta.
....**Diosaccidae** [106] (Part 2)

P2-P4 exopod-1 without inner seta
....**115**

---

[102] *Talpina* (male part.)
[103] *Cylindronannopus*, ***Paranannopus*** (male part.)
[104] *Dizahavia* (part.)
[105] *Nitocrellopsis*
[106] ***Pseudodiosaccus***

115. Maxilliped as in Fig. 40C; P2-P4 exopod-3 with 3 or 4 setae / spines; P3 endopod-2 male without inner apophysis.
....**Diosaccidae** [107]

Maxilliped as in Fig. 40D; P2-P4 exopod-3 with at least 5 setae / spines; P3 endopod-2 male with inner apophysis (Fig. 40E).
....**Canthocamptidae** [108]

116. Mandibular palp as in Figs 23H-I (basis elongated, endopod twisted over exopod and with long, posteriorly-directed setae); rostrum typically triangular, often incised near the apex (Fig. 28F); P5 exopod laterally displaced (as in cyclopoids) (Fig. 23K).
....**Diosaccidae** [109] (Part 2)

These characters not combined.
....**117**

117. Body as in Fig. 40F; maxilliped with long syncoxa and basis (Fig. 40G); P1 as in Fig. 40H, exopod-3 with 3 setae / spines; planktonic.
....**Miraciidae** [110] (Part 1: p. 322)

These characters not combined.
....**118**

118. Body as in Fig. 40I; maxilla (Fig. 40J) and maxilliped (Fig. 40K) modified as grasping appendages; ectoparasitic on gills of teleost fish.
....**Tisbidae** [111]

These characters not combined.
....**119**

---

[107] *Schizoperoides, Schizoperopsis*
[108] *Attheyella* (part.), *Bryocamptus* (part.), *Canthocamptus* (part.)
[109] **Stenhelia** (***Delavalia***) (part.), **Stenhelia** (***Stenhelia***)
[110] ***Macrosetella***
[111] *Neoscutellidium*

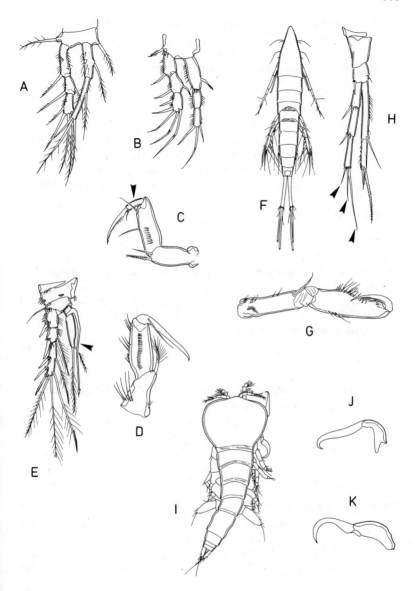

Fig. 40. Key to families of Harpacticoida. Couplets 112-118.

119. Antennary exopod 4-segmented (Fig. 41A); P1 as in Fig. 41B.
....**Tisbidae** [112]

Antennary exopod at most 3-segmented; P1 different.
....**120**

120. Rostrum large, bell-shaped (Figs 41C, D); antennules short, with numerous pinnate setae / spines (Fig. 41C); P1 as in Fig. 41E, endopod 2- or 3-segmented (with 1 (or 2) inner and 2 distal spines); P5 with widely separated exopod(al lobe) and endopodal lobe (Figs 41F, G).
....**Thalestridae** [113] (Part 2)

These characters not combined.
....**121**

121. Labrum with anteriorly-directed bifid extension (visible in dorsal aspect) (Figs 41H, I).
....**Diosaccidae** [114]

Labrum without such extension.
....**122**

122. P1 endopod 2-segmented, not prehensile, endopod-2 with 1 inner and 3 distal setae / spines (basically as in Fig. 41K).
....**123**

P1 endopod different
....**126**

123. P1 exopod-3 with 4 setae / spines (Fig. 41K).
....**124**

P1 exopod-3 with 5 setae / spines.
....**125**

---

[112] *Drescheriella*
[113] ***Pseudotachidius*** (part.)
[114] *Cladorostrata*

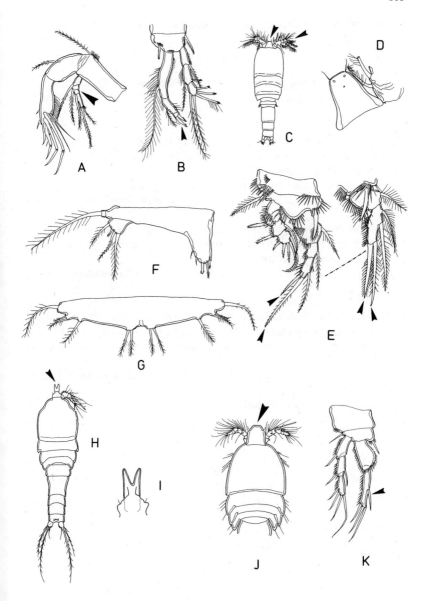

Fig. 41. Key to families of Harpacticoida. Couplets 119-124.

124. Rostrum large, defined at base (Fig. 41J); P2-P4 exopod-1 without inner seta.

....**Diosaccidae** [115] (Part 2)

Rostrum minute, fused to cephalothorax; P2-P4 exopod-1 with inner seta.

....**Argestidae** [116]

125. Rostrum defined at base (Figs 42A, B); antennule female short, at most 6-segmented (Fig. 42A); antennary exopod 3-segmented (Fig. 42C); male with spinous apophysis on P2 endopod-2 (and/or endopod-3) (Figs 42D, E) or with hooked apophysis on P3 endopod-2 (Fig. 42F)

....**Danielsseniidae** [117] (Part 1 p. 236)

Rostrum fused to cephalothorax; antennule female slender, at least 7-segmented (Fig. 42G); antennary exopod 1-segmented (Fig. 42H); P2-P3 endopod male not modified

....**Argestidae** [118] (Part 3)

126. Rostrum large, shaped as in Fig. 42I; maxilliped small (Fig. 42J); P1 with 3-segmented, non-prehensile endopod and armature as in Fig. 42K; P5 a single plate with exopodal and endopodal setae widely separated (Fig. 42L).

....**Thalestridae** [119] (Part 2)

These characters not combined.

....**127**

---

[115] *Pseudomesochra* (part.)
[116] *Dizahavia* (part.), *Odiliacletodes*
[117] *Afrosenia, Archisenia, Bathypsammis, **Danielssenia, Fladenia**, Leptotachidia, **Micropsammis, Paradanielssenia, Psammis, Jonesiella, Telopsammis**. Idomene aberrans* Por really belongs to the Paranannopidae.
[118] *Fultonia, Neoargestes* (part.)
[119] *Pseudotachidius* (part.)

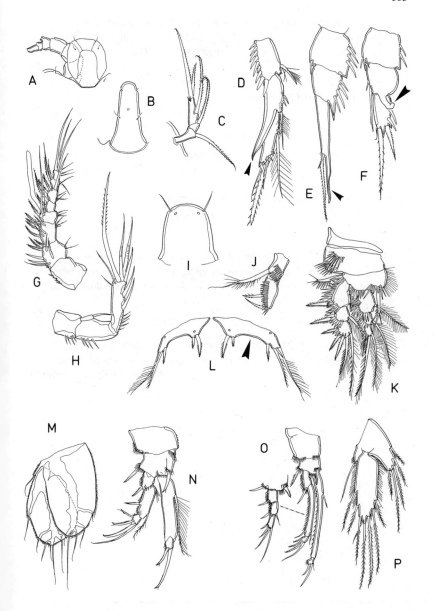

Fig. 42. Key to families of Harpacticoida. Couplets 125-129.

127. Rostrum well developed, defined at base; P1 exopod-3 with 4 setae / spines; P1 endopod 2-segmented, endopod-1 longer than exopod, inner seta inserted in proximal half of segment (Figs 42N, O).

....**128**

These characters not combined.

....**130**

128. P2-P4 exopod-3 with 5, 6, 6 setae / spines, respectively.

....**Thalestridae** [120]

P2-P4 exopod-3 with different armature formula.

....**129**

129. P1 as in Fig. 42N; P2-P3 endopod-2 with 2 inner setae; P2 endopod male 2-segmented with distal apophysis on endopod-2; P5 female with large, foliaceous exopod and baseoendopod (Fig. 42M); P5 baseoendopod male with 3 spines.

....**Thalestridae** [121]

P1 as in Fig. 42O; P5 female without foliaceous rami (Fig. 42P); P5 baseoendopod male with 2 spines at most; other characters not combined.

....**Parastenheliidae** [122] (Part 2)

---

[120] *Marionobiotus*
[121] *Eudactylopus*
[122] This couplet not only keys out to **Parastenhelia** but also to *Karllangia*, currently placed in the Ameiridae. Both genera are heterogeneous assemblages and eventually might, to a certain extent, be related to each other. Any identification made should be checked against the relevant descriptions of both these two genera (Noodt, 1964; Wells, 1967; Kunz, 1975; Wells *et al.*, 1982; Wells & Rao, 1987; Mielke, 1994).

130. Rostrum large, defined at base, reaching to at least the distal margin of first antennulary segment (Fig. 43A); maxillipedal endopod an elongated segment bearing claw and 1-3 setae (Fig. 43B); P2 endopod male 2-segmented (Figs 43C-E); two egg-sacs.
....**Diosaccidae** [123] (Part 2)

These characters not combined
....**131**

131. Rostrum large, defined at base; P1 endopod-1 elongated, inner seta inserted in distal quarter of segment near boundary with endopod-2 (Figs 43F-I).
....**Diosaccidae** [124] (Part 2)

These characters not combined.
....**132**

132. P1 exopod-2 more than twice as long as exopod-1, outer spine inserted medially or subdistally (Figs 25D; 43J-M).
....**133**

These characters not combined.
....**134**

133. First antennulary segment with one long seta in both sexes; antennule, at most, 11-segmented in male; P3 endopod not modified in male.
....**Thalestridae** [125] (Part 2)

First antennulary segment without a seta in both sexes; antennule 14-segmented in male; P3 endopod modified in male.
....**Ambunguipedidae** (Part 2)

---

[123] *Actopsyllus*, **Amonardia** (part.), **Amphiascoides**, **Amphiascopsis** (part.), **Amphiascus**, *Antiboreodiosaccus*, *Balucopsylla*, **Bulbamphiascus**, *Dactylopodamphiascopsis*, **Diosaccus** (part.), **Eoschizopera**, **Haloschizopera**, *Helmutkunzia*, *Metamphiascopsis* (part.), *Miscegenus*, **Paramphiascella**, *Paramphiascoides*, **Paramphiascopsis**, *Pararobertsonia*, *Pholenota*, **Protopsammotopa**, **Psammotopa**, **Pseudamphiascopsis**, **Rhyncholagena**, **Robertgurneya**, **Robertsonia**, **Schizopera**, **Typhlamphiascus**
[124] **Amonardia** (part.), **Amphiascopsis** (part.), *Diosaccopsis*, **Diosaccus** (part.), *Ialysus*, *Metamphiascopsis* (part.), *Parialysus*, *Pseudodiosaccopsis*, *Teissierella*, *Tydemanella*
[125] **Amenophia**, **Dactylopusia** (part.), **Parathalestris**, *Peltthestris*, **Phyllothalestris**, **Rhynchothalestris**, *Thalestris*

134. P1 endopod distinctly 2-segmented.

....**135**

P1 endopod 3-segmented (Fig. 43N) or endopod-2 and endopod-3
separated by incomplete suture (Fig. 43O).

....**140**

135. P2-P4 exopod-1 without inner seta.

....**136**

P2-P4 exopod-1 with inner seta.

....**138**

136. P2-P4 endopod-1 without inner seta.

....**Ameiridae** [126](Part 2)

P2-P4 endopod-1 with inner seta.

....**137**

137. P1 endopod-2 with 2 armature elements (Fig. 44A); P5 female with fused
exopod and baseoendopod (Fig. 44C); P4 exopod male modified (Fig.
44B); P6 male paired, with 2 setae (Fig. 44D).

....**Latiremidae** [127]

P1 endopod-2 with 3 armature elements (Fig. 44E); P5 female with
separate exopod and baseoendopod (Fig. 44G); P4 exopod male not
modified; P6 male a median unarmed operculum (Fig. 44F).

....**Cancrincolidae** [128]

---

[126] ***Interleptomesochra*** (part.), *Parapseudoleptomesochra* (?) *reductus*, ***Psyllocamptus***
(Psyllocamptus)
[127] *Latiremus*
[128] Associates of intertidal and terrestrial crabs. Revision given by Fiers (1990). Contains the
genera *Cancrincola*, *Antillesia*, *Abscondicola* and *Neocancrincola*.

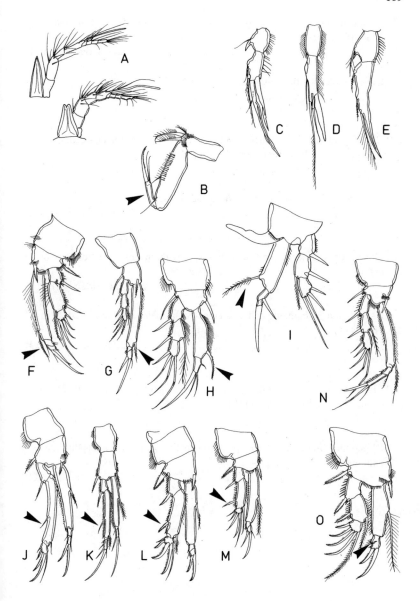

Fig. 43. Key to families of Harpacticoida, Couplets 130-135.

138. Rostrum large, bell-shaped (Fig. 44H); P1 endopod-2 with 4 setae / spines (Fig. 44I).

....**Thalestridae** [129] (Part 2)

These characters not combined.

....**139**

139. P3 endopod-2 with 2 inner setae; P1 basis male with inner basal spine modified and/or P5 baseoendopod male with 3 spines

....**Thalestridae** [130] (Part 2)

P3 endopod-2 with 1 inner seta; these male characters absent

....**Thalestridae** [131] (Part 2)

140. P2 endopod 2-segmented in both sexes, without any modifications in male

....**Ameiridae** [132] (Part 2)

P2 endopod 3-segmented; if 2-segmented in male, then modified as in Figs 44J-L.

....**141**

141. P1 endopod not prehensile, endopod-1 shorter than endopod-2 and endopod-3 combined (Figs 44M-O).

....**142**

P1 endopod prehensile or endopod-1 distinctly longer than endopod-2 and endopod-3 combined (Figs 44P-Q).

....**145**

---

[129] *Pseudotachidius* (part.)
[130] *Dactylopodopsis*, *Neodactylopus*, *Sewellia*
[131] *Dactylopodella* (part.), *Idomene* (part.)
[132] *Interleptomesochra* (part.), *Praeleptomesochra*, *Pseudoleptomesochra*

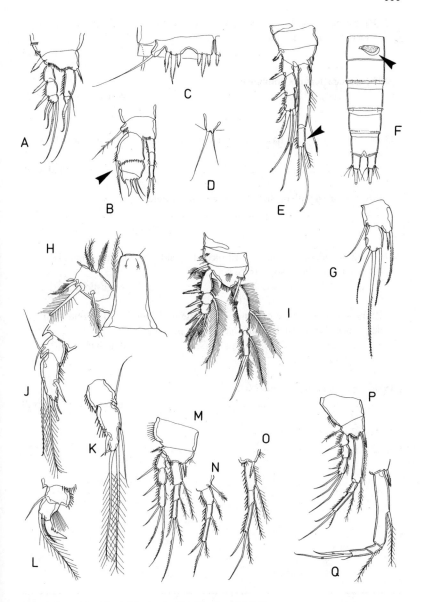

Fig. 44. Key to families of Harpacticoida, Couplets 136-141.

112

142. P1 exopod-2 with inner seta, exopod-3 with 5 setae / spines; P2-P3 exopod-1 with inner seta

....**143**

These characters not combined

....**Ameiridae** [133] (Part 2)

143. Rostrum defined at base (Fig. 45B); antenna robust in appearance (Figs 45A-C).

....**Ameiridae** [134]

Rostrum fused with cephalothorax; antenna different

....**144**

144. P5 baseoendopods female fused medially, endopodal lobe vestigial (Fig. 45D); P1 inner basal spine male not modified.

....**Argestidae** [135] (Part 3)

P5 baseoendopods female not fused medially, endopodal lobe well-developed (Fig. 45E); P1 inner basal spine male modified.

....**Ameiridae** [136] (Part 2)

145. P3 endopod-2 with 2 inner setae.

....**Thalestridae** [137] (Part 2)

P3 endopod-2 with 1 inner seta.

....**146**

---

[133] *Ameiropsyllus, Limameira, **Nitokra** (part.), Parapseudoleptomesochra (part.), **Proameira** (part.), **Pseudameira**, Psyllocamptus (**Langpsyllocamptus**)*
[134] *Parameiropsis*
[135] *Argestes, Parargestes, **Neoargestes** (part.); Abyssameira*, formerly placed in the Ameiridae, is herein transferred to the Argestidae.
[136] ***Sarsameira** (part.), **Argestigens**.* There is evidence to believe that the latter genus really belongs to the Ameiridae.
[137] ***Dactylopusia** (part.), **Dactylopusioides**, **Paradactylopodia** (part.), Protolatiremus*

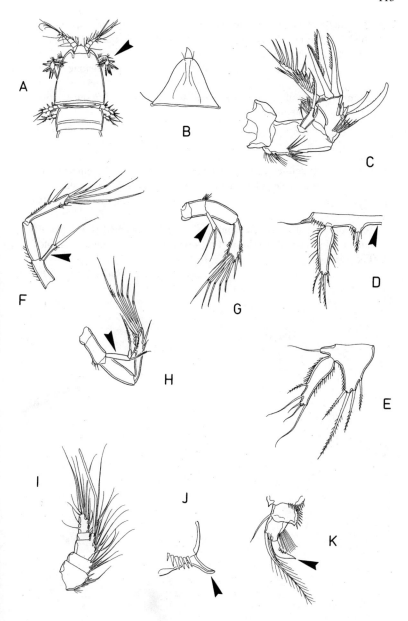

Fig. 45. Key to families of Harpacticoida, Couplets 142-146.

114

146. Antennary exopod 1- or 2-segmented with a total of 2 or 3 setae (Figs 45F-H); P1 inner basal spine male modified; P2 endopod male 3-segmented, not modified.
....**Ameiridae** [138] (Part 2)

Antennary exopod 2- or 3-segmented with a total of 5-7 setae; other characters not combined.
....**147**

147. Rostrum not defined at base; antennule female 6- or 7-segmented; P1 inner basal spine male not modified; P2 endopod male 3-segmented.
....**Thalestridae** [139] (Part 2)

Rostrum defined at base; antennule female 5-segmented (Fig. 45I); P1 inner basal spine male modified (Fig. 45J); P2 endopod male 2-segmented (Fig. 45K).
....**Thalestridae** [140] (Part 2)

---

[138] *Ameira*, *Ameiropsis,* Haifameira, *Nitokra* (part.), *Parapseudoleptomesochra* (part.), *Proameira* (part.), *Psammameira*, *Sarsameira* (part.), *Sicameira, Stenocopia*
[139] *Idomene* (part.)
[140] *Paradactylopodia* (part.)

Family LONGIPEDIIDAE Brady, 1880.

Diagnosis.

Body (Fig. 46A). Large, fusiform in dorsal view, without marked distinction between prosome and urosome. Cephalothorax with very large rostrum defined at base. Female genital double-somite with large triangular, lateral processes (arrowed in Fig. 46A); genital field compact, with median copulatory pore immediately posterior to a common genital aperture. Characteristic anal operculum prominent (Fig. 46B) with a strong median spine and 2 to 7 small lateral spines on each side.

Antennule. Female indistinctly 6-segmented, with two aesthetascs midway on outer margin and two modified apical setae on terminal segment; many pinnate and pectinate setae. Chirocer in male.

Antenna (Fig. 46C). Exopod 8-segmented, endopod 3-segmented; protopod and proximal segment of endopod and exopod all fused.

Mandible. Basis with two setae; endopod 2-segmented; exopod 3-segmented.

Maxillule. Coxal epipodite with five setae. Baso-exite represented by one small seta. Exopod 1-segmented; endopod indistinctly 2-segmented.

Maxilla. Praecoxa and coxa separate, each with two endites; endopod 3-segmented.

Maxilliped. Phyllopodial (similar to Fig. 10E), syncoxa with one very large plumose seta and eight or nine smaller setae; basis with two setae; endopod 1-segmented with eleven setae.

P1-P4. Coxa of each limb with inner seta / spine; rami 3-segmented. P1 exopod-1 with inner seta, endopod not prehensile; P2 endopod characteristic, with distal segment extremely elongate with strong spines (Fig. 46D). Male P2 sometimes with one fewer spine on endopod-3 and less well-developed unguiform process on endopod-1 than in female.

P5. Basis and endopod separate (Fig. 47C). Outer portion of basis an elongate cylinder with a terminal seta; endopod with a fused, long whiplash-shaped structure and one small articulating seta; exopod separate and 1-segmented. In female, bases not fused medially; in male, bases fused medially and exopod differs in shape, ornamentation and setation.

Male P6. Asymmetrical, with a spine and two setae.

Females with a single egg-sac; males with one spermatophore.

Monogeneric.

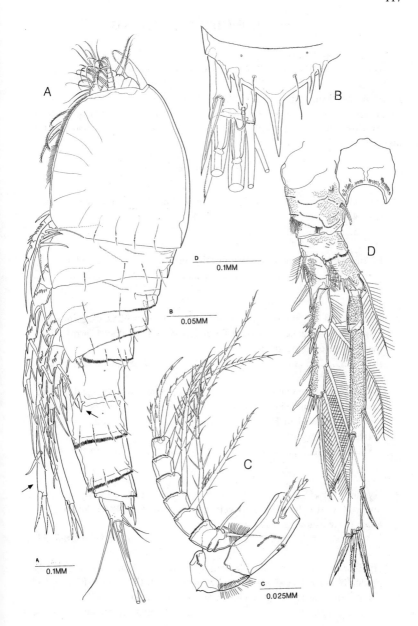

Fig. 46. *Longipedia minor*: A, body in lateral view, arrows indicate elongate P2 endopod and lateral process of genital double-somite; B, operculum; C, antennary protopod, exopod and proximal (fused) endopod segment; D, P2.

Genus LONGIPEDIA Claus, 1863

Diagnosis: As for family.
Latest revision by Wells (1980). Eleven species known world-wide.

Local species. Four. Setal formulae in Appendix Table 1 (p. 340).
Adult females and males can be distinguished by the following keys but the full descriptions in Wells (1980) should be consulted for confirmation of any identification.

FEMALES

1. P2 endopod-1 with large unguiform projection distally on anterior face (Fig. 47B).
   ....**2**

   P2 endopod-1 with no projection distally on anterior face (Fig. 48B).
   ....**3**

2. Hyaline frill of genital double-somite not toothed at 625x magnification (Fig. 47A). Articulating seta on P5 endopod well-developed (arrowed in Fig. 47C); exopod rectangular.
   .... ***Longipedia coronata*** Claus

   Hyaline frill of genital double-somite with pronounced teeth equal in size, dorsal and ventral (Fig. 47D). Articulating seta on P5 endopod small and smooth (arrowed in Fig. 47E); exopod with inner and outer margins noticeably divergent.
   .... ***Longipedia scotti*** Sars

3. Hyaline frill of genital double-somite with large teeth ventrally, grading abruptly ventro-laterally into very small teeth (Fig. 48A). P5 exopod about twice as long as wide (Fig. 48C).
   .... ***Longipedia helgolandica*** Klie

   Hyaline frill of genital double-somite with large ventral teeth, grading gradually dorso-laterally into smaller dorsal teeth (Fig. 48E). P5 exopod about three times as long as wide, sides nearly parallel (Fig. 48F).
   .... ***Longipedia minor*** T. & A. Scott

119

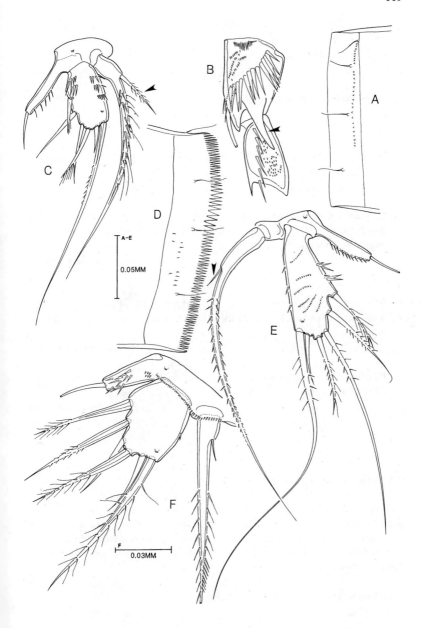

Fig. 47. *Longipedia coronata*: A, lateral hyaline frill on female genital double-somite; B, proximal two segments of P2 endopod; C, female P5. *L. scotti:* D, lateral hyaline frill on female genital double-somite; E, female P5; F, male P5

MALES

1. P5 exopod with six setae.
    ....**2**

    P5 exopod with seven or eight setae.
    ....**3**

2. Hyaline frill of third urosomite with moderately large and broad teeth all round body. P2 endopod-1 with unguiform process.
    .... *Longipedia scotti*

    Hyaline frill of third urosomite with ventral teeth larger than lateral or dorsal but with all teeth slender and finely pointed. P2 endopod-1 without unguiform process.
    .... *Longipedia helgolandica*

3. P5 exopod with seven setae (Fig. 48G). Hyaline frill of third urosomite with rather slender closely set teeth larger ventrally and laterally than dorsally.
    .... *Longipedia minor*

    P5 exopod with eight setae. Hyaline frill of third urosomite not dentate at 625x magnification (Fig. 47A).
    .... *Longipedia coronata*

All species

Morphological descriptions: Wells (1980).

Habitat: Found from the lower (or, much less often, the middle) part of the shore down to about 150m, predominantly on mixtures of sand and mud, less often on clean sand, pure mud or amongst algae; sometimes in the plankton, where they are most numerous just above the bottom. In small numbers almost anywhere in fully marine waters, locally common.

Distribution: Throughout north-west Europe.

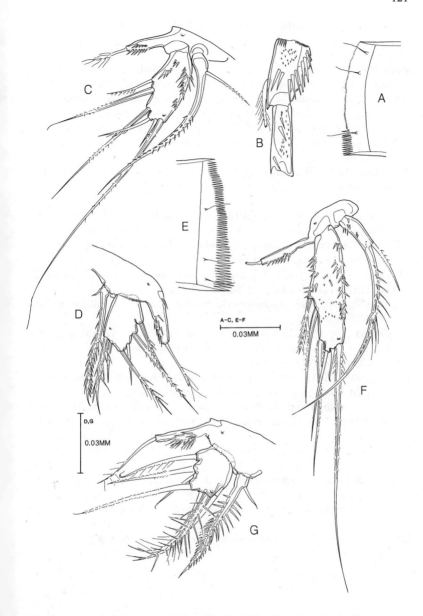

Fig. 48. *Longipedia helgolandica*: A, lateral hyaline frill on female genital double-somite; B, proximal two segments of P2 endopod; C, female P5; D, male P5. *L. minor*: E, lateral hyaline frill on female genital double-somite; F, female P5; G, male P5

Family CANUELLIDAE Lang, 1944

Diagnosis.

Body (Fig. 2). Large (1-2mm), elongate, sub-cylindrical, without marked distinction between prosome and urosome. Rostrum large, defined at base. Female genital double-somite completely fused, cylindrical, without lateral processes; genital field with paired copulatory pores and gonopores (Fig. 50D). Operculum weakly-developed or replaced by pseudoperculum. Caudal rami usually divergent and much longer than broad (Fig. 51D-G); sometimes sexually dimorphic.

Antennule. In female, indistinctly 4- or 5-segmented, with two aesthetascs midway on anterior margin; with many pinnate or pectinate setae. Variable in male.

Antenna (Fig. 49A). With well defined basis and 6- to 8-segmented exopod. Endopod 2- or 3-segmented.

Mandible. Coxa and gnathobase well developed. Basis with two setae. Exopod 2- to 4-segmented; endopod 2-segmented.

Maxillule. Coxal epipodite represented by two or three setae. Endopod 2-segmented; exopod 1-segmented with heavily plumose setae.

Maxilla (Fig. 49B). Praecoxa and coxa incompletely fused, each with two endites, endopod 1-segmented.

Maxilliped (Fig. 49C). Non-prehensile, phyllopodial. Syncoxa with numerous setae. Basis with two setae. Endopod 1-segmented or indistinctly 2-segmented with many heavily plumose setae.

P1 (Fig. 50A). Coxa with inner seta (arrowed in Fig. 50A). Rami 2- or 3-segmented; exopod-1 without inner seta, endopod not prehensile.

P2-P4. Coxa with or without inner seta. Rami 3-segmented except P4 endopod which may be 2-segmented. Sexual dimorphism variable but usually present on endopod of one leg.

P5. Not sexually dimorphic. Limb incorporated into somite and represented only by four setae.

Male P6. Symmetrical, represented by one to three setae.

Females with two divergent egg-sacs, males with two spermatophores.

Seventeen genera known world-wide. Latest key to genera given by Huys (1995b).

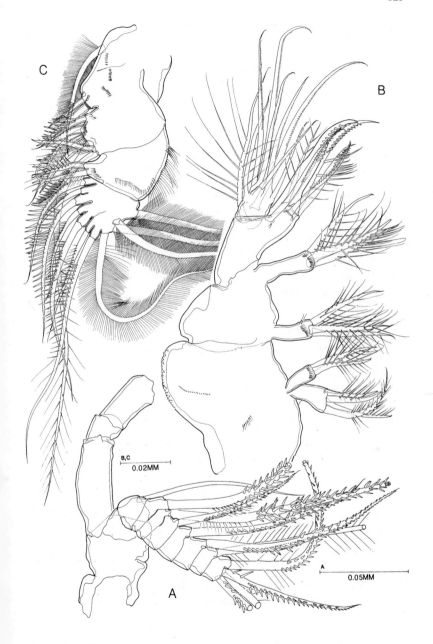

Fig. 49. *Canuella perplexa*: A, antenna (armature and ornamentation of endopod omitted); B, maxilla; C, maxilliped.

Key to world genera of Canuellidae

READ THREE ALTERNATIVES

1. P4 endopod distal segment with two setae / spines.
    ....***Microcanuella*** Mielke, 1994

    P4 endopod distal segment with three setae / spines.
    ....**2**

    P4 endopod distal segment with four setae / spines.
    ....**7**

2. P4 endopod 2-segmented.
    ....**3**

    P4 endopod 3-segmented.
    ....**5**

3. Distal segments of both rami of P3 with four setae / spines; P4 exopod-2 without inner seta.
    ....***Ellucana*** Sewell, 1940 [141]

    P3 exopod-3 and endopod-3 with five and three setae / spines, respectively; P4 exopod-2 with inner seta
    ....**4**

4. Maxilla sexually dimorphic, allobasal claw strongly chitinised, dark brown and recurved in female, much smaller, straight and with blunt teeth in male; antennule with enormous sub-chela in male.
    ....***Parasunaristes*** Fiers, 1982

    Maxilla not sexually dimorphic, allobasal claw short and accompanied, at base, by four accessory setae; antennule with moderately-developed subchela.
    ....***Intersunaristes*** Huys, 1995

---

[141] *Canuellina nicobaris* Wells & Rao, 1987, whose taxonomic status is unresolved, keys out to the genus *Ellucana*.

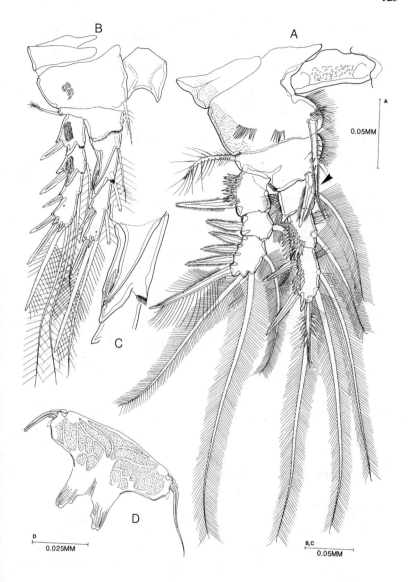

Fig. 50. *Canuella perplexa*: A, P1, anterior; B, P2 anterior; C, P2 endopod-1 and -2, anterior; D, female genital field.

5. P1 exopod-3 and endopod-3 with six and four setae / spines, respectively.
....*Galapacanuella* Mielke, 1979

P1 exopod-3 and endopod-3 with seven and five or six setae / spines, respectively.
....**6**

6. Distal segment of both rami of P3 with four setae / spines; P4 exopod-2 without inner seta.
....*Canuellina* Gurney, 1927

P3 exopod-3 and endopod-3 with five and three setae respectively; P4 exopod-2 with inner seta.
....*Sunaristes* (p.132)

7. P1 exopod 2-segmented.
....*Canuellopsis* (p. 136)

P1 exopod 3-segmented.
....**8**

8. P3 exopod-3 with four setae / spines.
....**9**

P3 exopod-3 with five setae / spines.
....**10**

READ FOUR ALTERNATIVES

9. P2 exopod-3 with four setae / spines.
....*Brianola* (p. 134)

P2 exopod-3 with five setae / spines.
....*Nathaniella* Por, 1984

P2 exopod-3 with six setae / spines.
....*Ifanella* Vervoort, 1964

P2 exopod-3 with seven setae / spines.
....*Intercanuella* Becker & Schriever, 1979

10. P4 exopod-3 with four setae / spines.
....**11**

P4 exopod-3 with five setae / spines.
....**12**

11. P1-bearing somite fused to cephalosome; P4 exopod-2 without inner seta.
....*Coullana* Por, 1984 [142]

P1-bearing somite not fused to cephalosome; P4 exopod-2 with inner seta.
....*Scottolana* Por, 1964

12. P4 endopod-2 without inner seta.
....**13**

P4 endopod-2 with inner seta.
....*Elanella* Por, 1984

13. Female caudal rami distinctly longer than wide; P3 and P4 coxae with inner seta; free-living.
....*Canuella* (p. 128)

Female caudal rami not longer than wide; P3 and P4 coxae without inner seta; endo-associates of sea urchins.
....*Echinosunaristes* Huys, 1995

---

[142] *Brianola pori* Hamond, 1972 keys out to the genus *Coullana*. Por (1984) suggested that this species does not belong to the genus *Brianola* and should probably be placed in a separate genus.

Genus CANUELLA T. & A. Scott, 1893

Diagnosis: Canuellidae.

Body. (Fig. 2). P1-bearing somite not fused to cephalosome. Rostrum elongate. Urosome without distinct spinule rows, hyaline frills plain. Genital double-somite in female with lateral sub-cuticular rib. Female genital field (Fig. 50D) large; paired copulatory pores posteriorly displaced and covered by flaps with free lateral margins; gonopores covered by opercula with one seta. Anal somite with weakly-developed operculum. Caudal rami (Fig. 51 D-G) markedly divergent, sometimes sexually dimorphic.

Antennule. Haplocer in male.

Antenna. (Fig. 49A). Exopod 8-segmented, as long as endopod; spinulose setae on segments 2-8. Endopod indistinctly 3-segmented.

Mandible. Exopod 3-segmented.

Maxillule. Coxal epipodite with two setae.

P1-P4. Rami 3-segmented, coxa with inner seta. Setal formula constant in all species (see Appendix Table 1 (p.340)). P2 endopod-1 with apophysis fitting into groove with bordering spinule rows on endopod-2 (Fig. 50B, C). P3-P4 endopod-1 and 2 outer distal corner attenuated. P4 endopod longer than exopod. No sexual dimorphism.

Male P6. (Fig. 51A-C). Large and complex; with three setae, proximal seta minute, middle seta very long and barbed; distal margin with triangular extension. Inner margin of plate produced into membranous flap with bifid distal extension. Urosomite-3 with mid-ventral spinulose ridge.

Three described species known world-wide.

Local species. Three. Setal formula in Appendix Table 1 (p.340). All three species can be distinguished by the following key or on the structure of the male P6 (see Fig. 51A-C).

1. Caudal ramus at least as long as last three urosomites (Fig. 51G).
    .... *Canuella furcigera*

    Caudal ramus at most as long as last two urosomites.
    ....**2**

2. Urosomites and caudal rami (Fig. 51D,E) with distinct pattern of denticles; seta IV heavily spinulose, modified in female (Fig. 51E).
    .... *Canuella perplexa*

    Urosomites and caudal rami (Fig. 51F) without denticles; seta IV not heavily spinulose, not modified in female (Fig. 51F).
    ....*Canuella* sp.

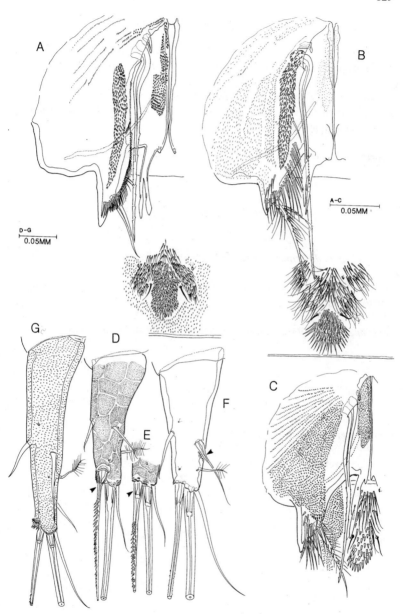

Fig. 51. Male P6 (right only) of, A, *Canuella perplexa*; B, *Canuella* sp.; C, *Canuella furcigera*. Caudal ramus of, D, *Canuella perplexa* male; E, *Canuella perplexa* female; F, *Canuella* sp. female; G, *Canuella furcigera* female.

Canuella perplexa T. & A. Scott, 1893

Morphological descriptions: T. & A. Scott (1893); Bodin (1970); Mielke (1975).

Habitat: Usually on clean sand with a variable proportion of silt, from low intertidal to about 30m, and occasionally in the plankton. Can be extremely abundant on decaying *Ulva*.

Distribution: Widely distributed throughout north-west Europe.

Canuella furcigera Sars, 1903

Morphological descriptions: Sars (1911), Sars (1920).

Habitat: Muddy bottom, shallow subtidal. Can be locally abundant, especially on estuarine mudflats.

Distribution: Oslofjord, southern North Sea and English Channel coasts.

Canuella sp.

Morphological description: Undescribed.

Habitat: Brackish water lagoon.

Distribution: Dievengat (north-west Belgium).

Genus SUNARISTES Hesse, 1867

Diagnosis: Canuellidae.

Body (Fig. 52A,B). Very large (approx. 2mm) and slender. P1-bearing somite fused to cephalosome which is somewhat laterally compressed. Urosomites without spinule rows, hyaline frills plain. Genital double-somite without sub-cuticular rib; female genital field (Fig. 52C) with paired opercula (vestigial P6 bearing one seta and a median process) covering separate paired gonopores and copulatory pores. Anal somite with operculum. Caudal rami longer in female than in male; divergent, tapering, without scales or spinules; seta V about as long as urosome.

Antennule. Chirocer in male.

Antenna. Exopod 8-segmented, armature elements on all segments. Endopod 3-segmented.

Mandible. Exopod 3-segmented.

Maxillule. Coxal epipodite with two setae.

P1. Rami 3-segmented.

P2-P4. Rami 3-segmented; without inner seta on coxa. P4 endopod shorter than exopod. In male, P2 endopod-1 with large, and endopod-2 with small, apophysis (Fig. 52D).

Male P6. A triangular plate with two setae, inner seta modified.

Four species known world-wide. Latest key to species in Hamond (1973).

Local species. One. Setal formula in Appendix Table 1 (p.340).

Sunaristes paguri Hesse, 1867

Morphological descriptions: Sars (1911); Sars (1920); Codreanu & Mack-Fira (1961).

Habitat: Copepodites and adults commensal on hermit crabs, mostly *Pagurus bernhardus* but occasionally other species. Found from below low water mark to about 20m, rarely deeper.

Distribution: In suitable habitats throughout north-west Europe, the Mediterranean and the Black Sea.

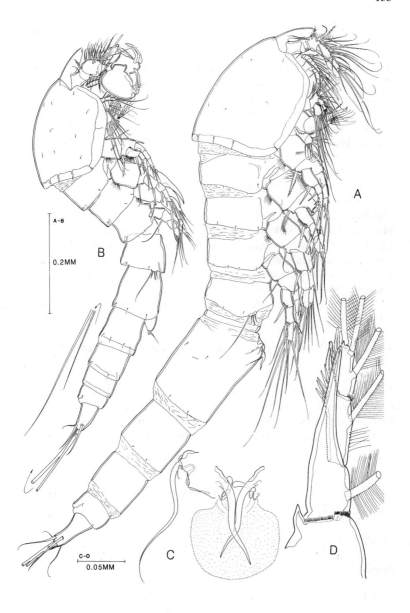

Fig. 52. *Sunaristes paguri*: A, female body, lateral; B, male body, lateral; C, female genital field; D, male P2 endopod.

Genus BRIANOLA Monard, 1927

Diagnosis: Canuellidae.

Body (Fig. 53A). P1-bearing somite fused to cephalosome. Rostrum very large, exceeding length of antennules. Urosomites variously ornamented with rows of fine spinules; hyaline frills markedly incised. Female genital field small; opercula closing off gonopores with one seta (vestigial P6); copulatory pores median under a membranous flap. Penultimate urosomite with deeply-incised pseudoperculum (Fig. 53E). Caudal rami slightly divergent; seta I minute; with rows of scales and two rows of spinules on outer margin (Fig. 53E).

Antenna (Fig. 53B). Exopod 8-segmented (arrowed in Fig. 53B) with setae absent on at least four segments, distinctly shorter than endopod. Endopod 3-segmented.

Mandible. Exopod indistinctly 2-segmented.

Maxillule. Epipodite with three setae.

P1. (Fig. 53C). Rami 3-segmented. Outer spines of exopod-1 and -2 strongly pectinate (arrowed in Fig. 53C)

P2-P4. Rami 3-segmented. Coxa without inner seta. P4 endopod longer than exopod. No sexual dimorphism.

P5. Limbs connected by a deeply-incised symmetrical hyaline frill (arrowed in Fig. 53D).

Seven species known world-wide, latest revision and key to species in Hamond (1973).

Local species. One. Setal formula in Appendix Table 1 (p.340). Monard (1935) recorded *Brianola stebleri* (Monard, 1926) from the "vivier" (holding tanks) of the biological station at Roscoff. This is the only record of this species outside the Mediterranean region and therefore of doubtful validity.

Brianola sp.

Morphological description: Undescribed.

Habitat: Intertidal mud.

Distribution: Percuil Creek in the Fal estuary, Cornwall.

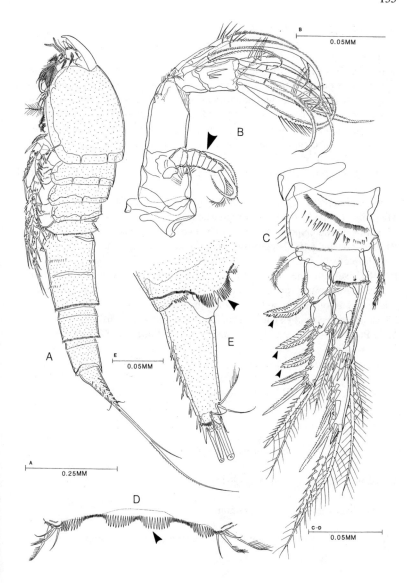

Fig. 53. *Brianola* sp: A, female body, lateral; B, antenna; C, P1; D, P5; E, pseudoperculum and caudal ramus.

Genus CANUELLOPSIS Lang, 1936

Diagnosis: Canuellidae.

Body (Fig. 54A). Heavily chitinised and brown in colour. P1-bearing somite fused to cephalosome. Rostrum large and spatulate. Urosomites with deeply-incised hyaline frill. Female genital double-somite with lateral and dorsal sub-cuticular rib. Female genital field simple (Fig. 54D) with paired opercula of vestigial P6s without setae and covering common gonopore and copulatory pore. Anal somite with operculum and pronounced dorsal posterior extensions (arrowed in Fig. 54C). Caudal rami (Fig. 54C) distinctly longer in male than in female; divergent, tapering; covered in minute scales but without spinule rows on lateral margin; seta I minute.

Antenna. Exopod 7-segmented with armature elements on all segments.

Mandible. Exopod indistinctly 4-segmented.

Maxillule. Coxal epipodite represented by two or three setae.

P1. Exopod (Fig. 54B) 2-segmented, outer spines finely pinnate. Endopod 2- or 3-segmented.

P2-P4. Coxa with inner seta. Rami 3-segmented, anterior face of rami ornamented with dense rows of spinules; P2 and P3 exopod-1 outer spine very elongate. P4 endopod as long as exopod. Without sexual dimorphism.

P5. Limbs connected by symmetrical, deeply-incised hyaline frill.

Male P6 (Fig. 54E). A simple triangular plate with three setae (inner one small).

Three species known world-wide.

Local species. One. Setal formula in Appendix Table 1 (p.340).

Canuellopsis swedmarki Por, 1964

Morphological description: Por (1964b).

Habitat: Sandy mud or mud, 150-450m. Rare.

Distribution: Known only from the Skagerrak between Denmark and Sweden.

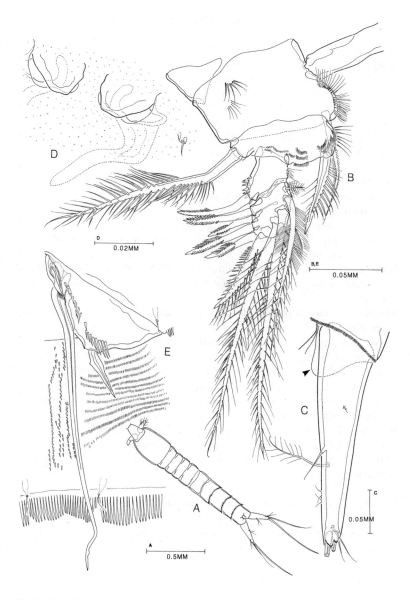

Fig. 54. *Canuellopsis swedmarki*: A, female body; B, P1 (endopod omitted); C, male caudal ramus, ventral; D, female genital field; E, male P6.

Family CERVINIIDAE Sars, 1903

Diagnosis.

Body. With clear distinction between prosome and urosome, former sometimes with pronounced ornamental projections. P1-bearing somite not fused to cephalosome (except in *Cerviniella*). Rostrum not defined at base. Vestigial P6 on female genital double-somite a cylindrical process with two or three setae. Anal somite elongate, tapering posteriorly. Caudal rami elongate, often extremely so, and either slightly to markedly divergent (Fig. 56A) or juxtaposed and fused along their entire length (Fig. 56B); caudal setae I, II and VI often minute.

Antennule. In female, 5- to 8-segmented with at least one aesthetasc on segment 3. In male, at most weakly haplocer with three or more aesthetascs (Fig. 58A).

Antenna (Fig. 55A). Allobasis or incomplete basis. Exopod 4-segmented, middle two segments small bearing one seta. Endopod 1-segmented.

Mandible (Fig. 55B). Basis usually with four setae; endopod of one large segment; exopod usually 4-segmented.

Maxillule (Fig. 55C). Coxal epipodite represented by one or two setae; endopod indistinguishable from basis; exopod of one small segment or represented only by setae.

Maxilla (Fig. 55D). Syncoxa with four endites; endopod 3-segmented, often with geniculate setae.

Maxilliped (Fig. 55E). Weakly prehensile; syncoxa with incorporated endites represented by three curved spines and usually three or four setae; basis smaller, usually with one curved spine and a seta; endopod 2-segmented, proximal segment usually with two setae, distal segment with four setae.

P1-P4. Segmentation of rami variable and sometimes different between sexes. P1 exopod-1 with inner seta, endopod not prehensile.

P5. Baseoendopod reduced, endopodal lobe absent. Exopod of one elongate segment in female (Fig. 58C) and usually 2- or 3-segmented in male.

Male P6. Symmetrical. A broad plate usually with same number of setae as in female.

Females with one egg-sac, males with two spermatophores.

Eleven genera known world-wide, inhabiting deep water.

Fig. 55. *Hemicervinia stylifera*: A, antenna; B, mandible; C, maxillule; D, maxilla; E, maxilliped.

Key to world genera of Cerviniidae

1. Caudal ramus seta II implanted in proximal 60% of ramus length; rami more or less divergent (Fig. 56A).
   ....**2**

   Caudal ramus seta II implanted in distal 30% of ramus length; rami juxtaposed over whole length (Fig. 56B).
   ....**6**

2. P1 to P4 exopods 3-segmented.
   ....**3**

   P1 to P4 exopods 1- or 2-segmented.
   ....*Cerviniella* Smirnov, 1946

3. Caudal rami at least as long as anal somite; antennule 7- or 8-segmented.
   ....**4**

   Caudal rami at most half as long as anal somite; antennule 6-segmented.
   ....*Paracerviniella* Brotskaya, 1963

4. Female antennule 7-segmented; rostrum present.
   ....**5**

   Female antennule 8-segmented; rostrum absent; second free-prosomite expanded ventrally
   ....*Expansicervinia* Montagna, 1981

5. Postero-lateral border of free-prosomites not attenuated; caudal rami of equal length (Fig. 56A).
   ....*Cervinia* (p. 144) [143]

   Postero-lateral border of second to fourth free-prosomites attenuated; right caudal ramus usually longer than left (Fig. 59A).
   ....*Eucanuella* (p. 148)

---

[143] Following Montagna (1981), the genus *Pseudocervinia* Brotskaya, 1963 is a junior subjective synonym of *Cervinia*.

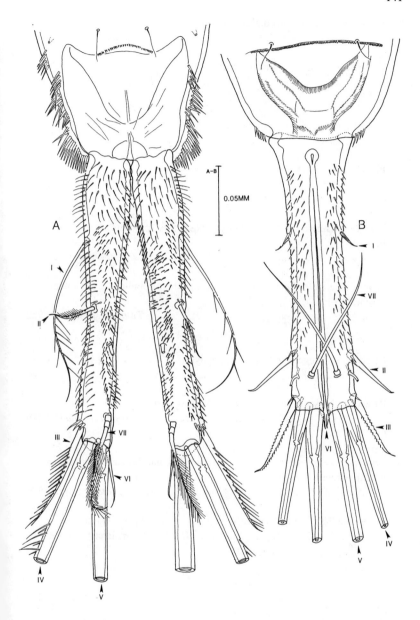

Fig. 56. Caudal rami of, A, *Cervinia synarthra*; B, *Cerviniopsis clavicornis*.

6. Prosome without ornamental projections.
....7

Prosome with large ornamental projections.
....*Pontostratiotes* Brady, 1883

7. Female antennule 5- to 7-segmented.
....**8**

Female antennule 8-segmented.
....**9**

8. Female antennule short, 5- to 6-segmented, with spinulose setae; antenna present.
....*Cerviniopsis* (p. 152)

Female antennule elongate, 7-segmented, without spinulose setae; antenna absent.
....*Tonpostratiotes* Itô, 1982

9. P1 endopod 3-segmented without apophysis.
....**10**

P1 endopod 2-segmented with apophysis (Fig. 60B).
....*Hemicervinia* (p. 150)

10. Antennule segments 1, 3 and 5 much longer than broad; endopod-1 of maxilliped with 3 setae.
....*Stratiopontotes* Soyer, 1970

Antennule fifth segment square, endopod-1 of maxilliped without setae.
....*Herdmaniopsis* Brotskaya, 1963 [144]

---

[144] Following Itô (1982), the genus *Ameliotes* described by Por (1969) is a junior subjective synonym of *Herdmaniopsis*.

Genus CERVINIA Norman in Brady (1878)

Synonym: Pseudocervinia Brotskaya, 1963.
Diagnosis: Cerviniidae.

Body (Fig. 57A). Without projections but sexually dimorphic in shape. Cephalosome of female broader than long with small triangular rostrum (Fig. 57A); in male, as long as broad with much larger rostrum (Fig. 58A). Free-prosomites with rounded postero-lateral margin in female and angular margins in male. Urosomites not attenuated, ornamented with spinule rows in male. Operculum smooth. Caudal rami (Fig. 56A) divergent, equal in length and at least as long as anal somite; sometimes ornamented with rows of spinules, particularly in male; setae I and II variable in length but former implanted at 20-30% of ramus length and latter at 50-60% of ramus length.
Antennule. With plumose, curled setae; 7-segmented in female (Fig. 57A), 8-segmented in male, unmodified or weakly haplocer with large aesthetascs (Fig. 58A).
Antenna (Fig. 57A). Longer than antennule. Allobasis with two setae on abexopodal margin. Exopod with two and three setae on proximal and distal segments respectively; endopod in most species with three lateral and six terminal, strongly-developed , spinulose spines or setae.
Mandible. Basis setae often reduced in number.
Maxillule. Coxal epipodite represented by one seta.
Maxilla. Second inner endite usually represented by one seta only; spine on allobasis sexually dimorphic.
Maxilliped. Syncoxa often with reduced number of setae; endopod-1 with only one seta.
P1-P4 (Figs 57B,C; 58B). Exopod 3-segmented. Endopod 2- or 3-segmented in female but 3-segmented in all known males (even if only 2-segmented in female) with some setae modified on P2-P4.
P5 (Fig. 58C). Exopod of one small segment in both sexes, but form and number of setae vary.
Male P6. With three setae.

Ten species known world-wide. Latest key to species in Montagna (1981).

Local species. Two. Setal formulae in Appendix Table 1 (p.340).
Adult females of the two local species can be distinguished from each other by the number of segments in the endopod of P2-P4; *C. bradyi* (Fig. 57C) has three and *C. synarthra* (Fig. 58B) has two. Only the male of *C. bradyi* has been described but it is likely that the male of *C. synarthra* also has a 3-segmented endopod in P2-P4. Males may therefore be extremely difficult to distinguish.

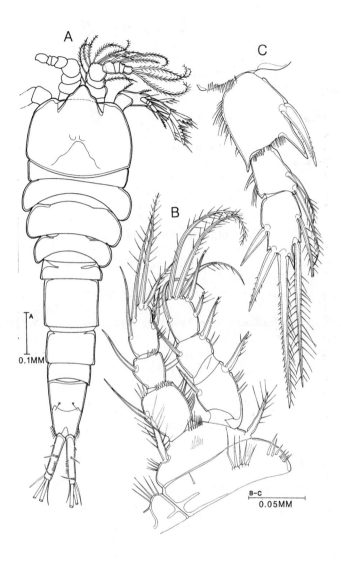

Fig. 57. *Cervinia bradyi* female: A, body, dorsal; B, P1; C, P2 endopod.

Cervinia bradyi Norman in Brady (1878)

Morphological descriptions: Brady (1878), Sars (1911), Por (1964a, 1967), Drzycimski (1969).

Habitat: Muddy sediments, 50-400m. Occasional.

Distribution: Irish Sea around Isle of Man, Oban, Moray Firth, Faroes and west coast of Norway and Sweden.

Cervinia synarthra Sars, 1903

Morphological descriptions: Sars (1911), Lang (1948), Por (1967).

Habitat: Muddy and clayey sediments, 50-1000m. Occasional.

Distribution: Irish Sea around Isle of Man, Loch Nevis, west coast of Norway; as far north as Iceland.

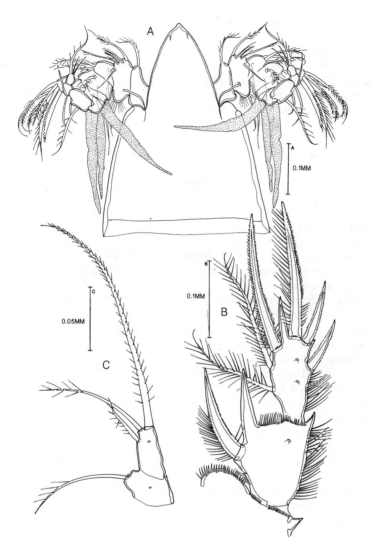

Fig. 58. *Cervinia bradyi* male: A, cephalosome and antennules. *Cervinia synarthra* female:
B, P2 endopod; C, P5.

Genus EUCANUELLA T. Scott, 1900

Diagnosis: Cerviniidae.

Body (Fig. 59A). Moderately sclerotised, without dorsal projections but sexually dimorphic in shape. Cephalosome rounded anteriorly with recurved pointed rostrum in female; tapering anteriorly with very large rostrum in male. Postero-lateral border of second to fourth free-prosomites with spiniform projection (stronger in male). Median lateral border of genital double-somite in female, and posterior border of genital somite in male, produced into strong spiniform projection. Anal somite longer than penultimate urosomite, with smooth semi-circular operculum. Female caudal rami (Fig. 59A) unequal in length, divergent, broad at base and tapering posteriorly; setae I and II implanted close together in proximal 30% of ramus; seta VI absent. Male caudal rami narrower and much longer than female, not always unequal; seta II implanted at mid-point of ramus.

Antennule. With plumose setae. In female (Fig. 59A), 7-segmented, distal three segments very small; with tooth-like projection on second segment and a very strong spinulose spine on fourth. In male, 8- or 9-segmented, haplocer, aesthetascs large.

Antenna. Shorter than antennule; allobasis with one seta on anterior margin. Exopod with two setae on both proximal and distal segments.

Maxillule. Coxal epipodite represented by one plumose seta.

Maxilla. Spine of allobasis in female transformed into a recurved hook in male.

Maxilliped. Endopod-1 with one seta.

P1 (Fig. 59B). Both rami 3-segmented. Endopod short, not reaching to distal border of exopod-2.

P2-P4. Rami 3-segmented. Male P4 endopod with larger segments and/or more setae than in female.

P5. In female, exopod of one small, narrow segment (Fig. 59C); in male 3-segmented.

Male P6. With three setae.

Four species known world-wide. Latest key in Soyer (1970).
Local species: One. Setal formula in Appendix Table 1 (p.340).

Eucanuella spinifera T. Scott, 1900

Morphological descriptions: T. Scott (1900), Sars (1911), Lang (1948).

Habitat: Muddy sediments, 60-250m. Rare or occasional.

Distribution: West coast of Scotland, Shetland Isles, west coast of Norway.

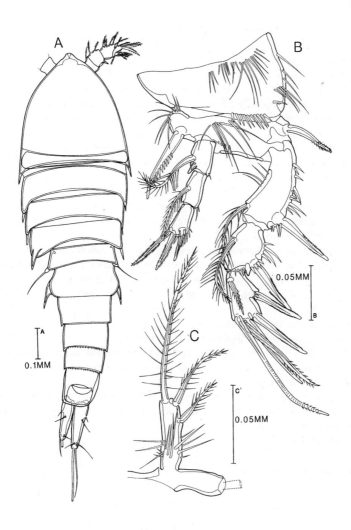

Fig. 59. *Eucanuella spinifera*: female; A, body, dorsal; B, P1; C, P5.

Genus HEMICERVINIA Lang, 1935

Synonym: Herdmania Thompson, 1893.

Diagnosis: Cerviniidae.

Body (Fig. 60A). Without projections, similar in both sexes. Cephalosome rounded anteriorly with small, triangular rostrum; postero-lateral border attenuated. Postero-lateral border of genital somite and following two urosomites attenuated. Operculum toothed. Caudal rami slender, as long as last three urosomites combined and, typically, swollen at base. In previous descriptions, caudal rami are equal and confluent but in two specimens we have examined (Fig. 60A) rami are partially or wholly divergent and unequal in length; seta I implanted at 25% of ramus length, seta II at 80%.

Antennule (Fig. 60A). In female, 8-segmented with no spinulose setae; proximal segment longest with pronounced tooth at anterior distal corner. In male, 8- or 9-segmented, haplocer.

Antenna (Fig. 55A). Shorter than antennule; allobasis with two setae on anterior margin; exopod with one and two setae on proximal and distal segments respectively; endopod with very long, fine lateral and terminal setae.

Maxillule. Coxal epipodite represented by two setae (lost from specimen drawn in Fig. 55C).

Maxilla. Without sexual dimorphism.

Maxilliped (Fig. 55E). Endopod-1 with three setae.

P1 (Fig. 60B). Exopod 3-segmented. Endopod 2-segmented, longer than exopod; distal segment with long finger-like apophysis at outer distal corner.

P2-P4. Both rami 3-segmented.

P5. In female (Fig. 60C), exopod elongate with three terminal and three lateral setae. In male, baseoendopods fused medially; exopod 2-segmented, distal segment with six setae.

Male P6. With two setae.

Monotypic. Setal formula in Appendix Table 1 (p.340).

Hemicervinia stylifera (Thompson, 1893).

Synonym: Hemicervinia ryforsi Lang, 1935

Morphological descriptions: Thompson (1893), Lang (1935), Por (1964a), Soyer (1970).

Habitat: Muddy sediment, 50-150m, Rare.

Distribution: Irish Sea around Isle of Man, west coast of Scotland.

151

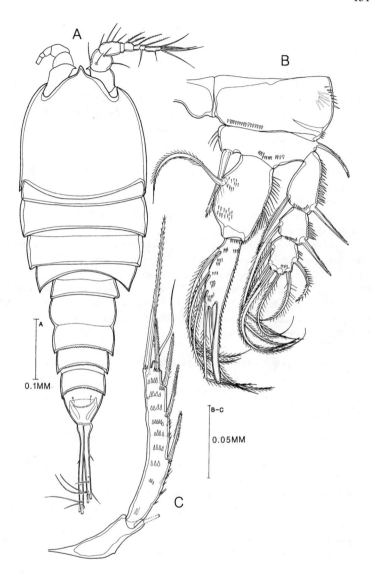

Fig. 60. *Hemicervinia stylifera* female: A, body, dorsal; B, P1; C, P5.

Genus CERVINIOPSIS Sars, 1903

Diagnosis: Cerviniidae.

Body (Fig. 61A). Without projections. Cephalosome large, rounded anteriorly with prominent triangular rostrum. Median lateral margin of female genital double-somite projecting to a variable degree. Operculum smooth. Caudal rami (Fig. 56B) equal in length, slender, confluent and always longer than last two urosomites combined; seta I implanted at 40-50% of ramus length, seta II at 90%.

Antennule. 5- or 6-segmented in female, proximal three segments robust with first segment longest, distal two or three segments markedly reduced; all segments with strongly-spinulose setae and fourth segment with a particularly large spinulose spine. In male, 7- or 8-segmented; no swollen segment.

Antenna. Shorter than antennule. Allobasis with two setae on anterior margin. Exopod with one or two setae on proximal segment and two on distal segment.

Maxillule. Coxal epipodite represented by one or two setae.

P1 (Fig. 61B). Rami 3-segmented and equal in length.

P2-P4. Rami 3-segmented. P4 endopod-3 with one terminal seta usually dwarfed.

P5. Exopod in female variable in length with three setae usually borne terminally (Fig. 61D); in male, 1- or 2-segmented with four or more setae.

Male P6. With two setae.

Thirteen known species world-wide. Latest key (in Russian) in Brotskaya (1963).

Local species. Two. Setal formula in Appendix Table 1 (p.340).

The two species recorded from north-west Europe can be distinguished as follows:

1. Caudal rami longer than last three urosomites combined; P2 and P3 endopod-1 with inner distal corner attenuated and inner seta transformed into strong spine; P5 exopod middle terminal seta small
   ....*Cerviniopsis longicaudata*

   Caudal rami not longer than last three urosomites combined; P2 and P3 endopod-1 normal (Fig. 61C); P5 exopod middle seta at least as long as outer seta (Fig. 61D)
   ....*Cerviniopsis clavicornis*

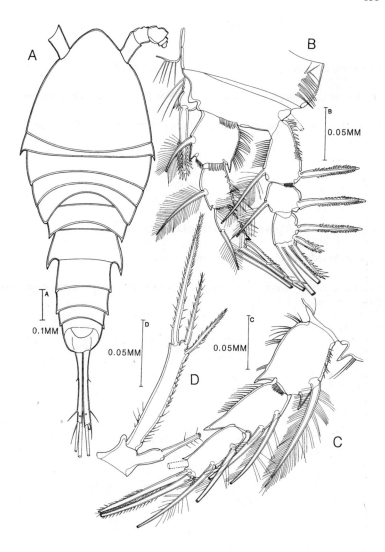

Fig. 61. *Cerviniopsis clavicornis* female: A, body, dorsal; B, P1; C, P2 endopod; D, P5.

Cerviniopsis clavicornis Sars, 1903

Morphological descriptions: Sars (1911, 1921), Lang (1948).

Habitat: Muddy and clayey sediments, 70-200m. Rare, occasionally common.

Distribution: West coast of Scandinavia from Lofoten Islands to Skagerrak

Cerviniopsis longicaudata Sars, 1903

Morphological descriptions: Sars (1911), Lang (1948).

Habitat: Muddy and clayey sediment in deep water. Rare.

Distribution: Only record in north-west Europe is of two specimens from west coast of Norway.

Family ECTINOSOMATIDAE Sars, 1903

Diagnosis.

Body. Two basic shapes in dorsal view, either characteristically fusiform (Fig. 62A) with a sub-triangular cephalothorax, or cylindrical with a sub-rectangular cephalothorax (Fig. 62B) in interstitial forms. Dorso-ventrally flattened in *Peltobradya*. Rostrum usually well-developed and not defined at base. No clear distinction between prosome and urosome.

Antennule. 5- to 8-segmented in female, distal segmentation often difficult to discern clearly in fusiform species; at most, weakly haplocer in male.

Antenna (Fig. 64A). With distinct basis. Endopod 2-segmented. Exopod 2- or 3-segmented (except in dubious genus *Tetanopsis*), distal segment bearing no lateral setae.

Mandible (Fig. 63B). Basis with 1-segmented rami (rarely exopod absent).

Maxillule (Fig. 63C). Without coxal epipodite.

Maxilla (Fig. 62C,D). Characteristic. Syncoxa with up to three endites. Allobasis very well-developed with distal endopod of one to three short segments (details of which are frequently very difficult to discern).

Maxilliped (Fig. 62E). Characteristic. Stenopodial, syncoxa with up to two setae, basis without setae, endopod 1-segmented usually with four setae.

P1-P4. Rami usually 3-segmented. P1 exopod-1 without inner seta, endopod usually unmodified (Fig. 64B).

P5. Characteristic (Fig. 62F). Baseoendopod with two setae on endopodal lobe; exopod generally with three or four setae, one of which may be inserted on anterior surface of exopod or, occasionally, of baseoendopod (arrowed in Fig. 62F). Sexually dimorphic.

Females with one egg-sac, males with one spermatophore.

Eighteen genera known world-wide.

Notes:
1. In the following generic descriptions the maxilla is classified according to its shape. The **geniculate maxilla** (Figs 62C, 63D) is bent at about 90 degrees, or more acutely, between the syncoxa and allobasis, whereas the **non-geniculate maxilla** (Fig. 62D) is straight or has a significantly more obtuse angle.
2. This is a very difficult family. Distinctions between species and genera are often slight and the small mouthparts provide important diagnostic characters. It is known that there are many species in British waters that remain undescribed, although the family is currently under revision. Many of the records of Ectinosomatidae are probably incorrect.
3. Members of this family are very prone to entrapment by surface films.

Key to world genera of Ectinosomatidae

1. Body cylindrical (Fig. 62B), cephalothorax rectangular (viewed dorsally).
  2

   Body fusiform (Fig. 62A), cephalothorax sub-triangular (viewed dorsally)
   or body robust, prosome distinctly wider than urosome (Fig. 63A).
  8

2. P2-P4 endopod 3-segmented.
  3

   P1-P4 endopod 2-segmented.
  7

3. Last somite with dorsal armature of claws, lappets or spiniform processes
   (Fig. 76H,I); P5 exopod with three marginal and one surface seta.
   ....*Arenosetella* (p. 192)

   Last somite without such armature.
  4

4. Maxilla geniculate, with major articulation between elongate syncoxa and
   elongate allobasis; P1 endopod 2- or 3-segmented; P5 exopod with three
   marginal and no surface setae.
   ....*Lineosoma* (p. 194)

   Maxilla with at most a slight angle between syncoxa and an often elongate
   allobasis bearing a very short endopod.
  5

5. Antenna exopod 1-segmented; (genus of dubious validity).
   ....*Tetanopsis* Brady, 1910

   Antenna exopod 2- or 3-segmented.
  6

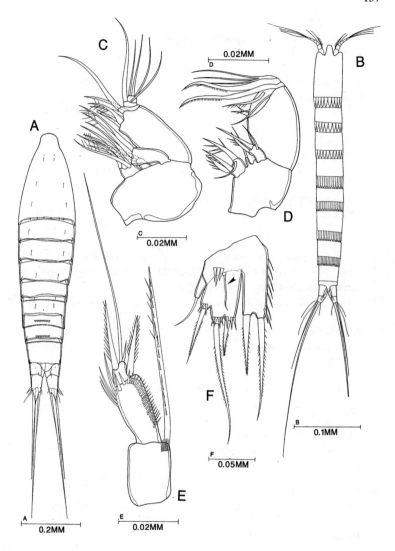

Fig. 62. Dorsal view of the body of, A, *Halectinosoma*; B, *Arenosetella*. Maxilla of, C, *Pseudobradya*. D, *Ectinosoma*. E, maxilliped of *Pseudobradya*. F, P5 of *Halectinosoma*.

6. Female P5 setae leaf-shaped, the exopod with three marginal and no surface setae; male P5 exopod with four normal marginal setae.
....*Oikopus* Wells, 1967

   P5 setae normal in both sexes, the exopod with three marginal setae and usually a surface seta (Fig. 75D, E).
....*Hastigerella* (p. 188)

7. Antenna exopod 2-segmented.
....*Noodtiella* (p. 196)

   Antenna exopod 3-segmented.
....*Ectinosomoides* Nicholls, 1945

8. P5 exopod poorly developed, short, fused with baseoendopod in female (Fig. 70D), distinct in male (Fig. 70E), with three marginal and usually no surface setae; body very small (<0.3mm).
....*Sigmatidium* (p. 178)

   Not like this.
....**9**

9. P1 endopod prehensile (Figs 68D, 69D).
....**10**

   P1 endopod non-prehensile (Figs 64B, 71B).
....**13**

10. P1 endopod 3-segmented.
....*Klieosoma* (p. 176)

   P1 endopod 2-segmented.
....**11**

11 P1 and P2 exopod-3 with two slender outer setae.
....*Bradyellopsis* Brian, 1924

   P1 and P2 exopod-3 with three outer spines or setae.
....**12**

12. Body fusiform (Fig. 68A); P1-P4 rami with slender segments (Fig. 68D).
....*Halophytophilus* (p. 174)

Prosome dorsoventrally flattened, clearly wider than urosome; P1-P4 rami with short, broad segments.
....*Peltobradya* Médioni & Soyer, 1967

13. P1-P4 endopod 2-segmented (Fig. 71B, C).
....*Pseudectinosoma* (p. 180)
P1-P4 endopod 3-segmented.
....**14**

READ THREE ALTERNATIVES

14. P5 exopod with three marginal setae and usually one surface seta.
....**15**

P5 exopod with four marginal setae and no surface seta (Fig. 67E).
....*Ectinosoma* (p. 172)

P5 exopod with four marginal and one surface seta, exopod fused to baseoendopod and left and right legs fused to form a plate.
....*Bradya confluens* Lang, 1936

15. Mandible with rudimentary coxa, basis elongate and bearing subterminally filiform rami, each terminating in two or three setae (Fig. 72C); antenna exopod distal segment without lateral spines (Fig. 72B).
....*Ectinosomella* (p. 182)

Not like this.
....**16**

16. Female antennule third segment three times longer than wide (Fig. 74B); mandibular endopod with one strong spiniform seta laterally (Fig. 74C); P1-P4 exopod-3 with only two outer spines (Fig. 73C); planktonic (occasionally in sediment).
....*Microsetella* (p. 184)

Not like this.
....**17**

17. P2-P4 exopod-1 without inner seta.
....*Halophytophilus aberrans* Wells & Rao, 1987

P2-P4 exopod-1 with inner seta.
....**18**

18. Body comparatively robust, prosome-urosome division comparatively distinct (Fig. 63A); antenna exopod-1 with two setae, endopod-1 or basis with one seta (Fig. 64A); mandibular exopod with at least five setae (Fig. 63B); maxilla geniculate (Fig. 63D); maxilliped robust with short distal segment fused at an angle with preceding segment and generally with four conspicuous setae (Fig. 63E).
....*Bradya* (p. 161, opposite)

Body comparatively slender with no sharp separation between prosome and urosome (Figs 65A, 66A); antenna exopod-1 with less than two setae (except *Pseudobradya ambigua* Sars, 1920 with two), endopod-1 with no setae; mandibular exopod generally with fewer than five setae; maxilla geniculate (Fig. 65B) or straighter (Fig. 66B); maxilliped as in Fig. 65C or Fig. 66C, distal segment generally distinct and carrying three conspicuous and one small setae.
....**19**

19. Antennule with or without dark pigment spot within the proximal three segments; maxilla geniculate (Fig. 65B), allobasis usually truncate distally and carrying 3-segmented endopod, although endopod sometimes very small and its morphology difficult to discern (maxilla reduced to a narrow 3-segmented cylinder in *P. leptognatha* Sars, 1920); maxilliped short and robust (Fig. 65C).
....*Pseudobradya* (p. 167)

Antennule without pigment spot; maxilla with at most a slight angle between syncoxa and allobasis (Fig. 66B), allobasis generally attenuating distally, endopod 3-segmented but always small, its morphology not clearly discernible; maxilliped generally slender (Fig. 66C).
....*Halectinosoma* (p. 170)

Genus BRADYA Boeck, 1872

Diagnosis: Ectinosomatidae.

Body (Fig. 63A). Fusiform but generally with more robust prosome which is distinct from urosome. Rostrum short.

Antennule. Short, 6- to 8-segmented in female.

Antenna (Fig. 64A). Exopod large, 3-segmented, basal segment bearing two setae. Endopod-1 with a proximal seta, endopod-2 with two or three setae or spines along inner margin.

Mandible (Fig. 63B). Basis with four setae, exopod with five or six setae.

Maxillule (Fig. 63C). Coxa with two slender setae.

Maxilla (Fig. 63D). Geniculate with three short but distinct endopod segments.

Maxilliped (Fig. 63E). Robust and highly characteristic; syncoxa with two setae; endopod fused to basis at an angle.

P1-P4 (Fig. 64B). Rami 3-segmented, exopod-3 with three outer spines.

P5. Baseoendopod and exopod distinct in sub-genus *Bradya* (Fig. 64C) or fused in sub-genus *Parabradya* (Fig. 64D); exopod with three (exceptionally four) marginal setae and one surface seta.

Fifteen species, in two sub-genera, are known world-wide. Latest key to species in Lang (1965).

Local species. Eight named species. Setal formulae in Appendix Table 2 (p. 341).

Note. The genus is in need of revision. The key overleaf is modified from Lang (1965). It should be used with caution, as additional unnamed species are known to be present and the scale of variability exhibited by the described species is not fully understood. It is valid only for females.

Key to females of local species in the genus *Bradya*

1. P5 well developed, exopod and baseoendopod not confluent (Fig. 64C)
....sub-genus ***Bradya*.....2**

    P5 poorly developed, exopod and baseoendopod confluent (Fig. 64D)
....***Bradya (Parabradya) dilatata***

READ THREE ALTERNATIVES

2. Caudal ramus about three times as long as wide.
....***Bradya (Bradya) furcata***

    Caudal ramus about twice as long as wide.
....***Bradya (Bradya) simulans***

    Caudal ramus distinctly shorter than either of the above.
....**3**

3. Middle marginal seta of P5 exopod and inner seta of P5 endopodal lobe
extending to about base of caudal rami.
....***Bradya (Bradya) macrochaeta***

    Middle marginal seta of P5 exopod and inner seta of P5 endopodal lobe
much shorter than above.
....**4**

4. Setae of endopodal lobe of P5 of subequal length.
....***Bradya (Bradya) proxima***

    Inner seta of endopodal lobe of P5 much longer than outer seta.
....**5**

5. Antennule 8-segmented; caudal ramus about as long as wide.
....***Bradya (Bradya) congenera***

    Antennule 7-segmented; caudal ramus longer than wide.
....**6**

6. Innermost marginal seta of P5 exopod longer than middle marginal seta.
....***Bradya (Bradya) typica***

    Innermost marginal seta of P5 exopod shorter than middle marginal seta.
....***Bradya (Bradya) scotti***

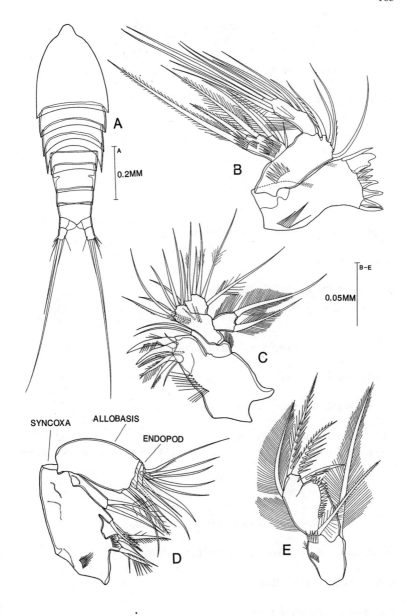

Fig. 63. *Bradya (Bradya) typica* female: A, body, dorsal; B, mandible; C, maxillule; D, maxilla; E, maxilliped.

Bradya (Bradya) typica Boeck, 1872

Morphological descriptions: Sars (1911), Lang (1948, 1965).

Habitat: Mud, littoral and sublittoral to 1074m. Occasional.

Distribution: Widely distributed throughout the region.

Bradya (Bradya) proxima T. Scott, 1912

Morphological description: T. Scott (1912).

Habitat: Unknown.

Distribution: One record from the North Sea.

Bradya (Bradya) scotti Sars, 1920

Morphological descriptions: Sars (1920), Lang (1948).

Habitat: Muddy sediments, 11-146m.

Distribution: Southern Norway, northern North Sea, Firth of Forth, Northumberland, Durham, Loch Creran, Isle of Mull, Firth of Clyde, Isle of Man, Celtic Sea, Isles of Scilly.

Bradya (Bradya) macrochaeta Sars, 1920

Morphological descriptions: Sars (1920), Lang (1948).

Habitat: Mud, 70-183m. Rare.

Distribution: Southern Norway.

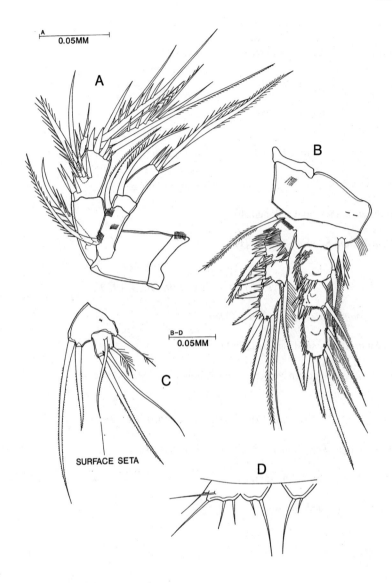

Fig. 64. *Bradya (Bradya) typica* female: A, antenna; B, P1; C, P5. *Bradya (Parabradya) dilatata* female: D, P5 (from Sars, 1911, no scale).

Bradya (Bradya) furcata Sars, 1920

Morphological descriptions: Sars (1920), Lang (1948).

Habitat: Mud, 30-110m. Rare.

Distribution: Southern Norway.

Bradya (Bradya) congenera Sars, 1920

Morphological descriptions: Sars (1920), Lang (1948).

Habitat: Muddy sand and mud, 40-120m. Rare.

Distribution: Southern Norway, Isle of Man.

*Bradya (Bradya) simulan*s Sars, 1920

Morphological description: Sars (1920).

Habitat: Muddy sand and mud, 87-110m. Rare.

Distribution: Southern Norway, Loch Creran, Isle of Man, Celtic Sea.

Bradya (Parabradya) dilatata Sars, 1904

Morphological descriptions: Sars (1911), Lang (1948).

Habitat: Mud, 40-422m. Rare.

Distribution: Southern Norway.

168

Genus PSEUDOBRADYA Sars, 1904

Diagnosis: Ectinosomatidae.

Body (Fig. 65A). Distinctly fusiform.

Antennule. Short, sometimes with dark pigment spot within proximal three segments; 5- to 7-segmented in female.

Antenna. Exopod 2- or 3-segmented, proximal segment bearing at most one seta (except in the aberrant *P. ambigua*). Endopod-1 with no setae; endopod-2 with two spines or setae on inner edge.

Mandible. Basis with one to three setae, exopod generally with fewer than five setae.

Maxillule. Coxa with fewer than two setae.

Maxilla (Fig. 65B). Geniculate. Allobasis typically truncate distally. Endopod of three short but usually distinct segments; the two strong setae issuing from the two basal endopod segments generally have a clearly defined suture at the point of insertion. (The maxilla of *P. leptognatha* is apparently reduced to a narrow 3-segmented cylinder.)

Maxilliped (Fig. 65C). Typically short and robust. Syncoxa with one seta. Endopod distinct with three conspicuous and one very small seta.

P1-P4 (Fig. 65D). Rami 3-segmented. Exopod-3 with two or three outer spines.

P5. Baseoendopod and exopod distinct in male and superficially distinct in female but, in most species, close scrutiny reveals a suture on the posterior face only (Fig. 65E). Exopod with three marginal setae. Surface seta issuing from either exopod or baseoendopod but occasionally absent.

Thirty-eight species and two subspecies known world-wide. Latest key to species in Lang (1965) but see below.

Note: Identification of many species within the genera *Pseudobradya*, *Halectinosoma* and *Ectinosoma* is just not possible at present. Distinctions between species can be very slight and some descriptions contain important errors. The three genera are very similar, with the result that some species have been ascribed to the wrong genus.

Pseudobradya has a similar P5 to *Halectinosoma* but differs from both *Halectinosoma* and *Ectinosoma* in the maxillae and maxillipeds (see diagnoses). Essentially, *Pseudobradya* has a geniculate maxilla and a short robust maxilliped, whereas the other genera possess a straighter maxilla, with the allobasis tending to be somewhat different in shape (see diagnoses), and a more elongate maxilliped. Although some species of *Pseudobradya* can be correctly identified using existing keys, these are all essentially unsound.

Local species. About twenty-five. Setal formulae in Appendix Table 2 (p. 341). Most common in mud and sand but can be found in a variety of other habitats, including algae.

169

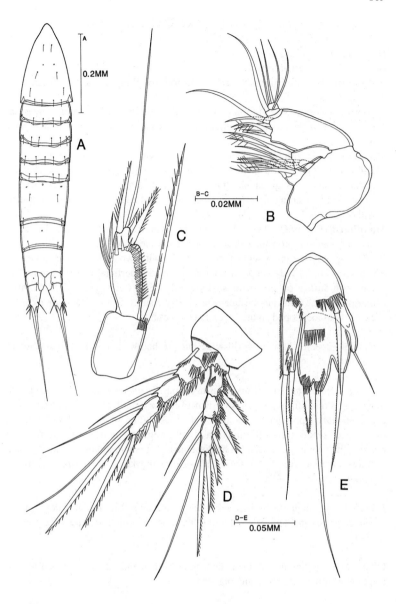

Fig. 65. *Pseudobradya fusca* female: A, body, dorsal; B, maxilla; C, maxilliped; D, P1; E, P5.

Genus HALECTINOSOMA Lang, 1944

Diagnosis: Ectinosomatidae.

Body (Fig. 66A). Fusiform.

Antennule. Without pigment spot, occasionally elongate, 5-7-segmented in female.

Antenna. Exopod 3-segmented, proximal segment with at most one seta. Endopod-1 with no setae, endopod-2 with two spines or setae along inner margin.

Mandible. Basis with two or three setae; exopod with fewer than five setae.

Maxilla (Fig. 66B). Non-geniculate. Allobasis commonly attenuating distally; endopod small, 3-segmented, although segmentation is generally very difficult to discern; two strong setae issuing from two basal endopod segments confluent with segments.

Maxilliped (Fig. 66C). Typically elongate. Syncoxa with two setae. Endopod distinct with three conspicuous and one usually inconspicuous seta.

P1-P4 (Fig. 66D). Rami 3-segmented; exopod-3 with two or three outer spines.

P5. Baseoendopod and exopod distinct in male and superficially distinct in female but with suture on posterior surface only (Fig. 66E). Exopod with three marginal setae and one surface seta clearly issuing from exopod or close to exopod/baseoendopod suture (occasionally absent).

Fifty-eight species known world-wide but see below. Latest key to species in Lang (1965).

Note: Halectinosoma can be distinguished from *Pseudobradya* by the form of the maxilla and maxilliped (see p. 168). However, the maxilliped of some species of *Halectinosoma* approaches the short, robust condition of *Pseudobradya* but in these cases reference to the maxilla should confirm the identification. With practice the necessary details can be discerned on a whole mount. Although some species can be correctly identified using existing keys, these are essentially unsound.

Local species. About twenty-seven but see *Note 2* on p. 155. Reliable descriptions of some species in Clément & Moore (1995). Setal formula in Appendix Table 2 (p. 341).

Often dominant members of the meiobenthos of mud and sand but can be found in a variety of other habitats, including algae.

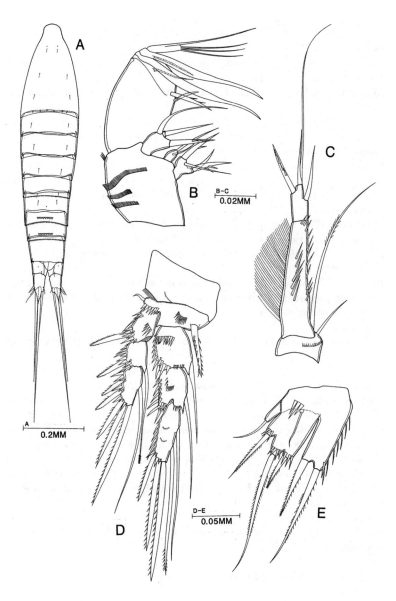

Fig. 66. *Halectinosoma brunneum* female: A, body, dorsal; B, maxilla; C, maxilliped; D, P1; E, P5.

Genus ECTINOSOMA Boeck, 1865

Diagnosis: Ectinosomatidae.

Body (Fig. 67A). Fusiform. Cuticle of somites with distinctive sub-rectangular pores. Caudal rami quadratic.

Antennule. Moderately elongated, lacking dark pigment spot, 6- or 7-segmented in female.

Antenna. Exopod 3-segmented, proximal segment with at most one seta. Endopod-1 with no setae, endopod-2 with two spines or setae on inner edge.

Mandible. Basis with two to four setae, exopod with two or three setae.

Maxilla (Fig. 67B). Non-geniculate. Allobasis commonly attenuating distally. Endopod small, 3-segmented, although segmentation very difficult to discern; two strong setae issuing from two basal endopod segments confluent with segments.

Maxilliped (Fig. 67C). Typically elongate. Syncoxa with one seta. Endopod distinct and carrying three conspicuous and one usually inconspicuous seta.

P1-P4 (Fig. 67D). Rami 3-segmented. Exopod-3 of P1 with three, of P2-P4 with two or three, outer spines.

P5. Baseoendopod and exopod distinct in male and superficially distinct in female but with a suture on posterior face only (Fig. 67E). Exopod with four marginal setae and no surface seta.

Twenty-two species and two subspecies known world-wide. Latest key to species in Lang (1965).

Note: Ectinosoma can be clearly separated from *Halectinosoma* only on the setation of the P5. *Ectinosoma* has a total of four marginal setae, whereas *Halectinosoma* has only three as a result of secondary migration of one seta onto the surface of the exopod. *Ectinosoma* shows a narrower range of variation than the other genera. For example, the caudal rami are always quadratic in shape. The cuticle of the body somites displays distinctive sub-rectangular pores (Fig. 67A), also found on the cephalothorax of *Halectinosoma porosum* Wells, 1967. Although some species can be correctly identified using existing keys, these are essentially unsound.

Local species. About twelve, but see *Note 2* on p. 155. Setal formulae in Appendix Table 2 (p. 341).

Can be common in mud and sand and among algae.

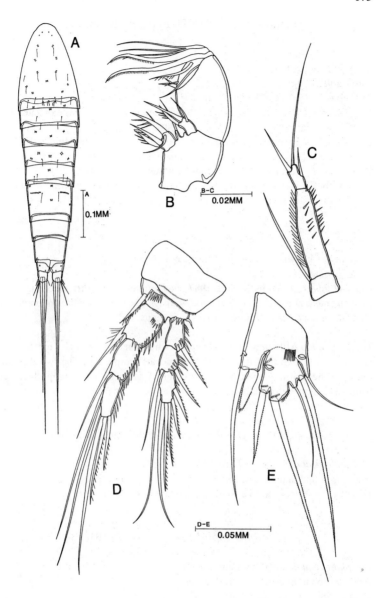

Fig. 67. *Ectinosoma melaniceps* female: A, body, dorsal; B, maxilla; C, maxilliped; D, P1; E, P5.

Genus HALOPHYTOPHILUS Brian, 1917

Diagnosis: Ectinosomatidae.
Body (Fig. 68A). Fusiform.
Antennule. 6-segmented in female.
Antenna. Exopod 2- or 3-segmented.
Maxilla (Fig. 68B). Geniculate, syncoxa with one endite, allobasis elongate.
Maxilliped (Fig. 68C). Non-geniculate, robust.
P1 (Fig. 68D). Exopod 3-segmented, exopod-3 with three outer spines. Endopod 2-segmented, prehensile, with distal segment much the shorter.
P2-P4. Rami 3-segmented; P2 exopod-3 with three outer spines.
P5 (Fig. 68E). Baseoendopod and exopod distinct; exopod with three marginal and one surface seta.

Males unknown.

Five species known world-wide. Latest key in Lang (1948).

Note: H. aberrans Wells & Rao, 1987 shows fundamental differences in the P1 (3-segmented, non-prehensile endopod with 1.1.221 setal formula; endopod-1 not elongate) and probably belongs to a distinct genus.

Local species. Although only two species have been recorded from the local region, it is known that other, unnamed species are present. The two described ones can be distinguished by the number of setae on P-1 endopod-2. Setal formulae in Appendix Table 2 (p. 341).

Halophytophilus spinicornis Sars, 1920

Morphological description: Sars, 1920.
Habitat: Found in mud, 18m. Rare.
Distribution: Known from a single female taken at Hvalør, Norway.

Halophytophilus similis Lang, 1948

Morphological description: Lang (1948).
Habitat: Found in mud and maerl, 2-20m. Rare.
Distribution: Loch Creran, Summer Isles.

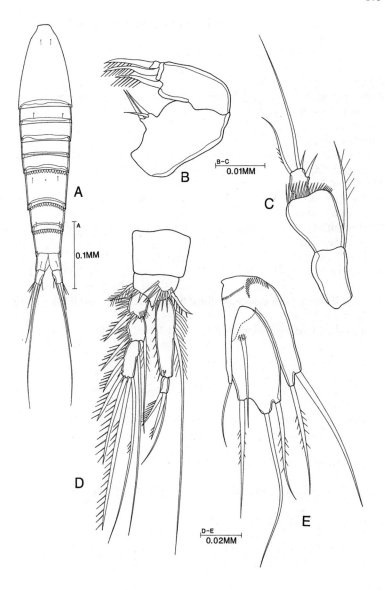

Fig. 68. *Halophytophilus similis* female: A, body, dorsal; B, maxilla; C, maxilliped; D, P1;
E, P5.

Genus KLIEOSOMA Hicks & Schriever, 1985

Synonym: Kliella Hicks & Schriever, 1983.

Diagnosis: Ectinosomatidae.

Body (Fig. 69A). Fusiform. Posterior marginal spinules ventrally on at least urosomites four and five.

Antennule. 6-segmented in female.

Antenna. Exopod 3-segmented.

Maxilla (Fig. 69B). Geniculate. Syncoxa with at most two endites. Allobasis elongate. Endopod segments may be indistinctly defined.

Maxilliped (Fig. 69C). Short, robust, syncoxa with one seta.

P1-P4. Rami 3-segmented. P1 (Fig. 69D) endopod prehensile, endopod-3 with four or five setae. P3 exopod-3 with two or three outer spines.

P5 (Fig. 69E) baseoendopod and exopod distinct; exopod with three marginal and one surface seta.

Males unknown.

Two species known world-wide. Revision by Hicks & Schriever (1983).

Local species. One. Setal formula in Appendix Table 2 (p. 341).

Klieosoma triarticulatum (Klie, 1949)

Synonyms: Halophytophilus? triarticulatus Klie, 1949; *Kliella triarticulatus* (Klie, 1949).

Morphological description: Hicks & Schriever (1983).

Habitat: On *Laminaria* and in gravel, down to 27m. Rare.

Distribution: Humberside, Helgoland.

177

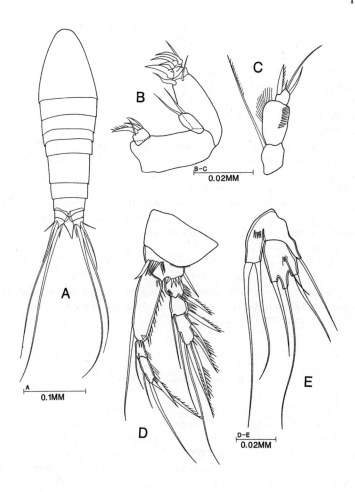

Fig. 69. *Klieosoma triarticulatum* female: A, body, dorsal; B, maxilla (from Hicks & Schriever, 1983); C, maxilliped; D, P1; E, P5.

Genus SIGMATIDIUM Giesbrecht, 1881

Diagnosis: Ectinosomatidae.

Body. Fusiform, very small (<270 μm).

Antennule. 5-segmented in female.

Antenna. Exopod 2- or 3-segmented.

Maxilla (Fig. 70A). Geniculate.

Maxilliped (Fig. 70B). Robust.

P1. Exopod 3-segmented, exopod-3 with two outer spines. Endopod (Fig. 70C) 2- or 3-segmented, prehensile when 2-segmented with distal segment much shorter than proximal.

P2-P4. Rami 3-segmented; exopod-3 with two outer spines.

P5. Baseoendopod and exopod fused in female (Fig. 70D), but distinct in male (Fig. 70E) and, apparently, in the female of *S. noodti* Kunz, 1974. Exopod short, with three marginal and usually no surface setae.

Six species known world-wide. Revision by Kunz (1974).

Local species. Although only one species has been recorded from north-west Europe, it is known that several other, unnamed species are present. Setal formula in Appendix Table 2 (p. 341).

Sigmatidium difficile Giesbrecht, 1881

Morphological description: Lang (1948); however, this and all currently available descriptions are inadequate and cannot be relied upon. British records of this species are dubious. Accordingly, *S. kunzi* Mielke, 1979 is illustrated (Fig. 70) as it provides a good example of the genus and a very similar species, with identical setal formula, is known to occur in Britain. *S. difficile* apparently differs from all other known species in the genus in possessing six setae on the distal segment of the endopod of the P1 and eight setae on the distal segment of the exopod of P2-P4 (see setal formula).

Habitat: Found amongst algae, in mud and sand, down to 146m.

Distribution: Northern North Sea, Ythan and Elbe estuaries, Loch Nevis.

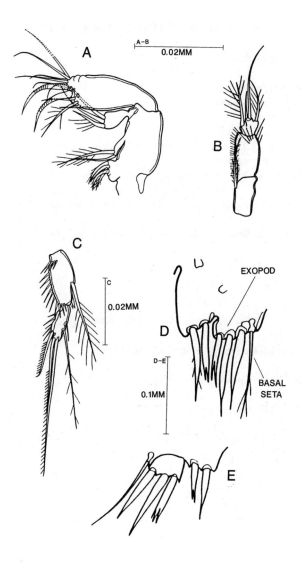

Fig. 70. *Sigmatidium kunzi* female: A, maxilla; B, maxilliped; C, P1 endopod; D, P5; E, male P5 (from Mielke, 1979).

Genus PSEUDECTINOSOMA Kunz, 1935

Diagnosis: Ectinosomatidae.
Body. Fusiform.
Antennule. 5-segmented in female.
Antenna. Exopod 2-segmented.
Maxilla. Geniculate.
Maxilliped (Fig. 71A). Robust.
P1-P4 (Fig. 71B,C). Exopod 3-segmented and exopod-3 with two outer spines or setae; endopod 2-segmented.
P5 (Fig. 71D,E). Reduced to a single plate-like lobe bearing two or five setae.

Two species known world-wide, but only one marine. Revision by Kunz (1974).

Local species. One. Setal formula in Appendix Table 2 (p. 341).

Pseudectinosoma minor Kunz, 1935

Synonym: Sigmatidium minor (Kunz) in Lang (1948).

Morphological description: Lang (1948).

Habitat: Brackish marsh. Rare.

Distribution: North Sea.

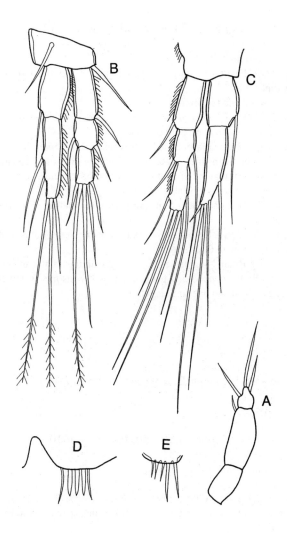

Fig. 71. *Pseudectinosoma minor*: A, maxilliped; B, P1; C, P2; D, female P5; E, male P5. After Kunz (1935), no scale.

Genus ECTINOSOMELLA Sars, 1910

Diagnosis: Ectinosomatidae.

Body (Fig. 72A). Fusiform, although tapering only slightly posteriorly. Rostrum large, hyaline.

Antennule. 6-segmented in female.

Antenna (Fig. 72B). Exopod 3-segmented, exopod-1 with two setae. Endopod segments without lateral armature of spines.

Mandible (Fig. 72C). Gnathobase with weakly-developed dentition. Basis elongate, slender, with three setae. Rami subterminal, each consisting of an elongate cylindrical region terminating in two or three slender setae.

Maxillule. Praecoxal arthrite weakly-developed.

Maxilla (Fig. 72D). Geniculate. Syncoxa with three endites. Endopod of three short segments.

Maxilliped (Fig. 72E). Robust. Syncoxa with one seta. Basis and endopod completely fused, with three setae.

P1-P4 (Fig. 73A). Rami 3-segmented. Exopod-3 with three outer spines.

P5 (Fig. 73B). Baseoendopod and exopod apparently distinct in female; exopod with three marginal and one surface seta.

Males unknown.

Monotypic.

Local species. One. Setal formula in Appendix Table 2 (p. 341).

Ectinosomella nitidula Sars, 1910

Morphological description: Sars (1911).

Habitat: Although Lang (1965: p. 14) describes this species as pelagic, the only information available on its habitat (Sars, 1911) is that specimens were taken from depths of 55-91 m.

Distribution: Known only from Southern Norway.

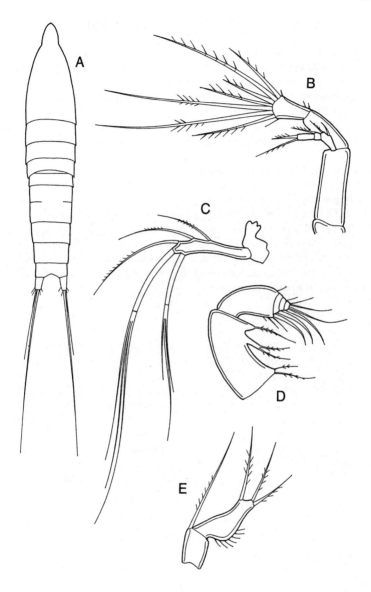

Fig. 72. *Ectinosomella nitidula* female: A, body, dorsal; B, antenna; C, mandible; D, maxilla; E, maxilliped. After Sars (1911), no scale.

Genus MICROSETELLA Brady & Robertson, 1873

Diagnosis: Ectinosomatidae.

Body (Fig. 74A). Fusiform, laterally compressed. Rostrum short, bent ventrally. Inner terminal seta of caudal ramus very long.

Antennule (Fig. 74B). 6-segmented in female, third segment elongate.

Antenna. Exopod 3-segmented.

Mandible (Fig. 74C). Basis with two setae. Exopod reduced. Endopod well developed, furnished with several slender setae and a strong spiniform lateral seta.

Maxilla (Fig. 74D). Not geniculate, with broad allobasis, resembling *Ectinosoma* and *Halectinosoma*.

Maxilliped (Fig. 74E). Robust.

P1-P4 (Fig. 73C). Rami 3-segmented. Exopod-3 with two outer spines.

P5. Baseoendopod and exopod distinct in male (Fig. 73E) and superficially distinct in female but with suture on posterior surface only (Fig. 73D). Exopod of female with three marginal setae and one surface seta. In male, exopod with only two marginal setae and one surface seta, endopodal lobe devoid of setae (male of one species only known).

Two species known world-wide.

Local species. Two. Setal formula in Appendix Table 2 (p. 341). They can be distinguished as follows:

Caudal ramus seta V (Fig. 74A) about as long as the body; female P5 baseoendopod inner seta much shorter than outer seta (Fig. 73D).
....*Microsetella norvegica*

Caudal ramus seta V twice as long as body; female P5 baseoendopod inner seta about as long as outer seta (Fig. 73F).
....*Microsetella rosea*

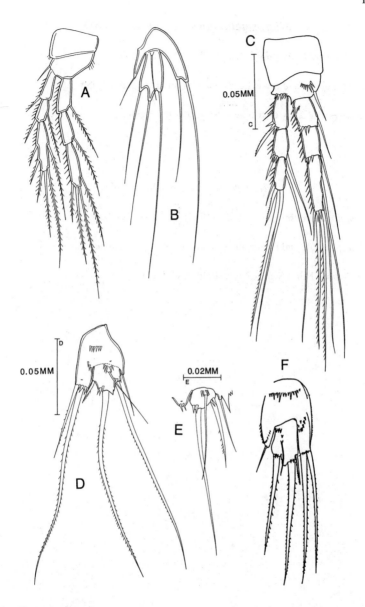

Fig. 73. *Ectinosomella nitidula* female: A, P1; B, P5: After Sars (1911), no scale. *Microsetella norvegica*: C, female P1; D, female P5; E, male P5. *Microsetella rosea*: F, female P5: After Lang (1948), no scale.

Microsetella norvegica (Boeck, 1865)

Morphological descriptions: Sars (1911), Boxshall (1979).

Habitat: Pelagic and found occasionally in mud and sand, 5-65m.

Distribution: Widely distributed throughout the region.

Microsetella rosea (Dana, 1848)

Morphological descriptions: Lang (1948), Boxshall (1979).

Habitat: Pelagic and found occasionally in sublittoral sediments.

Distribution: North Sea, Atlantic, English Channel.

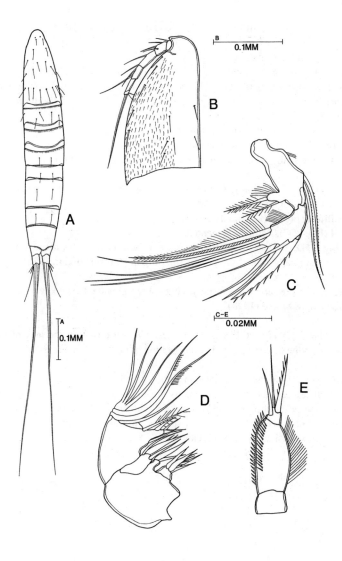

Fig. 74. *Microsetella norvegica* female: A, body, dorsal; B, antennule and cephalothorax, lateral; C, mandible palp; D, maxilla; E, maxilliped.

Genus HASTIGERELLA Nicholls, 1935

Diagnosis: Ectinosomatidae.

Body. Elongate, cylindrical, (as in *Arenosetella*, Fig. 76A), although *H. bozici* fusiform according to Kunz (1975); suture of female genital double-somite represented by discontinuous chitinous patches. Anal somite without dorsal armature.

Antennule. 5- to 8-segmented in female.

Antenna. Exopod 2- or 3-segmented.

Maxillule. Usually with 1-segmented exopod and endopod, but occasionally rami represented only by setae.

Maxilla (Fig. 75A). Non-geniculate, with elongate allobasis tapering distally for most of its length; endopod short.

Maxilliped (Fig. 75B). Usually slender.

P1-P4 (Fig. 75C). Rami 3-segmented.

P5 (Fig. 75D, E). Baseoendopod and exopod confluent or distinct; exopod with three marginal and one surface seta (missing in *H. soyeri* Bodin, 1976).

Seventeen species and two subspecies known world-wide. Latest key to species in McLachlan & Moore (1978).

Note: The genus is very similar to *Arenosetella* but differs in the lack of dorsal armature on the anal somite and in the setation of the swimming legs.

Local species. Four. Setal formulae in Appendix Table 2 (p. 341).
The local representatives of this genus are in need of revision as some of the records and descriptions of species are dubious and they are not included here. There are almost certainly additional species awaiting discovery. Known species may be distinguished by the following key:

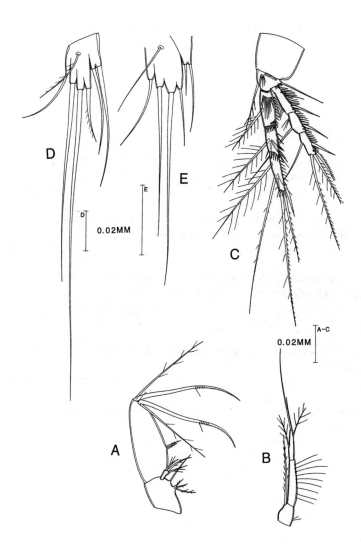

Fig. 75. *Hastigerella scheibeli*: A, maxilla; B, maxilliped; C, P1; D, female P5; E, male P5. After Mielke (1975).

Key to local species of Hastigerella

READ THREE ALTERNATIVES

1. P2-P4 endopod-3 with four setae and spines in all; female antennule 7-segmented; antennary exopod 3-segmented.
   ....*Hastigerella bozici*

   P2-P4 endopod-3 with five setae and spines in all; female antennule 5- or 6-segmented; antennary exopod 3-segmented.
   ....**2**

   P2-P4 endopod-3 with six setae and spines in all; female antennule 5-segmented; antennary exopod 2-segmented.
   ....*Hastigerella scheibeli*

2. P2-P4 exopod-3 with five setae and spines in all; female antennule 5-segmented.
   ....*Hastigerella leptoderma*

   P2-P4 exopod-3 with six setae and spines in all; female antennule 6-segmented.
   ....ᐧ....*Hastigerella psammae*

Hastigerella leptoderma (Klie, 1929)

Synonym: Pararenosetella leptoderma (Klie) in Lang (1948)

Morphological descriptions: Mielke (1975, 1981).

Habitat: Fine to coarse sand, littoral and sublittoral to 40m. Occasional.

Distribution: German North Sea coast, Aberdeenshire, Anglesey, Isles of Scilly, Finistère (France).

Hastigerella psammae (Noodt, 1955)

Synonym: Pararenosetella psammae Noodt, 1955.

Morphological description: Noodt (1955).

Habitat: Littoral sand, although the sole British record is from mud at 101m.

Distribution: Loch Nevis.

Hastigerella bozici Soyer, 1974

Morphological description: Soyer (1974). The description of South African material by Kunz (1975) may not be the same species.

Habitat: Littoral shell gravel and sublittoral sand to 108m.

Distribution: Finistère (France).

Hastigerella scheibeli Mielke, 1975

Morphological description: Mielke (1975).

Habitat: Littoral sand.

Distribution: Isle of Sylt (Germany).

Genus ARENOSETELLA C. B. Wilson, 1932

Diagnosis: Ectinosomatidae.

Body (Fig. 76A). Elongate, cylindrical. Female genital double-somite without trace of subdivision or with suture represented by discontinuous chitinous patches. Anal somite (Fig. 76H, I)) with dorsal armature of paired claws, lappets or spiniform processes.

Antennule. 5- or 6-segmented in female.

Antenna. Exopod usually 3-segmented.

Maxillule. 1-segmented exopod (with one exception) and endopod.

Maxilla (Fig. 76F). Non-geniculate. Allobasis typically elongate tapering distally for most of its length; endopod minute.

Maxilliped (Fig. 76G). Usually slender, endopod long.

P1-P4 (Fig. 76B, C). Rami 3-segmented ; exopod-3 with two outer spines.

P5 (Fig. 76D, E). Baseoendopod and exopod usually confluent. Exopod with three marginal and one surface seta.

Twenty species and two subspecies known world-wide. Keys to species in Bodin (1979) and McLachlan & Moore (1978).

Note: The genus is very similar to *Hastigerella* but differs in the presence of dorsal armature on the anal somite and in the setation of the swimming legs. The species of *Tetanopsis* Brady, 1910 described by Perkins (1956) from Whitstable almost certainly belong to this genus but their specific validity is questionable.

Local species. Two. Setal formulae in Appendix Table 2 (p. 341).

The species are distinguished from each other by the form of the dorsal armature (Fig. 76H,I) and by the setation of the endopods of P1-P4 (endopod-3 with four setae in *A. germanica* and three setae in *A. tenuissima*). There are almost certainly additional species awaiting discovery.

Arenosetella germanica germanica Kunz, 1937

Morphological descriptions: Mielke (1981, 1986).

Habitat: Often a dominant member of the interstitial fauna of sandy beaches and common in sublittoral sand.

Distribution: Widely distributed throughout the region.

Arenosetella tenuissima (Klie, 1929)

Synonym: A. monensis Moore, 1976.

Morphological description: Moore (1976).

Habitat: Often abundant in littoral and sublittoral sand, with an apparent preference for finer sand than *A. germanica germanica*.

Distribution: Widely distributed throughout the region.

193

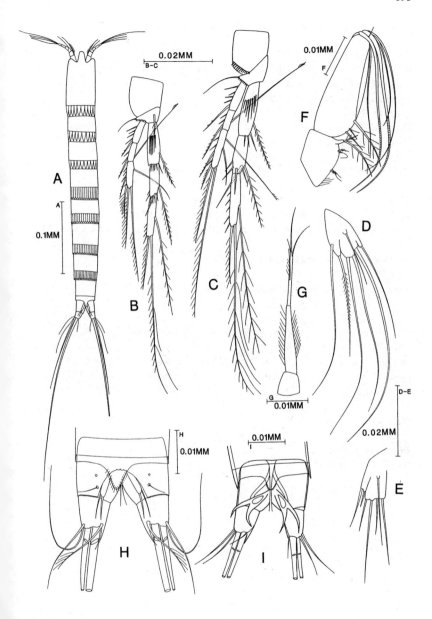

Fig. 76. *Arenosetella tenuissima*: A, female body, dorsal; B, P1; C, P4; D, female P5; E, male P5; F, maxilla; G, maxilliped; H, anal somite and caudal rami, dorsal; after Moore (1976). *Arenosetella germanica germanica*: I, anal somite and caudal rami, dorsal; after Lang (1965).

Genus LINEOSOMA Wells, 1965

Diagnosis: Ectinosomatidae.

Body. Elongate, cylindrical. Suture of female genital double-somite absent or represented by discontinuous chitinous lines.

Antennule. 6-segmented in female.

Antenna. Exopod 2-segmented.

Maxillule. 1-segmented exopod and endopod or rami can be fused to basis.

Maxilla. Geniculate. Syncoxa and allobasis elongate (very similar to *Noodtiella*, Fig. 78A).

Maxilliped. Slender but less so than in *Arenosetella* and *Hastigerella*.

P1-P4. Rami 3-segmented except that P1 endopod may be 2-segmented. Exopod-3 with one or two outer spines and no inner setae.

P5 (Fig. 77). Baseoendopod and exopod distinct in female but confluent in male (where this sex is known). Exopod with three marginal but no surface setae.

Four species known world-wide.

Local species. One. Setal formula in Appendix Table 2 (p. 341).

Lineosoma iscensis Wells, 1965

Morphological description: Wells (1965a). The only other known species of *Lineosoma* with a 3-segmented P1 endopod is *L. enertha* (Lindgren, 1975) from North Carolina, from which *L. iscensis* differs in the setal formula of P1- P4.

Habitat: Littoral sand. Rare.

Distribution: Exmouth.

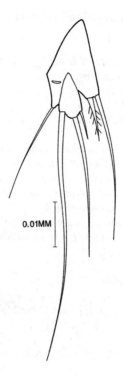

Fig. 77. *Lineosoma iscensis*: female P5.

Genus NOODTIELLA Wells, 1965

Diagnosis: Ectinosomatidae.

Body. Elongate, cylindrical. Suture of female genital double-somite absent or represented by weak chitinous markings.

Antennule. 6-segmented in female.

Antenna. Exopod 2-segmented.

Maxillule. Usually with 1-segmented exopod and endopod, but rami can be fused to basis.

Maxilla (Fig. 78A). Geniculate. Syncoxa and allobasis elongate.

Maxilliped (Fig. 78B). Slender but less so than in *Arenosetella* and *Hastigerella*.

P1-P4 (Fig. 78C). Exopods 3-segmented (may be 2-segmented on P4); exopod-3 with one or two outer spines and no inner setae (except *N. gracile* which has one inner seta on P4). Endopods 2-segmented.

P5 (Fig. 78D). Baseoendopod and exopod may be confluent or distinct. Exopod with three marginal setae (except for *N. tabogensis* Mielke, 1981 with two) but no surface setae.

Thirteen species known world-wide.

Local species. One. Setal formula in Appendix Table 2 (p. 341).

Noodtiella gracile Mielke, 1975

Morphological description: Mielke (1975). This species can be distinguished from all other local species in the family by the 2-segmented nature of the P4 exopod. Only one other known species of the genus shares this feature, *N. frequentior* Mielke, 1979 from South America, but this species differs in the setation of the P1-P4.

Habitat: Littoral sand.

Distribution: Isle of Sylt, Germany.

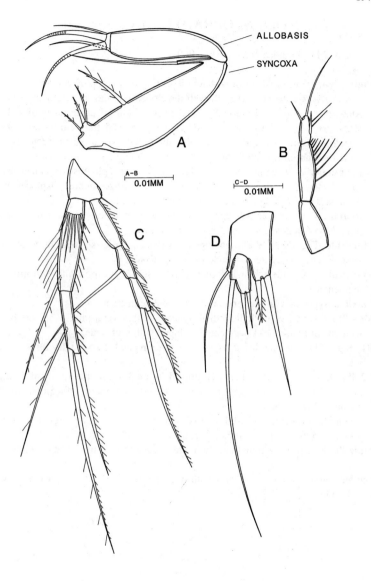

ALLOBASIS

SYNCOXA

A-B
0.01MM

C-D
0.01MM

A

B

C

D

Fig. 78. *Noodtiella gracile* female: A, maxilla; B, maxilliped; C, P1; D, P5. After Mielke (1975).

Family NEOBRADYIDAE Olofsson, 1917

Synonym. Marsteiniidae Drzycimski, 1969.

Diagnosis.

Body. Cylindrical or fusiform without distinction between prosome and urosome (Fig. 80A). Cephalothorax with well-developed rostrum, not defined at base. Anal somite short and markedly notched in middle of posterior border (Fig. 80B). Anal operculum absent, sometimes replaced by weakly-developed pseudoperculum. Caudal rami usually short, with six or seven setae (seta I sometimes absent); setae IV and V often fused at base.

Antennule. 8- or 9-segmented in female, with numerous plumose or pinnate setae and segment-1 shorter than segment-2. In male, 10-segmented, haplocer with aesthetasc on fourth and sometimes terminal segment.

Antenna. With basis and 2-segmented endopod, endopod-1 unarmed. Exopod (Fig. 79A) 4-segmented with 2.1.1.2 setal formula.

Mandible (Fig. 79B). Well-developed coxa and palp. Basis with three or four setae. Exopod 4-segmented; endopod 1-segmented.

Maxillule. Epipodite bearing one to four setae. Exopod and endopod 1-segmented.

Maxilla. Syncoxa with four endites. Endopod 3-segmented.

Maxilliped (Fig. 79C). Phyllopodial. Syncoxa with several pinnate spines. Basis with one or two setae. 1-segmented endopod with four setae.

P1 (Fig. 79D). Not modified; both rami 3-segmented. Exopod-1 without inner seta.

P2-P4. Exopod 3-segmented. Endopod 2- or 3-segmented; slight sexual dimorphism, variable except for long tube pore on anterior face of male P3 endopod-2 (Fig. 79E).

P5. Female with free or fused exopod, endopodal lobe sometimes marked by posterior suture. Sexually dimorphic.

Male P6 (Fig. 80B). Symmetrical with three setae and partially fused medially.

Females with one egg-sac, males with one spermatophore. Three genera known world-wide.

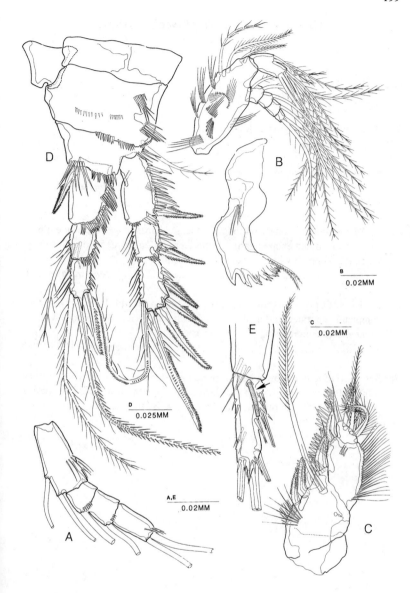

Fig. 79. *Neobradya pectinifera*: A, exopod of antenna; B, mandible with disarticulated palp and gnathobase; C, maxilliped; D, P1; E, male P3 endopod 2.

Key to world genera of Neobradyidae

1. P2-P4 endopod 2-segmented.
  2

   P2-P4 endopod 3-segmented; P1 endopod-3 with four setae / spines.
   ....*Marsteinia* (p. 203)

2. P2-P4 endopod-1 strongly prolonged, at least 3 times longer than wide; P5 baseoendopod and exopod partially confluent in female, exopod with five setae; P3 exopod-3 without sexual dimorphism.
   ....*Neobradya* (p. 202)

   P2-P4 endopod-1 almost square; P5 baseoendopod and exopod completely confluent in female, exopod with four setae; P3 exopod-3 with slight sexual dimorphism.
   ....*Antarcticobradya* Huys, 1987

Species of *Marsteinia* show a strong preference for bathyal or abyssal habitats down to 5000m, though a few species have been recorded from the west coast of Europe in 120-300m depth. *Antarcticobradya* is, thus far, confined to the Antarctic.

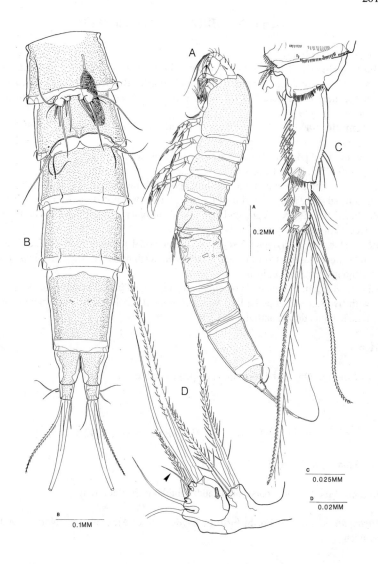

Fig. 80. *Neobradya pectinifera*: A, female body, lateral; B, male urosome, ventral; C, female P2 basis and endopod; D, female P5.

Genus NEOBRADYA T. Scott, 1892

Diagnosis: Neobradyidae.

Body. Cylindrical; urosomites without spinule rows (Fig. 80A). Penultimate somite nearly 3 times longer than anal somite. Rostrum broad, triangular, moderately developed. Caudal ramus short; seta V strongly-developed, others small (Fig. 80B).

Antennule. Slender, 9-segmented in female, with aesthetascs on fourth and terminal segments; setae plumose.

Antenna. Endopod-1 distinctly longer than endopod-2.

Mandible (Fig. 79B). Basis with three setae.

Maxillule. Epipodite with three setae. Exopod with four setae.

Maxilliped (Fig. 79C). Very long plumose seta on syncoxa. Basis with one spine.

P1 (Fig. 79D). Exopod-2 and endopod-1 without inner seta, endopod-3 with three setae / spines.

P2-P4 (Fig. 80C). Endopod 2-segmented; endopod-1 strongly prolonged, at least three times longer than average width, without inner seta. Male P3 exopod-3 without sexual dimorphism.

P5 (Fig. 80B,D). In female, baseoendopod and exopod partially confluent, exopod with five setae, endopodal lobe with two setae. In male, with same armature as female but endopod partially free.

Monotypic.

Local species. One. Setal formula in Appendix Table 3 (p.342).

Neobradya pectinifera T. Scott, 1892

Morphological description: Huys (1987).

Habitat: Muddy sand; coarse shell sand; subtidal in 20-90m. Rare.

Distribution: Firth of Forth, Firth of Clyde, Isle of Man, western Norway and Sweden.

203

Genus MARSTEINIA Drzycimski, 1968

Synonym: Tachidiopsis Sars (part.): Bodin (1968), Becker (1974), Dinet (1974).
Diagnosis: Neobradyidae.
Body (Fig. 81A). Fusiform; urosomites with or without spinule rows. Rostrum strongly-developed, bell-shaped, with two closely set sensilla at tip. Caudal ramus of variable length.
Antennule. Short, robust, 8- or 9-segmented in female with aesthetascs on fourth and sometimes terminal segments; setae mostly pinnate and spiniform.
Antenna. Endopod-1 not distinctly longer than endopod-2.
Mandible. Basis with one to four setae.
Maxillule. Epipodite with up to four setae. Exopod with two or four setae.
Maxilliped. Basis with two setae or spines.
P1. Exopod-2, endopod-1 and endopod-2 with inner seta, endopod-3 with four setae / spines.
P2-P4 (Fig. 81C,D). Endopods 3-segmented in female, endopod-1 not strongly prolonged, with inner seta. In male, P2-P3 endopods 2-segmented, inner seta of endopod-1 and outer terminal seta of P3 exopod-3 modified.
P5 (Fig. 81B,E,F). In female, baseoendopod and exopod with up to five and six setae respectively. In male, coxa, basis and endopod sometimes free; baseoendopod with 2 setae; exopod rarely two-segmented with up to five setae.

Seven species known world-wide.
Local species: Two. Setal formulae in Appendix Table 3 (p.342). The species can be distinguished as follows.

P3-P4 exopod-3 with two inner setae; female P5 with fused rami, baseoendopod with three setae (Fig. 81E); male P5 with fused rami (Fig. 81F).

....*Marsteinia typica*

P3-P4 exopod-3 with three inner setae; female P5 with free exopod, baseoendopod with five setae (Fig. 81B); male unknown.

....*Marsteinia similis*

Marsteinia typica Drzycimski, 1968

Morphological description: Drzycimski (1968).

Habitat: Subtidal sand with small stones, in 300m. Rare.

Distribution: West coast of Norway (Bergen).

Marsteinia similis Drzycimski, 1968

Morphological description: Drzycimski (1968).

Habitat: Subtidal mud in 122-242m. Rare.

Distribution: West coast of Norway (Bergen).

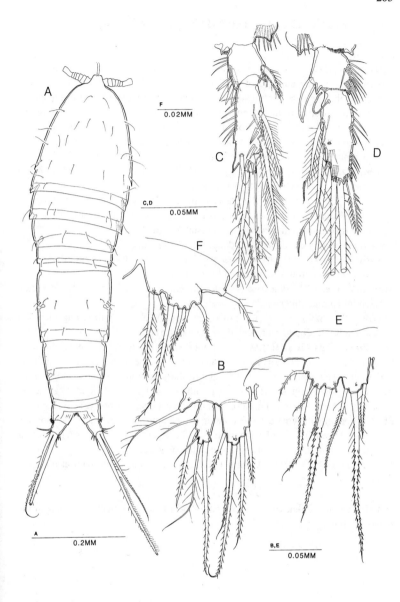

Fig. 81. *Marsteinia similis* female: A, body, dorsal; B, P5. *Marsteinia typica*: C, male P2 endopod; D, male P3 endopod; E, female P5; F, male P5.

Family DARCYTHOMPSONIIDAE Lang, 1936

Diagnosis.

Body (Figs 83A,E; 84A,B). Elongate, cylindrical, without marked distinction between prosome and urosome. Cephalothorax with triangular rostrum, with two sensilla. Female genital somite separate or completely fused to urosomite-3; female genital field extremely reduced, copulatory pore and gonopores concealed under common bilobed opercular structure without armature. Anal operculum usually weakly-developed, sometimes sexually dimorphic. Caudal rami short; only seta V well-developed; sometimes sexually dimorphic.

Antennule. In female, 5- to 7-segmented, with aesthetasc on third or fourth segment; in male, subchirocer or haplocer.

Antenna (Figs 82A, 83C). Allobasis without or with one seta on abexopodal margin. Exopod rudimentary, at most 1-segmented with, at most, two setae. Endopod without geniculate setae on distal margin.

Labrum. Strongly chitinised with densely packed teeth.

Mandible. Coxa and gnathobase well developed. Palp reduced, at most uniramous, sometimes represented by a single seta .

Maxillule (Fig. 82B). Praecoxa well developed. Coxa, basis and rami completely fused into a maxillulary palp.

Maxilla (Fig. 82C). Syncoxa with two endites. Allobasis with strong claw-like baso-endite. Endopod represented by one or two setae.

Maxilliped (Figs 82C; 83D). Absent or poorly developed and variable in form.

P1 (Fig. 82D). Non-prehensile. Inner seta of basis sometimes sexually dimorphic. Exopod 3-segmented with 0.0.022 setal formula. Endopod usually 2-segmented.

P2-P4. Exopod 3-segmented; exopod-1 without inner seta. Endopod 2-segmented usually with slight sexual dimorphism on at least one endopod (Fig. 82E,F).

P5. Very small, in female largely incorporated into somite. Baseoendopod and exopod fused, limbs of each side may be fused into single plate. Sexual dimorphism in degree of fusion and number of setae.

Male P6 (Figs 82G, 83H). Asymmetrical, a membranous plate with at most two setae.

Female egg-sacs unknown (possibly eggs laid free in sediment); males with one spermatophore.

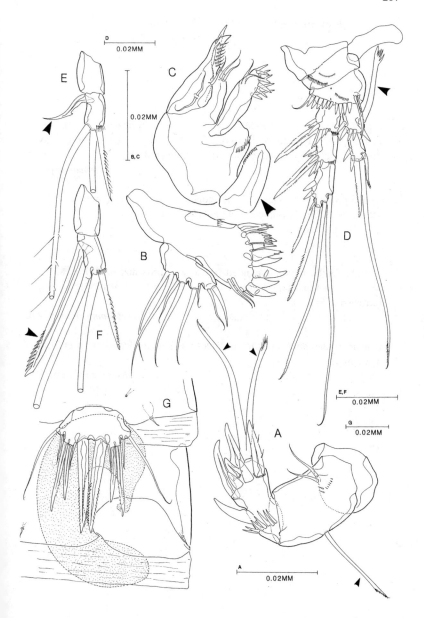

207

Fig. 82. *Leptocaris brevicornis*: A, antenna; E, male P3 endopod (dimorphic seta arrowed); F, male P4 endopod (dimorphic seta arrowed). *Leptocaris minutus*: C, maxilla and maxilliped; D, P1; G, male urosomite-1 and -2, showing P5, P6 and spermatophore. *Darcythompsonia fairliensis*: B, maxillule.

Key to world genera of Darcythompsoniidae

1. Maxilliped completely absent or reduced to small triangular lobe (arrowed in Fig. 82C); P1 endopod proximal or only segment with anteriorly directed seta with terminal comb (arrowed in Fig. 82D).
....*Leptocaris* (p. 212)

   Maxilliped present, moderately developed with at least one spine and two setae (Fig. 83D); P1 endopod-1 without inner seta.
....2

2. Female caudal ramus expanded laterally in proximal half (Fig. 83B). Males with fan-shaped dorsal organ and strongly bifid operculum (arrowed in Fig. 83E).
....*Darcythompsonia* (p. 210)

   Female caudal ramus cylindrical. Males without fan-shaped organ or bifid operculum.
....*Kristensenia* Por, 1983

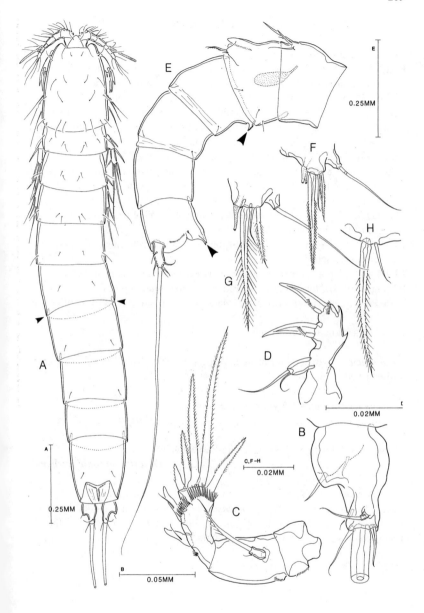

Fig. 83. *Darcythompsonia fairliensis*: A. female body, dorsal; B, caudal ramus, dorsal; C, antenna; D, maxilliped; E, male urosome, lateral; F, female P5; G, male P5; H, male P6.

Genus DARCYTHOMPSONIA T. Scott, 1906

Diagnosis: Darcythompsoniidae.

Body (Fig. 83A, E). Without somatic ornamentation. Rostrum defined at base. In female, genital somite completely separate from urosomite-3 (arrowed in Fig. 83A); in male, urosomite-3 with fan-shaped organ near dorsal anterior margin (arrowed in Fig. 83E). Anal operculum smooth in female; raised and strongly bifid in male (arrowed in Fig. 83E). Caudal rami in female with proximal half laterally expanded (Fig. 83B); cylindrical in male.

Antennule. In female, 7-segmented. In male, subchirocer.

Antenna (Fig. 83C). Allobasis without seta on abexopodal margin. Exopod 1-segmented with one well-developed seta. Endopod with five spines on distal margin.

Maxilliped (Fig. 83D). Not subchelate; with two terminal claw-like spines and a proximal lobe bearing one or two setae.

P1. Inner basal spine sexually dimorphic. Endopod 2-segmented; endopod-1 without inner seta.

P2-P4. P2 endopod-2 outer terminal seta transformed into a spine in male.

P5 (Fig. 83F, G). Not sexually dimorphic, with four setae / spines.

Male P6 (Fig. 83H). With two setae. Male spermatophore (Fig. 83E) small, ovoid.

Three species known world-wide.

Local species. Two. Setal formulae in Appendix Table 3 (p. 342). Species may be distinguished as follows.

P2-P4 exopod-3 with 4.5.5 setae / spines respectively.
.... ***Darcythompsonia neglecta***

P2-P4 exopod-3 with 5.6.6 setae / spines respectively.
.... ***Darcythompsonia fairliensis***

Note: A third species, *D. scotti* Gurney, 1920, described from Loch Fyne, is regarded as a synonym of *D. fairliensis* and therefore not included here. The distinguishing features (found only in the female of *D. scotti*) suggest that the description was based on a female copepodid V.

Darcythompsonia fairliensis (T. Scott, 1899)

Synonym: Darcythompsonia scotti Gurney, 1920.

Morphological descriptions: Sars (1911), Ceccherelli & Rossin (1979).

Habitat: Intertidal, brackish water pools, detritus-rich shell gravel.

Distribution: Shetland, Firth of Clyde, Loch Fyne, Anglesey, Dublin Bay, western Norway.

Darcythompsonia neglecta Redeke, 1953

Morphological description: Redeke (1953).

Habitat: Brackish water canal.

Distribution: Den Helder, Holland.

Genus LEPTOCARIS T. Scott, 1899

Synonym: Horsiella Gurney, 1920.

Diagnosis: Darcythompsoniidae.

Body (Fig. 84A,B). Rostrum not defined at base, usually ventrally deflected. Female genital somite either separate or completely fused to urosomite-3. Operculum semi-circular in both sexes. Caudal rami (Fig. 84C,E) cylindrical in both sexes.

Antennule. In female, 5- or 6-segmented; in male, subchirocer or haplocer.

Antenna (Fig. 82A). Allobasis with one seta on abexopodal margin. Exopod absent or represented by two small setae. Endopod distal margin with three spines and two basally fused setae (arrowed in Fig. 82A).

Maxilliped. Absent or reduced to small triangular lobe (arrowed in Fig. 82C).

P1 (Fig. 82D). Endopod 1- or 2-segmented, proximal or only segment with anteriorly directed inner seta with comb tip.

P2-P4 (Fig. 82E,F). Sexual dimorphism absent or on endopod.

P5 (Figs 82G; 84D,F,G). Sexually dimorphic.

Male P6 (Fig. 82G). Without setae. Male spermatophore (Fig. 82G) large, sausage-shaped and strongly curved.

Twenty-three species known world-wide. Latest key in Fleeger & Clark (1980).

Local species. Three.[145] Setal formulae in Appendix Table 3 (p.342). Species can be distinguished as follows.

1. P3 and P4 exopod-3 with four setae / spines.
    .... *Leptocaris minutus*

    P3 and P4 exopod-3 with five setae / spines.
   2

2. P2 endopod-1 with inner seta; P5 female with three setae; P5 male with six setae.
    .... *Leptocaris trisetosus*

    P2 endopod-1 without inner seta; P5 female with two setae; P5 male with four setae.
    .... *Leptocaris brevicornis*

---

[145] *Leptocaris ignavus* Noodt, 1953 has been omitted because it is almost certainly a synonym of *L. minutus*. The separation of these two forms was based on characters which were wrongly described or figured in the original description of *L. minutus*.

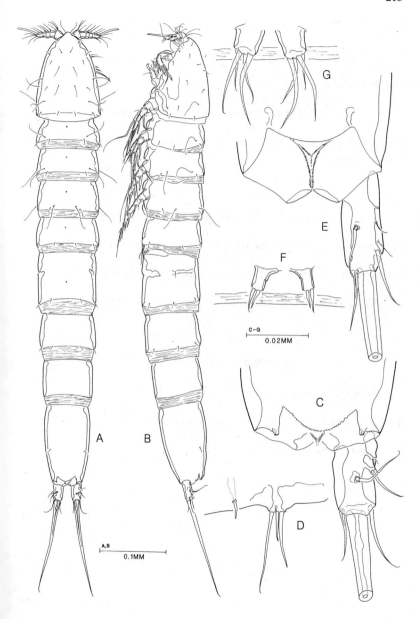

Fig. 84. *Leptocaris minutus*: A, body, dorsal; B, body lateral; C, anal somite, dorsal, showing operculum and caudal ramus; D, female P5. *Leptocaris brevicornis*: E, anal somite, dorsal, showing operculum and caudal ramus; F, female P5; G, male P5.

Leptocaris minutus T. Scott, 1899

Synonym: Leptocaris ignavus Noodt, 1953 ?

Morphological description: T. Scott (1899).

Habitat: Intertidal, brackish-water pools, estuarine muddy sand.

Distribution: Firth of Clyde; Exe estuary, Devon and, as *L. ignavus*, Anglesey and Dalkey, Ireland.

Leptocaris brevicornis (van Douwe, 1904)

Morphological descriptions: Gurney (1920, 1932), Kikuchi & Yokota (1984).

Habitat: Euryhaline, mud flats, salt marshes, amongst plant detritus.

Distribution: Norfolk; Exe estuary, Devon; North Sea coast of Germany.

Leptocaris trisetosus (Kunz, 1935)

Morphological descriptions: Kunz (1935), Bodin (1973).

Habitat: Euryhaline, brackish-water pools, amongst plant detritus.

Distribution: North Sea coast of Germany.

Family EUTERPINIDAE Brian, 1921

Diagnosis.

Body (Fig. 85A). Distinct separation between prosome and urosome. Cephalothorax with well-developed rostrum anteriorly directed, not defined at base. Anal somite short, with well-developed serrate anal operculum (Fig. 85B). Caudal rami longer than wide, slightly convergent (Fig. 85B); with six setae, seta I absent, setae IV and V fused at base.

Antennule (Fig. 85C,D). 7-segmented with smooth setae and aesthetasc on fourth and terminal segments in both sexes. Chirocer in male.

Antenna (Fig. 86A,B). With basis and 2-segmented endopod; basis and endopod-1 unarmed. Exopod 1-segmented, with four setae.

Mandible. Coxa and palp well developed. Basis with two setae. Exopod and endopod 1-segmented, with five and seven setae respectively.

Maxillule. Epipodite absent; exopod (one seta) and endopod (three setae) 1-segmented and incorporated in basis bearing six setae.

Maxilla. Syncoxa with three endites (3.3.4 setae). Allobasis with claw and four setae. Endopod 1-segmented with five setae.

Maxilliped (Fig. 85E). Sub-chelate. Syncoxa and basis unarmed. Endopod 1-segmented with spinulose claw and one accessory seta.

P1 (Fig. 86C,D). Not modified. Rami 2-segmented; exopod-1 without inner seta. Slightly sexually dimorphic.

P2-P4 (Fig. 86E-G). Rami 3-segmented in female. P2 endopod 2-segmented in male and with one or two fewer setae than in female.

P5. In female (Fig. 85F), a flattened rectangular plate with four spines on distal margin and two setae and a spine on outer margin. In male (Fig. 85G), both legs fused into a single plate with a median notch in the distal margin, each leg bearing two spines on distal margin and one spine and two setae on outer margin.

Male P6 (Fig. 85G). Symmetrical, with two spines.

Females with one egg-sac (Fig. 85A), males with one spermatophore.

Monotypic.

217

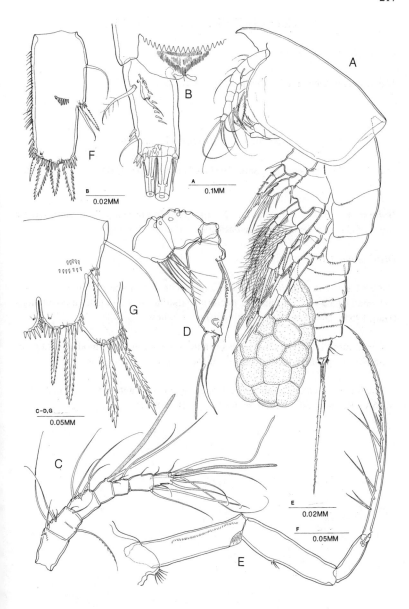

Fig. 85. *Euterpina acutifrons*: A, body of ovigerous female, lateral view; B, anal somite and caudal ramus, dorsal view; C, female antennule; D, male antennule (armature omitted); E, maxilliped; F, female P5; G, male P5 and P6.

Genus EUTERPINA Norman, 1903

Diagnosis: As for family.

Local species. One. Setal formula in Appendix Table 3 (p.342).

Euterpina acutifrons (Dana, 1848)

Morphological descriptions: Sars (1921), Chappuis (1936), Haq (1965), Boxshall (1979).

Habitat: Holoplanktonic, marine. Neritic, also in epipelagic and mesopelagic zones of ocean waters. Common, occasional in sediment samples.

Distribution: Cosmopolitan between 66°N and 40°S.

Note: Males of *E. acutifrons* are dimorphic with both large (0.65mm - 0.7mm) and small (0.52 - 0.6mm) morphs occurring simultaneously in natural populations (Haq, 1965). They can also be distinguished as follows:-

Large morph with twelve setae on antennule segment 3; modified rami of antenna (Fig. 86B); P2 endopod-2 with two inner setae (Fig. 86F).

Small morph with five setae on antennule segment-3; antenna as in female (Fig. 86A); P2 endopod-2 with three inner setae (Fig. 86G)

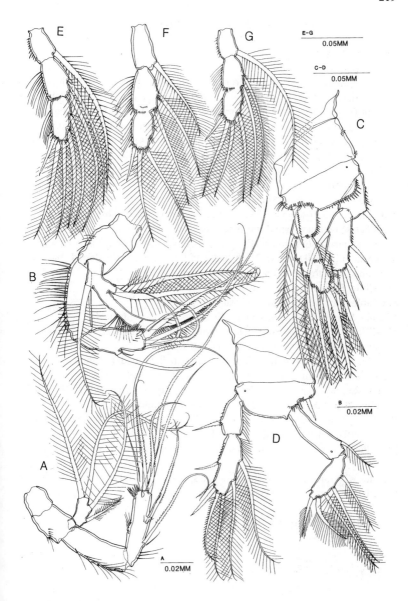

Fig. 86. *Euterpina acutifrons*: A, antenna of female and small male morph; B, antenna of large male morph; C, P1 of female and small male morph; D, P1 of large male morph; E, P2 endopod of female; F, P2 endopod of large male morph; G, P2 endopod of small male morph.

Family TACHIDIIDAE Boeck, 1865

Synonym. Microarthridioninae Lang, 1944.

Diagnosis.

Body. Cyclopoid-like in appearance, broad, rather flattened, with distinct separation between prosome and urosome. Cephalothorax with dorsal nuchal organ (Fig. 87A); paired accessory nuchal organs (Figs 87A, 88A) present on cephalothorax and somites bearing P2 to P4 (sometimes P5). Rostrum small, conical; not defined at base but hyaline zone at base sometimes present (Fig. 87A). Female genital somite free (Fig. 90B) or incorporated in double-somite (Fig. 88A). Anal somite short, with spinulose anal operculum. Caudal rami usually short, with six or seven setae (seta I sometimes absent); seta IV and V strongly-developed and spinulose.

Antennule. 6- to 9-segmented in female with numerous plumose or pinnate setae; aesthetasc on fourth and distal segments. Distinctive in male, up to 9-segmented and subchirocer or chirocer (Figs 87C, 89A), with two or three aesthetascs.

Antenna (Figs 87D; 88B). With basis and 2-segmented endopod; basis and endopod-1 unarmed. Exopod 1- or 2-segmented.

Mandible. Basis with two setae. Rami 1-segmented.

Maxillule. Rami incorporated in basis.

Maxilla. Syncoxa with three endites. Endopod 1- or 2-segmented.

Maxilliped (Fig. 87E). Sub-chelate. Syncoxa and basis unarmed. Endopod 1-segmented with claw and one or two small setae.

P1 (Fig. 87B). Not modified. Rami 3-segmented; exopod-1 without inner seta. Inner spine of basis sometimes slightly sexually dimorphic.

P2-P4. Rami 3-segmented in P2 and P3 and 2- or 3-segmented in P4. Usually both rami of P2 and exopod of P3 sexually dimorphic.

P5. A single plate in both sexes (Fig. 88C,E), occasionally incorporated in somite (Fig. 89B); armature variable. Sexually dimorphic.

Male P6. Symmetrical, with one seta and two spines; fused to supporting somite.

Females with one egg-sac, males with one spermatophore. Precopulatory clasping to the lateral margins of the cephalothorax.

Four genera known world-wide.

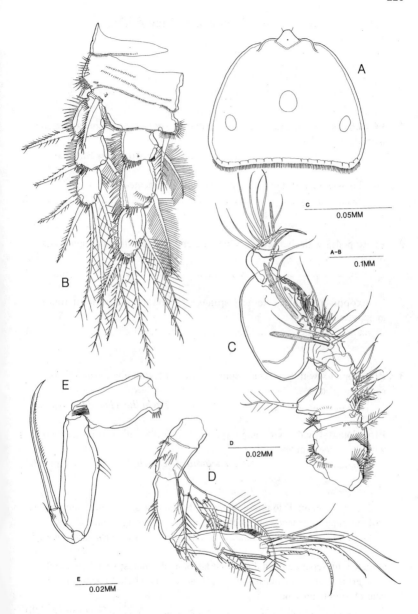

Fig. 87. *Tachidius (Tachidius) discipes*: A, cephalothorax, dorsal; B, P1. *Geeopsis incisipes*:
C, male antennule; D, antenna; E, maxilliped.

Key to world genera of Tachidiidae

1. P4 with 2-segmented rami; antenna exopod 1-segmented; associated with isopods.
   ....*Cithadius* Bowman, 1972

   P4 with 3-segmented rami; antenna exopod 2-segmented.
   ....**2**

2. P1 exopod-3 with five setae / spines; P2 endopod-2 with inner apophysis in male.
   ....**3**

   P1 exopod-3 with six setae / spines; P2 endopod-2 without inner apophysis in male.
   ....**4**

3. P1 endopod-3 with five setae / spines; female P5 with nine, male P5 with seven setae/ spines.
   ....*Tachidius (Tachidius)* (p. 224)

   P1 endopod-3 with four setae / spines; female P5 with seven, male P5 with five setae / spines.
   ....*Tachidius (Neotachidius)* Shen & Tai, 1963

4. Female with genital double-somite; P1-P4 endopod-1 a small segment without inner seta; accessory nuchal organ on P5-bearing somite absent.
   ....*Microarthridion* (p. 225)

   Female with separate genital and first abdominal somites; P1-P4 endopod-1 of normal size and with inner seta; accessory nuchal organ on P5-bearing somite present.
   ....*Geeopsis* (p. 228)

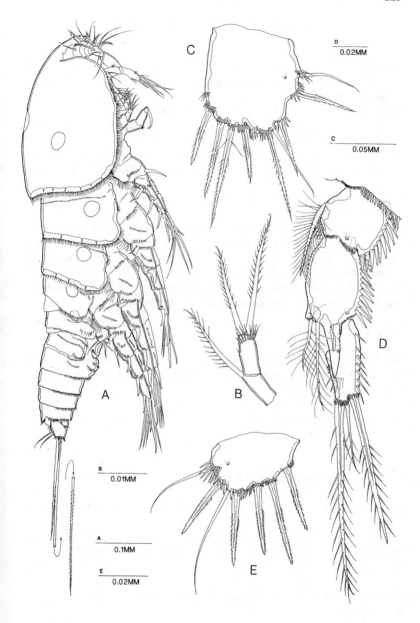

Fig. 88. *Tachidius (Tachidius) discipes*: A, female body, lateral; B, exopod of antenna; C, female P5; D, male P2 endopod; E, male P5.

Genus TACHIDIUS Lilljeborg, 1853

Diagnosis: Tachidiidae.

Body (Fig. 88A). Accessory nuchal organ on P5-bearing somite present. Genital and first abdominal somite fused in female with dorsal and lateral internal chitinous rib.

Antennule. 7-segmented in female. Chirocer in male.

Antenna (Fig. 88B). Exopod 2-segmented; proximal segment with one seta, distal segment with one (vestigial) lateral and two terminal setae.

P1 (Fig. 87B). Endopod-1 of normal size, with inner seta. Exopod-3 with five setae / spines. In male, inner basal spine more slender and longer than in female.

P2-P4. Endopod-1 of normal size with inner seta. Rami of P4 3-segmented. Male P2 with exopod outer spines shorter and stouter than female; endopod-2 with inner spinous apophysis overlapping deep notch of endopod-3 (Fig. 88D); endopod-3 outer spine minute and setiform, inner setae absent. Male P3 exopod (similar to Fig. 90F) longer than in female with exopod-3 often bent inwards; inner distal seta of exopod-3 vestigial.

P5 (Fig. 88C,E). In female, almost square, slightly bilobed, with nine setae / spines. In male, a broad undivided plate with seven setae / spines.

Three species known world-wide.

Two sub-genera, *Tachidius* and *Neotachidius*, are recognised on the basis of the P1 endopod and the P5 armature of both sexes (Shen & Tai, 1963) but only the former is represented in British waters.

Local species. One. Setal formula in Appendix Table 3 (p.342).

Tachidius (Tachidius) discipes Giesbrecht, 1881

Morphological descriptions: Gurney (1932), Chislenko (1967), Mielke (1975).

Habitat: Mud or fine muddy sand, occasionally in fine to medium clean sand; intertidal, rarely shallow subtidal. Polyhaline, occasionally in freshwater. One of the commonest littoral harpacticoids.

Distribution: Throughout the British Isles and European coast from Brittany to western Norway.

Genus MICROARTHRIDION Lang, 1944

Diagnosis: Tachidiidae.

Body (Fig. 89A). Accessory nuchal organ on P5-bearing somite absent. Female genital and first abdominal somites fused with dorsal and lateral internal chitinous rib.

Antennule. Short and blunt, 6-segmented in female. Chirocer in male.

Antenna. Exopod of antenna 2-segmented; proximal segment with one or two setae, distal segment with two or three setae.

P1. Endopod-1 very small and without inner seta; exopod-3 with six setae / spines. In male, inner basal spine longer and more slender than in female.

P2-P4. Rami 3-segmented. Endopod-1 very small, without inner seta. Male P2 exopod outer spines shorter and stouter than in female; endopod-2 without inner apophysis (Fig. 89C); endopod-3 distal outer spine very much reduced and spiniform. Male P3 exopod (similar to Fig. 90F) longer than in female with exopod-3 often bent inwards; inner distal seta of exopod-3 vestigial.

P5 (Fig. 89B,D). In female, consisting of outer basal seta on a laterally displaced minute knob and a small plate with four setae which is either free or incorporated in the somite. Vestigial in male, represented by five setae on posterior margin of somite.

Seven species known world-wide. Latest key to species in Bodin (1970).

Local species. Three. Setal formulae in Appendix Table 3 (p.342). Species can be identified as follows.

1. P2-P3 endopod-2 with one inner seta.
    ....***Microarthridion fallax***

    P2-P3 endopod-2 with two inner setae.
    ....**2**

2. Exopod of antenna with four setae (one on proximal segment).
    ....***Microarthridion littorale***

    Exopod of antenna with five setae (two on proximal segment).
    ....***Microarthridion reductum***

Microarthridion littorale (Poppe, 1881)

Morphological descriptions: Gurney (1932), Lorenzen (1969).

Habitat: Mud, muddy sand, less commonly fine sand; intertidal mudflats, organically-enriched estuarine and shallow subtidal localities. Euryhaline. Common to very common; occasionally in the plankton or in algal washings.

Distribution: Throughout north-west Europe.

Microarthridion fallax Perkins, 1956

Morphological descriptions: Lorenzen (1969), Bodin (1970).

Habitat: Mud, fine muddy sand and pure sand; intertidal flats. Brackish to fully marine. Common to very abundant; occasionally in washings of seagrasses.

Distribution: Estuaries of the Fal, Tamar, Teign, Exe, Swale and Forth; Anglesey, Whitstable, Norfolk; Brittany, Dutch and German North Sea coasts.

Microarthridion reductum (Monard, 1935)

Synonym. Microarthridion perkinsi Bodin, 1970.

Morphological description: Bodin (1970).

Habitat: Fine to medium sand; intertidal flats. Brackish to fully marine. Occasional to rare.

Distribution: Brittany, Galway Bay.

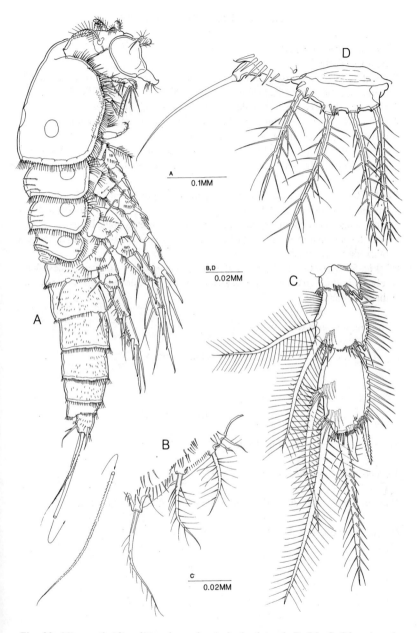

Fig. 89. *Microarthridion littorale*: male; A, body, lateral. B, P5; C, P2 endopod.
Microarthridion fallax: female; D, P5.

Genus GEEOPSIS Huys, 1996

Synonym: Tachidius (part.).

Diagnosis: Tachidiidae.

Body (Fig. 90A). Accessory nuchal organ on P5-bearing somite present. Female genital and first abdominal somite free (Fig. 90B).

Antennule. 9-segmented in female. Sub-chirocer in male (Fig. 87C).

Antenna (Fig. 87D). Exopod 2-segmented; proximal segment with two setae, distal segment with three or four setae.

P1 (Fig. 90E). Endopod-1 of normal size and with inner seta. Exopod-3 with six setae / spines. In male, inner basal spine more slender and longer than in female.

P2-P4. Rami 3-segmented. Male P2 exopod outer spines shorter and stouter than in female; endopod-2 without inner apophysis (Fig. 90E); endopod-3 distal outer spine reduced and spiniform, inner setae absent. Male P3 exopod (Fig. 90F) longer than in female with exopod-3 often bent inwards; inner distal seta of exopod-3 vestigial.

P5 (Fig. 90C, D). In female, distinctly bilobed, inner lobe with four spines, outer lobe with three spines and one seta. In male, slightly bilobed with two setae and three or four spines.

Two species known world-wide.

Local species. One. Setal formula in Appendix Table 3 (p.342).

Geeopsis incisipes (Klie, 1913).

Synonym: Tachidius incisipes Klie, 1913.

Morphological descriptions: Gurney (1932), Huys (1996).

Habitat: Sand or muddy sand, intertidal, brackish. Rare or occasional.

Distribution: Eden estuary, Norfolk, Weser estuary.

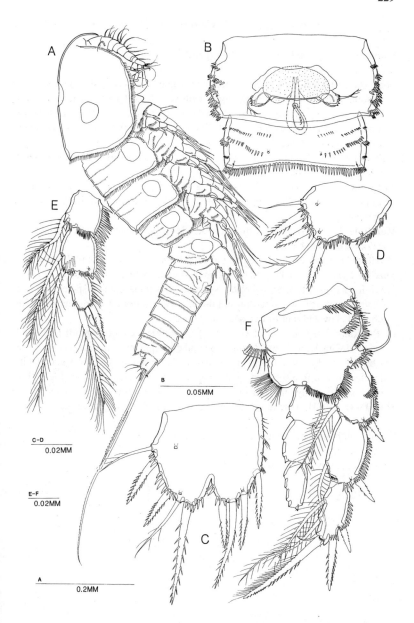

Fig. 90. *Geeopsis incisipes* female: A, body, lateral; B, genital and first abdominal somite, ventral; C, P5. Male: D, P5; E, P2 endopod; F, P3 (armature of endopod omitted).

Family THOMPSONULIDAE Lang, 1944

Synonym. Thompsonulinae Lang, 1944 (part.).

Diagnosis.

Body (Fig. 91A). Sub-pyriform or fusiform without marked distinction between prosome and urosome. Cephalothorax with very large hyaline rostrum defined at base, with one pair of sensilla. Female genital field (Fig. 92A) with separate gonopores. Anal operculum toothed. Caudal rami (Fig. 92E) broader than long, with seven setae, setae IV and V spinulose.

Antennule. 5- or 6-segmented, short, stout with numerous strongly pinnate setae in female. Subchirocer in male.

Antenna (Fig. 91B). Allobasis with a strong pinnate spine. Endopod 1-segmented. Exopod 3-segmented with 2.1.3 setae on proximal to distal segments.

Mandible (Fig. 92B). Basis with four setae. Rami 1-segmented, terminal setae on endopod fused at base.

Maxillule. Epipodite represented by one seta. Rami 1-segmented with four setae.

Maxilla. Syncoxa with three endites. Endopod indistinctly segmented.

Maxilliped (Fig. 91C). Sub-chelate. Syncoxa with three pinnate spines and one seta. Basis with two setae on palmar margin. Endopod 1-segmented with terminal claw and four or five accessory setae.

P1-P4. Rami 3-segmented. P1 (Fig. 91D) unmodified, exopod with 0.1.022 and endopod with 1.1.121 setal formula. Sexual dimorphism sometimes on P4.

P5. In female (Fig. 92C), legs not fused medially, endopodal lobe very well-developed with five setae, exopod separate, with six setae. In male (Fig. 92D), legs fused medially, baseoendopod with two setae, exopod with five setae.

Male P6 (Fig. 92D). One fused and one hinged plate, each with three setae.

Females with one egg-sac, males with one spermatophore.

Two genera known world-wide.

231

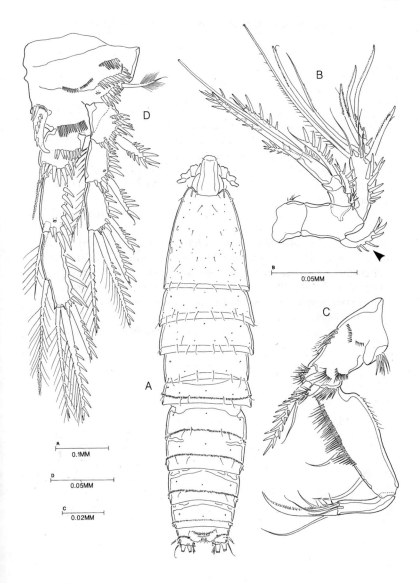

Fig. 91. *Thompsonula hyaenae*: A, female body, dorsal; B, antenna (abexopodal seta arrowed); C, maxilliped; D, P1.

Key to world genera of Thompsonulidae

1. Body markedly fusiform (Fig. 91A); genital double-somite without dorsal subcuticular ridge; urosomites with denticulate hyaline frill and continuous ventral spinule row on penultimate somite (Fig. 92A); P2 basis with naked outer seta; P5 endopodal lobe broadly rounded at distal margin which reaches beyond the exopod (Fig. 92C); no sexual dimorphism in swimming legs.
    ....***Thompsonula*** (p. 234)

    Body not markedly fusiform; genital double-somite with dorsal subcuticular ridge; urosomites with deeply divided hyaline frill and discontinuous ventral spinule row on penultimate somite; P2 basis with pinnate outer spine; P5 endopodal lobe distinctly triangular and narrow at distal margin which, at most, reaches distal margin of exopod; males with only two inner setae on P4 exopod-3.
    ....***Caribbula*** Huys & Gee, 1990

Genus THOMPSONULA T. Scott, 1905

Diagnosis: Thompsonulidae.

Body (Fig. 91A). Markedly fusiform. Rostrum large, recurved and reaching at least to distal margin of second segment of antennule. Female genital double-somite without dorsal sub-cuticular ridge. Urosomites with denticulate hyaline frill and continuous ventral spinule row on penultimate urosomite (Fig. 92A).

Antenna (Fig. 91B). Allobasis with short abexopodal seta reaching only to proximal third of endopod.

Maxilla. With proximal endite cylindrical (bifid in *Caribbula*).

P1-P4. Outer seta of P1 basis plumose in mid-region (Fig. 91D). Coxa of P2-P4 with only short spinules in row associated with tube pore. Basis of P2 with naked outer seta. No sexual dimorphism in swimming legs.

P5. In female (Fig. 92C), with endopodal lobe of baseoendopod broadly rounded at distal margin. Exopod almost circular with distal margin not reaching distal margin of endopodal lobe.

Two species known world-wide. Latest descriptions in Huys & Gee (1990).

Local species. One. Setal formula in Appendix Table 3 (p.342).

Thompsonula hyaenae (Thompson, 1889)

Morphological description: Huys & Gee (1990).

Habitat: Lower littoral and shallow sub-littoral fine sand and muddy sand sediment; fully marine. Rare to common.

Distribution: Throughout north-west Europe and extending into the Mediterranean.

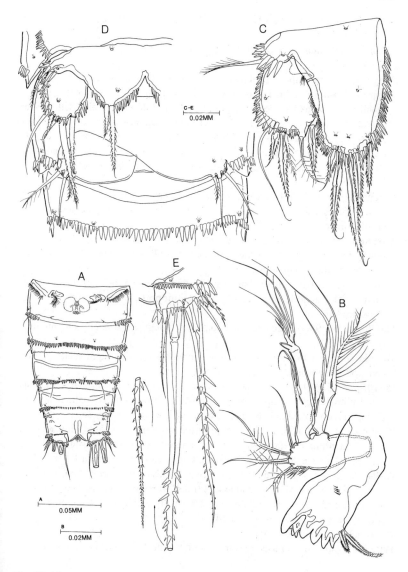

C-E
0.02MM

A
0.05MM

B
0.02MM

Fig. 92. *Thompsonula hyaenae*: A, female urosome, ventral (excluding urosomite-1); B, mandible; C, female P5; D, male P5 and P6; E, caudal ramus, ventral.

Family DANIELSSENIIDAE Huys & Gee, 1996

Synonym. Cletodidae T. Scott (part.), Paranannopidae Por.
Diagnosis.
Body. Variable in shape; dorsal hyaline frills of urosomites with minutely dentate margin. Rostrum defined at base, large, often hyaline, with either two pairs of sensilla or one pair of setae (Fig. 95A). Genital double somite with at least lateral internal chitinous ridge and two blind-ending openings always present just posterior to genital field (Fig. 93A, B); seminal receptacles usually transverse anterior to genital slit. Penultimate somite with pseudoperculum. Anal somite deeply divided. Caudal ramus seta I minute, setae IV and V spinulose.

Antennule (Fig. 93C). In female, 4- to 6-segmented, with pinnate or pectinate setae / spines at least on distal segments. In male, 7- to 9- segmented, chirocer or subchirocer.

Antenna (Fig. 94A). Allobasis bearing one abexopodal seta. Endopod 1-segmented. Exopod 3-segmented (except in *Carolinicola*) with 1(2).1.3 setae on proximal to distal segments.

Mandible (Fig. 97B). Gnathobase usually with one seta at inner distal corner. Basis with variable number of setae. Endopod always present, exopod sometimes absent.

Maxillule (Fig. 93D). Without coxal epipodite, 1-segmented rami each with three setae.

Maxilla (Fig. 94B). Syncoxa with three endites each with three setae / spines; endopod 1-segmented.

Maxilliped (Fig. 95C). Sub-chelate. Syncoxa usually with one large and one small pinnate seta on distal margin. Basis with one seta on palmar margin. Endopod represented only by a claw with one or two accessory setae.

P1 (Figs 94C; 95C). Basis with inner spine ventrally directed, outer element usually a pinnate seta. Exopod 3-segmented, with setal formula 0.1.023. Endopod 2-segmented, non-prehensile, usually with setal formula 1.121.

P2-P4. Exopods 3-segmented (except in two species of *Paranannopus*), endopods 0- to 3-segmented. Male P3 endopod-2 (Figs 94D; 96B) with hooked apophysis at outer distal corner. Male P2 endopod-2 usually with apophysis at outer distal corner and setae of endopod-3 modified.

P5. Variable, sexually dimorphic.

Male P6. Symmetrical. Fused to somite, with two or three setae on each side.

Females with one egg-sac, males with one spermatophore.

Seventeen (fourteen described) genera known world-wide.

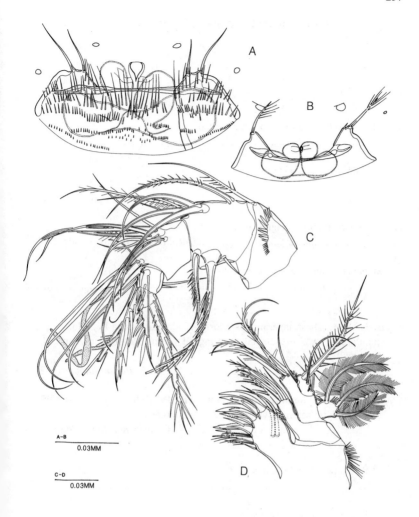

Fig. 93. Female genital field of: A, *Paranannopus* sp.; B, *Psammis longisetosa*: *Fladenia robusta*; C, female antennule; D, maxillule.

Key to world genera of Danielsseniidae

1. P4 endopod absent or 1- to 2-segmented.
   ....**2**

   P4 endopod 3-segmented.
   ....**4**

2. Antennary exopod 1-segmented.
   ....*Carolinicola* Huys & Thistle, 1989[146]

   Antennary exopod 3-segmented.
   ....**3**

3. Body short, robust, tapering posteriorly; caudal ramus seta IV-V long and
   spinulose; P5 well-developed covering all ventral width of urosomite-1
   (Fig. 96C).
   ....*Paranannopus* (p. 244)

   Body slender, cylindrical; caudal ramus setae IV-V short and plumose: P5
   minute, only in centre of ventral face of urosomite-1.
   ....*Cylindronannopus* Coull, 1973

4. P2-P4 exopod-1 without inner seta.
   ....**5**

   P2-P4 exopod-1 with inner seta.
   ....**7**

5. Antennules without plumose or pinnate spines / setae.
   ....*Danielssenia minuta* Coull, 1969[147]

   Antennules with plumose and/or pinnate spines / setae.
   ....**6**

---

[146] The genus *Carolinicola* is placed *incertae sedis* in this family (Huys & Thistle, 1989).
[147] *Danielssenia minuta* is to be placed in the new genus *Sentiropsis*.

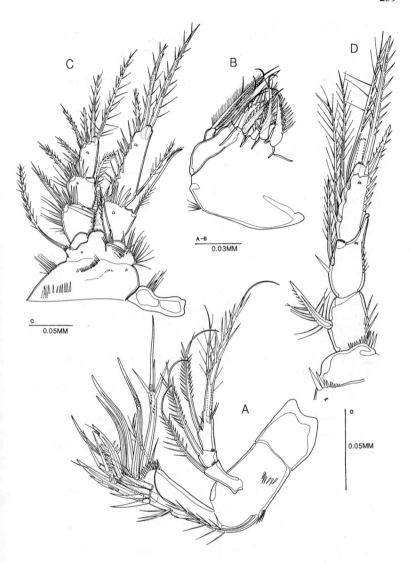

Fig. 94. *Fladenia robusta*: A, antenna; B, maxilla; C, P1; D, male P3 endopod.

6. Caudal ramus with distinct cluster of long setules at inner distal corner; P2 endopod-2 with large apophysis in female (and presumably in male also).
    ....*Mucrosenia* Gee & Huys, 1994

    Caudal ramus without such cluster, P2 endopod-2 with large apophysis in males only.
    ....*Danielssenia* (p. 250)

7. P4 exopod-3 with eight setae / spines.
    ....**8**

    P4 exopod-3 with at most seven setae / spines.
    ....**13**

8. P2 endopod-2 with two inner setae.
    ....**9**

    P2 endopod-2 with one inner seta.
    ....**10**

9. Caudal rami 5 times as long as maximum width; P1 endopod shorter than exopod; female P5 with fused exopod and baseoendopod.
    ....*Bathypsammis* Huys & Gee, 1993

    Caudal rami broader than long; P1 endopod longer than exopod; female P5 with separated exopod and baseoendopod.
    ....*Jonesiella* (p. 253)

10. Body dorso-ventrally flattened; caudal rami setae IV and V stubby and spiniform; P1 endopod-1 1.5 times as long as endopod-2.
    ....*Idomene aberrans* Por, 1964[148]

    Body not dorso-ventrally flattened; caudal rami setae IV and V long and setiform; P1 endopod-1 at most as long as endopod-2.
    ....**11**

---

[148] *Idomene aberrans* is to be placed in the new genus *Peltisenia*.

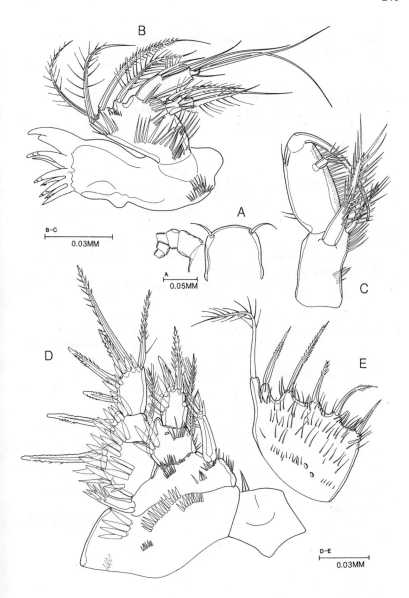

Fig. 95. *Paranannopus* sp.: A, rostrum and female antennule; B, mandible; C, maxilliped; D, P1; E, female P5.

11. Female antennule 4-segmented; club-shaped aesthetascs (Fig. 101B,C) present on mandible (endopod), maxillule (basis) and maxilla (endopod); male P2 endopod-2 without distinct apophysis.
.... *Paradanielssenia* (p. 256)

Female antennule 6-segmented; no club-shaped aesthetascs on mouthparts; male P2 endopod-2 with long outer apophysis.
....**12**

12. Antennary exopod-1 with one seta; P3 exopod-3 with seven setae / spines; male P2 endopod-3 with inner distal seta transformed into large pinnate spine reaching beyond apophysis of endopod-2.
....*Danielssenia spinipes* Wells, 1967[149]

Antennary exopod-1 with two setae; P3 exopod-3 with eight setae / spines; male P2 endopod-3 with inner distal seta not transformed and shorter than apophysis of endopod-2.
....*Archisenia* Huys & Gee, 1993[150]

13. P2 endopod-2 with two inner setae.
....*Psammis* (p. 248)

P2 endopod-2 without or with one inner seta.
....**14**

14. Club-shaped aesthetascs present on mandible (endopod), maxillule (basis) and maxilla (endopod); P2 exopod-3 with at most six setae / spines.
....**15**

No club-shaped aesthetascs present on mouthparts; P2 exopod-3 with seven setae / spines.
....*Fladenia* (p. 246)

---

[149] *Danielssenia spinipes* is to be placed in the new genus *Afrosenia*.
[150] There is one unconfirmed record of *Archisenia* (as *Danielssenia sibirica*) from a Scottish Loch (Wells, 1965b). All other records of this genus are from within the Arctic Circle.

15. P1 endopod-2 with one terminal seta geniculate (Fig. 102B); female P5 baseoendopod and exopodal lobes distinguishable, with three and four setae respectively; male P2 endopod-2 with small apophysis; male P6 with three setae.

....*Micropsammis* (p. 258)

P1 endopod-2 with two terminal setae geniculate; female P5 baseoendopod and exopod indistinguishable, with five setae; male P2 endopod-2 without apophysis; male P6 with two setae.

....**16**

16. Antennule in both sexes with densely opaque, bulbous appendage on distal segment; P2-P4 exopod-2 without inner seta.

....*Leptotachidia* Becker, 1974

Antennule in both sexes without densely opaque, bulbous appendage on distal segment; P2-P4 exopod-2 with inner seta.

....*Telopsammis* (p. 260)

Genus PARANANNOPUS Huys & Gee, 1996

Diagnosis: Danielsseniidae.

Body. Short, robust and heavily ornamented with spinules. Rostrum (Fig. 95A) not hyaline, rounded-quadratic and with one pair of setae. Vestigial P6 on female genital double-somite with two setae (Fig. 93A).

Antennule. 5- or 6-segmented with some pinnate setae in female; only slightly modified in male.

Antenna. Exopod-1 with two setae.

Mandible (Fig. 95B). Coxa with long, fine teeth; basis with four setae, rami 1-segmented, exopod only half as long as endopod.

Maxilliped (Fig. 95C) with very short, stout pinnate seta on inner margin of basis.

P1 (Fig. 95D). Basis with short, stout, pinnate outer spine. Exopod-2 and endopod-2 with or without inner seta; endopod segments equal in length.

P2-P4. Exopod usually 3-segmented but with more setae in male than in female. Endopods 0- to 2-segmented in female; in male P2-P3 endopods 3-segmented and P2 endopod-2 bears an apophysis reaching at least to distal margin of endopod-3 which has modified setae (Fig. 96A).

P5. In female (Fig. 95E), limbs usually not fused medially but baseoendopod and exopod fused and indistinguishable; in male (Fig. 96C), limbs fused medially to form a single plate.

Male P6. With two setae.

Note: This genus is badly in need of revision and is almost certainly an amalgam of a number of genera. At present 22 species have been described but for no species are both sexes known. The reason for this may be that the extreme sexual dimorphism in segmentation and setation of the swimming legs had not been recognised; or that the species are relatively rare deeper water forms, and only a few specimens, usually of one sex, have been found in samples from any one locality.

Local species. Two. Setal formulae in Appendix Table 4 (p.343).
Wells (1965b) found both sexes in muddy sand at 140m on the Fladen Ground in the North Sea but named them as two species, the females as *P. triarticulatus* and the males as *P. langi*. Gee & Huys (1990) provided morphological evidence that they represent the male and female of a single species, and *P. langi* therefore, is formally relegated to a junior subjective synonym of *P. triarticulatus*. A further female specimen, close to *P. philistinus* Por, 1964 has been recorded from muddy sand at 100m in the Celtic Sea.

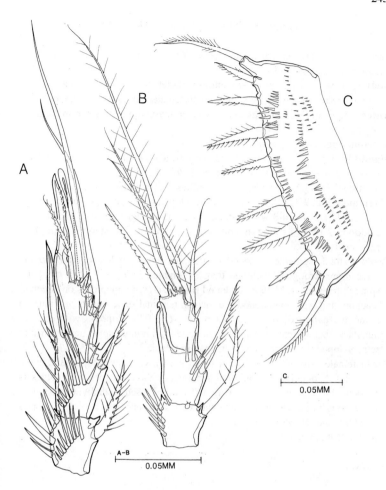

Fig. 96. *Paranannopus triarticulatus* male: A, P2 endopod; B, P3 endopod; C, P5.

Genus FLADENIA Gee & Huys, 1990

Synonym: Danielssenia (part.) Sars, 1921; Wells, 1965.

Diagnosis: Danielsseniidae.

Body (Fig. 97A). Slightly dorso-ventrally flattened. Rostrum elongate, hyaline, with two pairs of sensilla. Vestigial P6 on female genital somite with one seta.

Antennule (Fig. 93C). 5-segmented with numerous pinnate setae in female. 7-segmented, sub-chirocer in male.

Antenna (Fig. 94A). Exopod-1 with one seta.

Mandible (Fig. 97B). Coxa with slender cuspidate teeth. Basis with four setae. Exopod 2-segmented, only half as long endopod.

Maxillule (Fig. 93D). Coxal and basal endites each with six setae.

Maxilliped (Fig. 97C). Basis with well-developed pinnate seta on palmar margin.

P1 (Fig. 94C). Exopod-3 with distal outer spine shorter than middle outer spine. Endopod-2 twice as long as endopod-1; inner seta on endopod-2 implanted proximally.

P2-P4. Rami 3-segmented. Exopod-1 with inner seta; in male exopod-3 with inner setae more strongly-developed than in female. Endopod-1 with large inner spine in both sexes. Male P2 endopod (Fig. 97D) with apophysis on endopod-2 reaching half way up endopod-3 on which terminal setae minute and inner and outer seta enlarged compared to female. Male P3 endopod-3 with one more inner seta than in female. Male P4 endopod-1 with inner spine transformed to a seta; endopod-3 with one more seta than in female.

P5. In female (Fig. 97E), limbs not fused medially; baseoendopod and exopod fused but distinguishable and well separated; endopodal lobe with four setae, exopod with five setae. In male (Fig. 97F), limbs fused medially; baseoendopod and exopod fused; endopodal lobe with two setae (one very reduced); exopodal lobe with one seta very reduced.

Male P6. With three setae.

Monotypic.

Local species. One. Setal formula in Appendix Table 4 (p.343).

Fladenia robusta (Sars, 1921)

Synonyms. Danielssenia robusta Sars, 1921; *D. intermedia* Wells, 1965; *Fladenia intermedia* (Wells, 1965).

Morphological description: Gee & Huys (1990).

Habitat: Muddy sand, 90-150m. Occasional.

Distribution: The Fladen Ground and off Cullercoats in the North Sea.

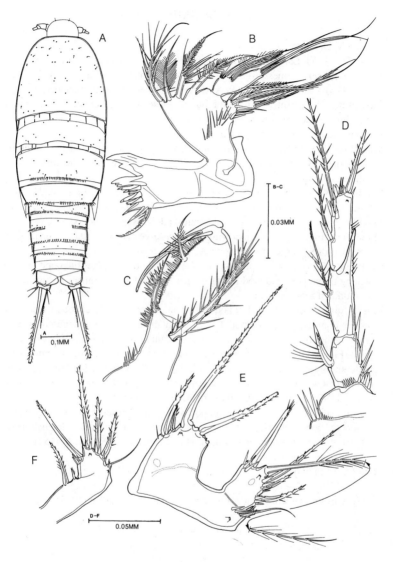

Fig. 97. *Fladenia robusta*: A, female body, dorsal; B, mandible; C, maxilliped; D, male P2 endopod; E, female P5; F, male P5.

Genus PSAMMIS Sars, 1910

Diagnosis: Danielsseniidae.

Body (Fig. 98A). Large, slightly fusiform. Rostrum not hyaline, with two pairs of sensilla, anterior ones large. Vestigial P6 of female genital field with 1 seta (Fig. 93B). Caudal rami (Fig. 98A) divergent, tapering, longer than broad.

Antennule. 4-segmented with numerous plumose setae in female. 9-segmented, sub-chirocer, segment-6 swollen in male.

Antenna. Exopod-1 with two setae.

Mandible (Fig. 98B). Coxa with long, finely pointed teeth and two setae on gnathobase. Basis with four setae. Rami 1-segmented, equal in length and with reduced armature.

Maxillule. With two comb-like spines and three tubular setae on coxal endite. Basal endite with three plumose setae, one tubular seta and one spine.

Maxilla. With tubular setae on coxal endites, allobasis and endopod.

Maxilliped (Fig. 98C). Syncoxa with one very large and one minute pinnate seta. Basis with very large, strongly pinnate seta on palmar margin.

P1. Exopod-3 distal outer spine longer than middle outer spine. Endopod at least as long as exopod; endopod-2 longer than endopod-1 with inner seta implanted in middle of inner margin.

P2-P4. Rami 3-segmented. Exopod-1 with an inner seta. P2 endopod distinctly longer than exopod; endopod-1 with outer distal margin attenuated in both sexes; endopod-2 with two setae (one implanted on posterior surface) and in male (Fig. 98D) with outer apophysis not reaching distal margin of endopod-3; male endopod-3 with outer spine transformed into non-articulating process, distal setae reduced and inner seta enlarged compared to female. Inner distal seta of P3-P4 endopod-3 extremely reduced in both sexes.

P5. In female (Fig. 98E), baseoendopod and exopod fused but distinguishable; endopodal lobe with five setae; exopod with four or five setae. In male (Fig. 98F), not fused medially, baseoendopod and exopod separate with two and four setae / spines respectively.

Male P6. With two setae.

Two species known world-wide. Latest revision in Huys & Gee (1993).

Local species. One. Setal formula in Appendix Table 4 (p.343).

Psammis longisetosa Sars, 1910

Morphological descriptions: Gee (1988b), Huys & Gee (1993)

Habitat: Sublittoral muddy sediments, 11-120m. Rare.

Distribution: Loch Creran and Loch Nevis in Scotland, Oslofjord and around Bergen in Norway.

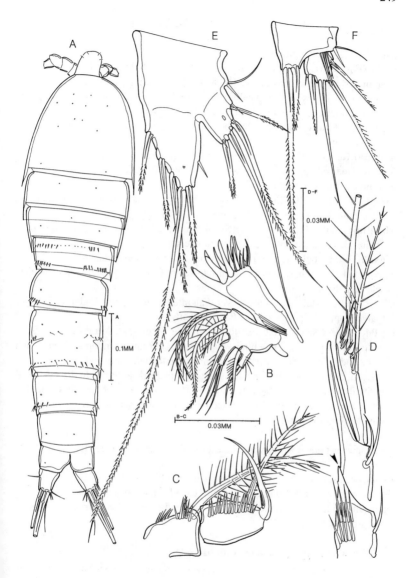

Fig. 98. *Psammis longisetosa:* A, female body, dorsal; B, mandible; C, maxilliped; D, male P2 endopod (apophysis on endopod-1 arrowed); E, female P5; F, male P5.

Genus DANIELSSENIA Boeck, 1872

Diagnosis: Danielsseniidae.

Body (Fig. 99A). Variable in size (0.4 - 1.0mm), slightly fusiform and dorso-ventrally flattened; dorsal hyaline frill on P5-bearing somite deeply incised. Rostrum large, hyaline, typically deflexed with two pairs of sensilla. Vestigial P6 of female genital double-somite with one seta; seminal receptacle with paired, anteriorly directed chambers extending to anterior margin of somite. Caudal rami parallel, broader than long.

Antennule. 4-segmented with numerous pinnate setae in female. 8- or 9-segmented, subchirocer, segment-6 very swollen in male.

Antenna. Exopod-1 with one seta.

Mandible (Fig. 99B). Coxa with short, bluntly rounded teeth on gnathobase. Basis with three setae. Rami 1-segmented, equal in length.

Maxillule. With three tubular setae, one pinnate seta and one spine on coxal endite. Basal endite with four setae and one spine.

Maxilla. With tubular setae on coxal endites, allobasis and endopod.

Maxilliped (Fig. 99C). Syncoxa with two setae. Basis with a very small pinnate seta on palmar margin.

P1. Exopod-3 distal outer spine longer than middle outer spine. Endopod-2 longer than endopod-1, inner seta implanted medially.

P2-P4. Rami 3-segmented; exopod-1 without inner seta. Male P2 (Fig. 99F) endopod-2 apophysis reaching well beyond margin of endopod-3 on which distal and outer setae reduced and inner setae enlarged compared to female.

P5. Exopod and baseoendopod separate. In female (Fig. 99D), limbs not fused medially; endopodal lobe with three or five setae; exopod with four or five setae. In male (Fig. 99E), limbs fused medially, endopodal lobe with two setae.

Male P6. With two setae.

Three species known world-wide. Latest revision in Huys & Gee (1993).

Local species. One. Setal formula in Appendix Table 4 (p.343).
However, *D. quadriseta* Gee, 1988a may have been confused previously with *D. typica* and both species could be present around the North Sea coasts. They can be distinguished as follows.

P3 endopod-3 and P5 exopod with five setae.
.... *Danielssenia typica*

P3 endopod-3 and P5 exopod with four setae.
.... *Danielssenia quadriseta*

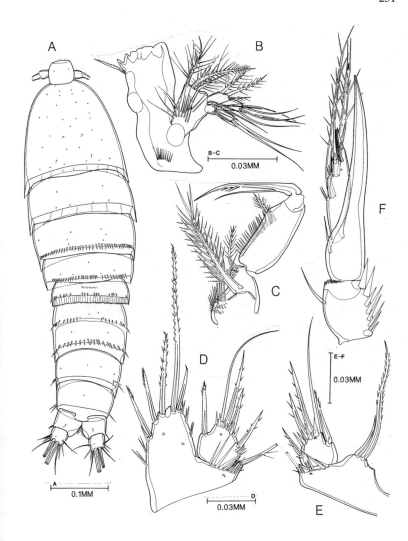

Fig. 99. *Danielssenia typica*: A, female body, dorsal; B, mandible; C, maxilliped; D, female P5; E, male P5; F, male P2 endopod.

Danielssenia typica Boeck, 1872

Synonym: Danielssenia fusiformis (Brady, 1880) *sensu* Sars (1910).

Morphological descriptions: Gee (1988a), Huys & Gee (1993).

Habitat: In sandy mud and mud sediments, occasionally in *Laminaria* holdfasts, sublittoral down to 130m. Occasional, locally common.

Distribution: German Bight, west coast of Norway, northern England, coast of Scotland, Irish Sea, Co. Mayo in Ireland, Isles of Scilly and off Devon coast.

Genus JONESIELLA Brady, 1880

Synonyms: Danielssenia (part.); *Sentirenia* Huys & Gee, 1992.
Diagnosis: Danielsseniidae.
Body (Fig. 100A). Slightly dorso-ventrally flattened. Rostrum large, hyaline, tapering posteriorly, with two pairs of sensilla. Vestigial P6 of female genital double-somite with three setae. Caudal rami broader than long.
Antennule. 5- to 6-segmented with numerous pinnate setae in female. 7-segmented, subchirocer, segment-5 moderately swollen in male.
Mandible. Coxa with moderately slender teeth and one seta on gnathobase. Palp (Fig. 100B) slender, all segments elongate; basis with two pinnate and one naked setae; both rami 2-segmented, an aesthetasc on distal margin of endopod-2.
Maxillule. Coxal endite with six setae. Basal endite with three setae and an aesthetasc on distal margin. Exopod always folded under basis (arrowed in Fig. 100C).
Maxilla. Endopod with aesthetasc on distal margin.
Maxilliped. Basis with small pinnate seta on palmar margin.
P1. Exopod-3 with distal outer spine longer than middle outer spine. Endopod distinctly longer than exopod, endopod-2 slightly longer than endopod-1, with inner seta implanted medially.
P2-P4. Rami 3-segmented; exopod-1 with inner seta. P2 endopod-2 with two inner setae. Male P2 endopod-2 (Fig. 100E) with proximal inner seta reduced or absent and apophysis reaching almost to distal margin of endopod-3 on which terminal and outer setae reduced compared to female but distal inner seta enlarged into spinulous spine.
P5. In female (Fig. 100D), legs not fused medially; exopod and baseoendopod separate; endopodal lobe large rectangular, with five deeply embedded setae; exopod only slightly longer than broad with five setae of which inner longest and deeply embedded. In male (Fig. 100F), element of each side fused medially; endopodal lobe with two deeply embedded setae; exopod with five setae, second inner longest.
Male P6. With three setae.

Two species known world-wide.

Local species. One. Setal formula in Appendix Table 4 (p.343).

Jonesiella fusiformis Brady, 1880

Synonyms: Danielssenia perezi Monard, 1935; *D. paraperezi* Soyer, 1970; *Sentirenia perezi* (Monard, 1935).

Morphological description: Huys & Gee (1992).

Habitat: Sandy sediments at 15-26m depth. Occasional.

Distribution: Firth of Clyde, Liverpool Bay, Isles of Scilly and Roscoff but extending southwards into the Mediterranean.

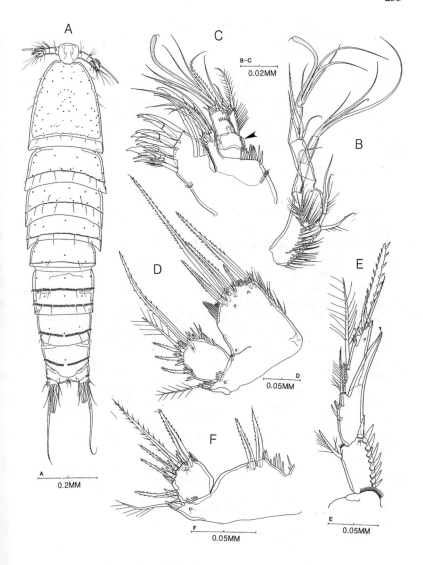

Fig. 100. *Jonesiella fusiformis*; A, female body, dorsal; B, mandibular palp; C, maxillule (folded under exopod, arrowed); D, female P5; E, male P2 endopod; F, male P5.

256

Genus PARADANIELSSENIA Soyer, 1970

Diagnosis: Danielsseniidae.

Body. Small, slightly dorso-ventrally flattened. Rostrum (Fig. 101A) not hyaline, triangular with two pairs of sensilla. Vestigial P6 on female genital field with one seta. Caudal rami about as long as broad, tapering slightly.

Antennule. 4-segmented, with pinnate spines on distal segment in female. 6-segmented, segment-4 only slightly swollen in male.

Antenna. Exopod 1- or 3-segmented, when 3-segmented proximal segment with one seta.

Mandible (Fig. 101B). Coxa with bluntly rounded teeth on gnathobase. Basis robust with four setae. Endopod 1-segmented with two setae and a club-shaped aesthetasc; exopod absent.

Maxillule (Fig. 101C). With club-shaped aesthetasc on basis and sometimes on exopod.

Maxilla. With club-shaped aesthetasc on endopod and sometimes on endites.

Maxilliped. Basis with small pinnate seta on palmar margin.

P1. Exopod-3 distal outer spine as long as middle outer spine. Endopod only slightly longer than exopod; endopod-2 only slightly longer than endopod-1; inner seta on endopod-2 implanted near base of segment.

P2-P4. Rami 3-segmented; exopod-1 with an inner seta; inner element of endopod-1 a dentate spine on P2-P3. Male P2 endopod-2 (Fig. 101E) with small apophysis, endopod-3 outer seta on distal margin transformed into rigid process, terminal two setae reduced and distal inner seta enlarged compared to female.

P5. In female (Fig. 101D), legs not fused medially; baseoendopod and exopod separate; endopodal lobe large with five setae; exopod with four or five setae. In male (Fig. 101F), limbs fused medially; baseoendopod and exopod separate; endopodal lobe with two setae, outer minute; exopod with four or five setae.

Male P6. With three setae.

Four species known world-wide. Latest key to species in Gee & Huys (1994).

Local species. One. Setal formula in Appendix Table 4 (p.343).

Paradanielssenia biclavata Gee, 1988

Morphological descriptions: Gee (1988b), Gee & Huys (1991).

Habitat: Muddy sand, 100m, rare.

Distribution: The only record is of three specimens from the southern Celtic Sea.

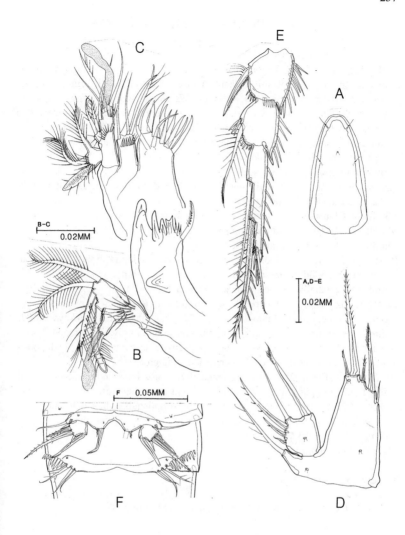

Fig. 101. *Paradanielssenia biclavata*; A, rostrum; B, mandible; C, maxillule; D, female P5; E, male P2 endopod; F, male P5 and P6.

Genus MICROPSAMMIS Mielke, 1975

Diagnosis: Danielsseniidae.

Body (Fig. 102A). Small, not dorso-ventrally flattened, without spinule rows; hyaline frill of all urosomites deeply incised. Rostrum not hyaline, elongate, bell-shaped with two pairs of sensilla. Female genital double-somite completely fused; vestigial P6 with two setae; seminal receptacles fused, not anterior to genital slit. Caudal rami slightly conical, as long as broad; seta VI minute.

Antennule. 6-segmented with pinnate setae in female. 6-segmented, sub-chirocer, segment-4 moderately swollen in male.

Antenna. Exopod-1 with two setae.

Mandible. Basis slender with one seta. Endopod with two setae and a club-shaped aesthetasc. Exopod absent.

Maxillule. Club-shaped aesthetasc on basis.

Maxilla. Club-shaped aesthetasc on endopod.

Maxilliped. Basis with a small naked seta.

P1 (Fig. 102B). Exopod-3 terminal setae geniculate. Endopod slightly longer than exopod; endopod segments about equal in length; inner seta on endopod-2 implanted medially; one terminal seta geniculate.

P2-P4. Rami 3-segmented; exopod segments all with inner seta, P4 exopod-3 with only two outer spines. Endopods (Fig. 102C) tapering distally, always shorter than exopod, endopod-3 inner terminal seta minute, only P3 endopod-2 with inner seta. Male P2 (Fig. 102E) endopod-2 with small apophysis, endopod-3 with distal seta transformed into non-articulating process.

P5. In female (Fig. 102D), legs fused medially at base; baseoendopod and exopod fused but distinguishable, lobes with four and three setae respectively. In male (Fig. 102F), limbs fused medially but distinguishable; baseoendopod and exopod fused and indistinguishable, with four setae and two marginal pores (arrowed in Fig. 102F).

Male P6. With three setae.

Monotypic.

Local species. One. Setal formula in Appendix Table 4 (p.343).

Micropsammis noodti Mielke, 1975

Morphological descriptions: Mielke (1975), Gee & Huys (1991).

Habitat: Intertidal sand. Rare.

Distribution: The only record of this species is from the Island of Sylt (Germany) in the southern North Sea.

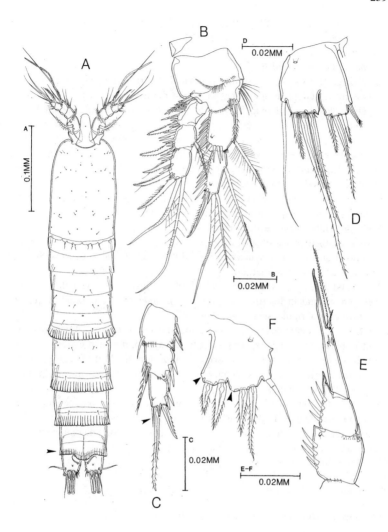

Fig. 102. *Micropsammis noodti*; A, female body, dorsal (hyaline frill of penultimate somite arrowed); B, P1; C, P3 endopod (minute inner distal seta arrowed); D, female P5; E, male P2 endopod; F, male P5.

Genus TELOPSAMMIS Gee & Huys, 1991

Synonym: Micropsammis Mielke, 1975 (part.).

Diagnosis: Danielsseniidae.

Body (Fig. 103A). Small, semi-cylindrical; hyaline frills of first to fourth urosomites deeply divided, that of penultimate somite entire. Rostrum not hyaline, elongate, bell-shaped with two pairs of sensilla. Female genital double-somite completely fused, vestigial P6 with two setae; seminal receptacle multi-chambered. Caudal rami slightly conical, as long as broad, seta VI small.

Antennule. 6-segmented with pinnate setae, aesthetasc on fourth segment in female. Chirocer, 6-segmented, segment-5 slightly swollen in male.

Antenna. Exopod-1 with one seta.

Mandible. Basis slender, elongate, with one seta. Endopod 1-segmented with two setae and a club-shaped aesthetasc. Exopod absent.

Maxillule. Club-shaped aesthetasc on basis.

Maxilla. Club-shaped aesthetasc on endopod.

Maxilliped (Fig. 103B). Syncoxa with only one seta (small). Basis with small pinnate seta on palmar margin.

P1. Exopod-3 terminal setae geniculate. Endopod distinctly longer than exopod; segments equal in length; endopod-2 with inner seta implanted at base of segment, two terminal setae geniculate.

P2-P4. Rami 3-segmented. Exopod-3 without inner setae and on P4 with only two outer spines. Endopods tapering distally, always shorter than exopod, with no inner setae, endopod-3 inner terminal seta minute. Male P2 (Fig. 103D) endopod-2 without apophysis, endopod-3 with distal outer seta transformed into non-articulating process.

P5. In female (Fig. 103C), legs not fused medially at base, baseoendopod and exopod completely fused and indistinguishable, with five setae. In male (Fig. 103E), legs fused medially at base; baseoendopod and exopod completely fused and indistinguishable, with four setae.

Male P6. With two pinnate setae.

Monotypic.

Local species. One. Setal formula in Appendix Table 4 (p.343).

Telopsammis secunda (Mielke, 1975)

Synonym: Micropsammis secunda Mielke, 1975.

Morphological descriptions: Mielke (1975), Gee & Huys (1991).

Habitat: Sand. Intertidal. Rare.

Distribution: The only record is from the Island of Sylt (Germany) in the southern North Sea.

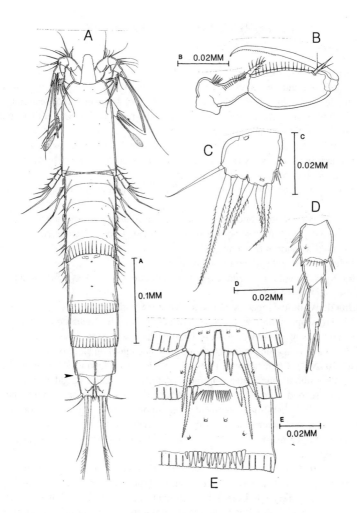

Fig. 103. *Telopsammis secunda*: A, female body, dorsal (hyaline frill of penultimate somite arrowed); B, maxilliped; C, female P5; D, male P2 endopod; E, male P5 and P6.

Family HARPACTICIDAE Sars, 1904

Diagnosis.

Body. Variable in shape. Cephalothorax with rostrum (Fig. 104C) defined at base, often deflexed, with two pairs of sensilla. Urosome always smaller in male than in female, ornamented, in both sexes, with rows of spinules. Anal operculum transparent, semi-circular, smooth. Caudal rami more or less cylindrical and seldom longer than broad; with seven setae.

Antennule. In female, 7- to 9-segmented with naked setae and aesthetascs on fourth and distal segments (Fig. 104C). In male, sub-chirocer or chirocer with aesthetascs on swollen and distal segments.

Antenna. With allobasis bearing one seta on abexopodal margin. Exopod 1- to 4-segmented with a total of three to six setae.

Mandible. Coxa with one pinnate seta at inner distal corner of gnathobase. Basis broad, usually with four setae. Rami well-defined, 1- or 2-segmented, exopod always slightly shorter than endopod.

Maxillule. Exopod and endopod 1-segmented.

Maxilla. Syncoxa with three endites, proximal endite more or less bifid. Endopod represented only by setae.

Maxilliped. Well-developed, subchelate. Syncoxa with one or two setae. Basis variable in shape, with one small seta on palmar margin. Endopod represented by a claw, always shorter than basis, bearing three accessory setae on posterior surface, and a spiny tongue (much shorter than the claw) on anterior surface.

P1 (Fig. 104A,B). Characteristic. Exopod longer than endopod, of two elongate segments without inner setae, rudiment of third segment embedded in distal margin of second segment and bearing four unhinged claws, one hinged claw and a seta. Endopod 2- or 3-segmented, endopod-1 about as long as exopod-2 with, at most, one inner seta; distal margin of endopod with a large outwardly-hooked unhinged major claw, a minor claw (which may or may not be hinged) and a simple seta.

P2-P4 (Fig. 105A,B). Rami usually 3-segmented (P3-P4 endopods sometimes 2-segmented), exopod always longer than endopod. Outer basal seta stoutly setiform (or weakly spiniform) and bipinnate on P2 (and P1) but slenderly setiform and naked on P3 and P4. Sexual dimorphism usually on P2 endopod, sometimes in either ramus of P3.

P5. In female, with baseoendopods separate but touching in mid-line, exopod separate. Male P5 baseoendopods fused medially; baseoendopod and exopod fused or separate.

Male P6. With up to three setae.

Females with a single egg-sac, males with one spermatophore (two in *Harpacticella* spp., *Tigriopus* spp. and *Zaus goodsiri*). Precopulatory clasping to posterior border of cephalothorax.

Nine genera known world-wide.

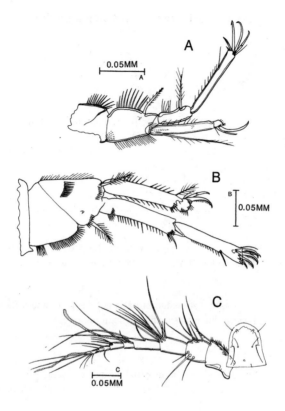

Fig. 104. A, *Perissocope* sp., P1; B, *Harpacticus obscurus*, P1; C, *Harpacticus littoralis*, female rostrum and antennule.

Key to world genera of Harpacticidae

1. P3-P4 endopod 2-segmented; area between maxillae, maxillipeds and P1 transformed into large sucker-like organ.
   .... *Discoharpacticus* Noodt, 1954

   P3 endopod 3-segmented, P4 endopod 2- or 3-segmented; no such sucker-like organ present.
   ....**2**

2. P1 (Fig. 104A) with distal edge of basis stepped, so that exopod is implanted distal to endopod; P2-P4 exopod-1 without inner seta.
   ....**3**

   P1 (Fig. 110C, F) with distal edge of basis not stepped; inner seta of P2-P4 exopod-1 present, but occasionally difficult to discern.
   ....**4**

3. P1 endopod-1 with inner seta in proximal third of segment.
   ....*Perissocope* (p. 267)

   P1 endopod-1 without inner seta.
   ....*Zausodes* C. B. Wilson, 1932

4. P4 endopod-2 without inner seta; antennary exopod 3- or 4-segmented.
   ....**5**

   P4 endopod-2 with inner seta; antennary exopod 1- or 2-segmented.
   ....**6**

5. P5 exopod with five setae in female and four or five setae in male; P2 endopod-2 with distinct outer apophysis in male; around UK in rockpools at HWST.
   ....*Tigriopus* (p. 270)

   P5 exopod with four setae in female and three setae in male; P2 endopod-2 without outer apophysis in male; found (in Japan) inside shells of rock barnacles.
   ....*Paratigriopus* Itô, 1969

265

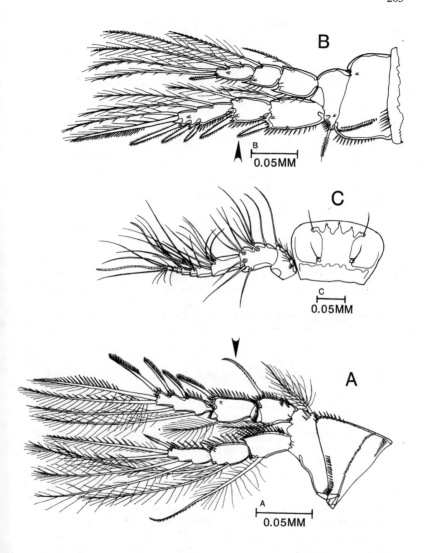

Fig. 105. A, *Zaus caeruleus*, female P2; B, *Harpacticus chelifer*, female P2; C, *Zaus goodsiri*, female rostrum and antennule.

6. P2-P4 outer spine of exopod-1 setiform (Fig. 105A) .
   7

    P2-P4 outer spine of exopod-1 spiniform (Fig. 105B) .
   8

7. Antennule in female 7-segmented; proximal outer spine on P3-P4 exopod-3 smooth, inserting at about 3/4 of the segment's length: antiboreal only.
    ....*Zausopsis* Lang, 1934

    Antennule in female 9-segmented; proximal outer spine on P3-P4 exopod-3 with denticulate hyaline outer margin inserting at or above middle of outer margin of segment; boreal.
    ....*Zaus* (other than *Z. goodsiri*) (p. 272)

8. Antennule 7-segmented in female; P2 endopod not transformed in male.
    ....*Harpacticella* Sars, 1908

    Antennule 9-segmented in female (8-segmented in *Harpacticus chelifer*).
   9

9. Body elongate (Fig. 109D), distinctly flattened; integument heavily sclerotised, clear golden yellow, sculptured and pitted; rostrum very large, twice as broad as long, its width about half the length of the antennule (Fig. 105C); urosomites-3 and -4 with well-developed, backwardly-pointing, lateral processes (Fig. 109D); caudal rami about twice as long as broad, seta IV inserted directly on top of seta V (Fig. 109F); male P2-P4 as in female.
    ....*Zaus goodsiri* (p. 276)

    Body at most only slightly flattened; integument thin, more or less colourless, transparent and without sculpturing; rostrum at most 1.6 times broader than long, its width at most one third length of antennule (Fig. 104C); urosomites without lateral processes; caudal rami never much longer than wide and seta IV inserted external to seta V; male P2 endopod-2 with long pointed apophysis.
    ....*Harpacticus* (p. 278)

Genus PERISSOCOPE Brady, 1910

Diagnosis: Harpacticidae.

Body (Fig. 106A). Small, somewhat dorso-ventrally flattened, widest at posterior part of cephalothorax which narrows anteriorly to a broad rostrum (Fig. 106B) rounded at apex. Free prosomites with posteriorly directed epimera. Urosome tapering posteriorly; genital double-somite in female with lateral cuticular ridge; anal somite partially cleft dorsally, completely cleft ventrally. Caudal rami only just broader than long.

Antennule (Fig. 106B). In female, 7- or 8-segmented, first four segments moderately elongate, remaining segments small. In male, 9-segmented, chirocer or sub-chirocer.

Antenna (Fig. 106C). Exopod 2- or 3-segmented. Subterminal spines of endopod slender, almost setiform.

Mandible (Fig. 106D). Basis with three or four setae; exopod and endopod 1-segmented, about equal in length.

Maxilliped (Fig. 106G). Basis slender, palmar margin straight. Endopodal claw slender, almost as long as basis.

P1 (Fig. 104A). Distal margin of basis stepped and exopod implanted distal to endopod; exopod-1 not more than half as long as exopod-2. Endopod 2-segmented, inner seta of elongate proximal segment arising in proximal fifth of segment.

P2-P4. Exopod outer spines moderately slender and bipectinate, exopod-1 without inner seta. Male P2 endopod always (Fig. 106H), and P3 endopod usually (Fig. 106I), with outer distal corner of endopod-2 and/or endopod-3 attenuated and some ramal setae modified.

P5. In female, baseoendopod and exopod separate; baseoendopod usually with five setae. In male, baseoendopod and exopod separate; endopodal lobe with two setae.

Eight species known world-wide. Latest key to species in Watkins (1987).

Local species. Only one species has been described from north-west Europe (Wells, 1968) but another, as yet unnamed, species has been recorded by Moore (1973). Setal formulae in Appendix Table 4 (p.343).

Perissocope adiastaltus Wells, 1968

Morphological description: Wells (1968).

Habitat: Amongst the epifauna of sublittoral rocks, 27-30m. Rare.

Distribution: St. Mary's, Isles of Scilly.

Perissocope sp.

Morphological description: Undescribed, see Fig. 106. *P. xenus*, incompletely-described from Banyuls by Monard (1926), is probably identical to this species.

Habitat: Amongst holdfasts of *Laminaria hyperborea*, 1-5m (Moore, 1973). Rare.

Distribution: St. Abbs Head and Burniston, north-east England.

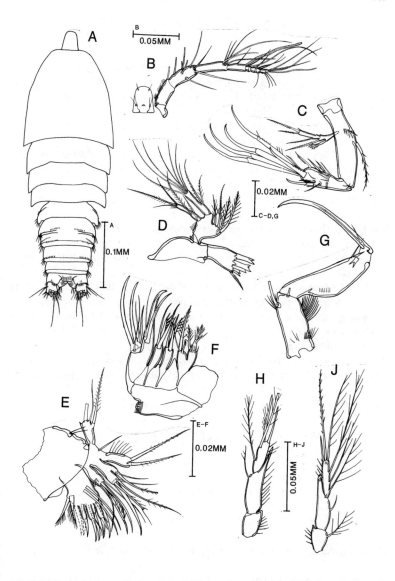

269

Fig. 106. *Perissocope* sp.: A, female body, dorsal; B, rostrum and female antennule; C, antenna; D, mandible; E, maxillule; F, maxilla; G, maxilliped; H, male P2 endopod; J, male P3 endopod.

Genus TIGRIOPUS Norman, 1868

Diagnosis: Harpacticidae.

Body (Fig. 107A). With marked distinction between prosome and urosome; free prosomites and urosomites without extended epimera. Genital double somite in female with a faint internal rib. Anal somite not completely divided ventrally. Caudal rami at least as long as broad.

Antennule. In female, 9-segmented, proximal four segments almost square. In male, 8-segmented, sub-chirocer.

Antenna (Fig. 107B). Exopod 3- or 4-segmented with six setae, proximal segment much longer than others. Terminal spines of endopod naked or microserrate.

Mandible (Fig. 107C). Basis with two setae. Exopod 2-segmented, endopod 1-segmented.

Maxilliped (Fig. 107D). Strongly-developed. Basis short and palmar margin straight. Endopodal claw stout.

P1 (Fig. 107E). Endopod 3-segmented, distal two segments at least half as long as proximal segment.

P2-P4. P4 endopod-2 without inner seta. Male P2 (Fig. 107F) endopod-2 with inner seta transformed into a strong stiff pectinate spine, outer distal apophysis reaching only as far as distal border of endopod-3; endopod-3 reduced in width compared to female, with three slender naked terminal setae and one strongly bipinnate inner seta.

P5. In both sexes, baseoendopod and exopod separate. Endopodal lobe projecting beyond exopod and with five setae in female; reduced with one seta in male.

Eleven species known world-wide. Latest key to species in Bradford (1967).

Local species. One. Setal formula in Appendix Table 4 (p.343).

Tigriopus brevicornis (O. F. Müller, 1776).

Synonym: Tigriopus fulvus (Fischer, 1860) *sensu* Sars (1911).

Morphological descriptions: Sars (1911), Božić (1960), Carli & Fiori (1977).

Habitat: In rock pools at or above mean high water where it can be very abundant.

Distribution: On rocky shores throughout north-west Europe. (It is replaced in the Mediterranean by *T. fulvus*).

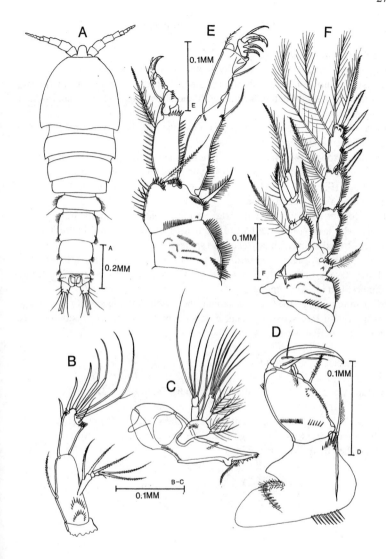

Fig. 107. *Tigriopus brevicornis*: A, female body dorsal; B, antenna; C, mandible; D, maxilliped; E, P1; F, male P2.

Genus ZAUS Goodsir, 1845

Diagnosis: Harpacticidae.

Body (Fig. 108A,D). Dorso-ventrally flattened, with marked distinction between prosome and much narrower urosome; epimera of prosome projecting posteriorly. Genital double-somite with lateral chitinous ridge. Caudal rami as long as broad.

Antennule. In female, 9-segmented, terminal three segments very small. In male, sub-chirocer with segment 3 elongate.

Antenna. Exopod 2-segmented with five bipinnate and one smooth setae. Distal spines of endopod (Figs 108E; 109A) with denticulate hyaline margins.

Maxilliped (Figs 108F; 109B). Usually rather small. Basis with palmar margin at most only slightly emarginate.

P1. Endopod 3-segmented but distal two segments very small, inner seta of endopod-1 arising in distal half of segment. Terminal claws of both rami more or less frilled as in antennary endopod spines.

P2-P4. Outer spine of exopod-1 setiform, all outer spines more or less distinctively ornamented. P4 endopod-2 with an inner seta. No sexual dimorphism in swimming legs.

P5. In female (Fig. 108C,G), baseoendopod well-developed with four setae; exopod with five setae. In male, baseoendopod very reduced, without setae, exopod with five setae.

Twelve species known world-wide.

Local species. Four. Setal formulae in Appendix Table 4 (p.343).

Zaus goodsiri is distinctly different from the others (see key to genera, p. 266) and probably belongs to a new genus. The remaining three species can be distinguished by the key on p. 274:

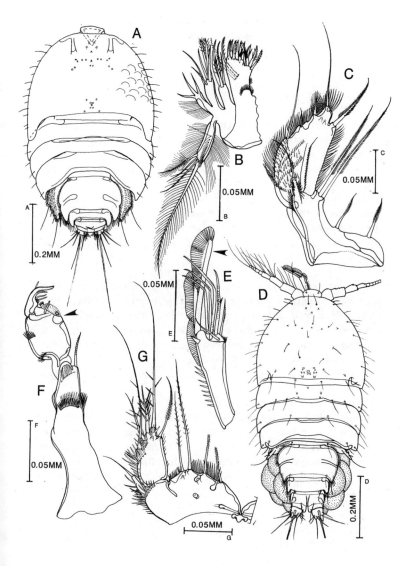

Fig. 108. *Zaus abbreviatus*: A, female body, dorsal; B, maxillule; C, female P5. *Zaus spinatus*: D, female body, dorsal; E, endopod of antenna; F, maxilliped; G, female P5.

Key to local species of Zaus
(except Z. *goodsiri* - for which see p. 266)

1. Body extremely broad and flattened (Fig. 108A); maxillule exopod with one of the four setae very large and strongly pinnate (Fig. 108B); female P5 baseoendopod strongly emarginate (Fig. 108C).

    .... *Zaus abbreviatus*

    Body only moderately broad and flattened (Fig. 108D); maxillule exopod with all four setae approximately the same size; female P5 baseoendopod not emarginate (Fig. 108G) .

   2

2. Antennary endopod terminal pectinate seta (arrowed in Fig. 108E) reaching well beyond end of terminal geniculate setae; maxilliped basis weakly-developed, almost rectangular, palmar margin sharply angled (arrowed in Fig. 108F); P1 endopod-3 with only one large pectinate claw; P5 exopod relatively short, the setal insertions strongly step-like (Fig. 108G); male P2 endopod-2 with one seta.

    .... *Zaus spinatus*

    Antennary endopod terminal pectinate seta (arrowed in Fig. 109A) not reaching end of terminal geniculate setae; maxilliped basis slender and markedly oval, palmar margin weakly angled (arrowed in Fig. 109B); P1 endopod-3 with two large claws, one pectinate the other hinged and smooth; P5 exopod long and tapering, setal insertion steps weak in female (Fig. 109C), moderate in male; male P2 endopod-2 with two setae.

    .... *Zaus caeruleus*

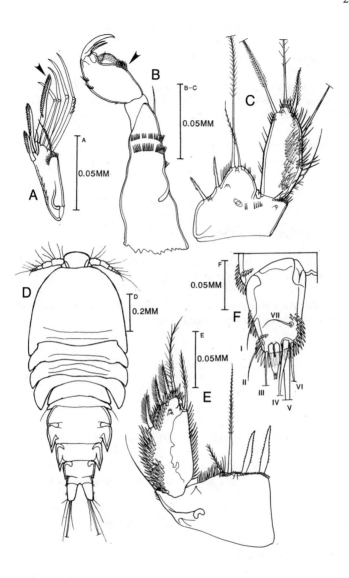

Fig. 109. *Zaus caeruleus*: A, endopod of antenna; B, maxilliped; C, female P5. *Zaus goodsiri*: D, female body, dorsal; E, female P5; F, caudal ramus, dorsal.

Zaus spinatus Goodsir, 1845

Morphological descriptions: Sars (1911), Itô (1974).

Habitat: On small macroalgae and amongst holdfasts of *Laminaria* on rocky shores from mid-tide level to about 20m. Common, often abundant. Occasionally found in the plankton or among algae on other types of shore.

Distribution: All round coasts of north-west Europe, from Concarneau (Itô, 1974) northwards.

Zaus abbreviatus Sars, 1904

Morphological description: Sars (1911)

Habitat: On red algae in strong clear-water currents of full salinity and oceanic origin, from low-water to about 20m. Rare.

Distribution: Around northern England, Scotland, east and west coasts of Ireland and the west coast of Norway around Bergen.

Zaus caeruleus Campbell, 1929

Morphological descriptions: Campbell (1929), Sars (1909) as *Z. aurelii*, Klie (1949) as *Z. schaeferi*.

Habitat: Similar to *Z. spinatus* but very rare in north-west Europe.

Distribution: Principally an Arctic north-eastern Pacific species but recorded from Blakeney Harbour, (Norfolk) and from Helgoland in the southern North Sea area.

Zaus goodsiri Brady, 1910

Morphological description: Sars (1911).

Habitat: Sometimes found amongst algae with other members of this family but more frequently among communities of other sessile organisms on rocky shores from the lower intertidal down to 30m and sometimes deeper. Occasionally found in the plankton.

Distribution: Around the coasts of Britain and northern Europe from Brest to Bergen; widely distributed but never common.

Genus HARPACTICUS Milne-Edwards, 1840

Diagnosis: Harpacticidae.

Body. Shape variable, at most only slightly flattened, integument without sculpturing; urosomites without lateral processes but with clearly defined rows of spinules. Rostrum (Fig. 104C) with, at most, only slightly convex sides, at most 1.6 times broader than long.

Antennule. In female, 8- or 9-segmented. In male, chirocer.

Antenna. Exopod 2-segmented. Distal spines of endopod usually finely pectinate.

Maxilliped (Figs 110B,E; 113B). Well-developed, usually with inner margin of basis slightly convex to deeply excavated.

P1. Basis distal margin square cut with rami arising level with one another; in male inner seta of basis sometimes smooth. Endopod 2- or 3- segmented; inner seta of endopod-1 implanted in distal half of segment; distal one or two segments very short.

P2-P4 (Fig. 105B). Exopod outer spines usually finely pectinate. P4 endopod-2 with an inner seta. Male P2 endopod-2 with outer distal corner extended to beyond distal border of terminal segment but with inner seta normal i.e., not fused to the segment. Male P3 exopod segments and setae more strongly built than in female.

P5 (Figs 111E; 112D; 113D). In female endopodal lobe well-developed with four setae. In male endopodal lobe very reduced without setae.

Thirty-four species and three subspecies known world-wide. The key in Lang (1948) is not reliable.

Local species. Eight described. Setal formulae in Appendix Table 4 (p.343).

The following key will facilitate identification of species from north-west Europe. However, note that *H. obscurus*, *H. littoralis* and *H. giesbrechti* are extremely difficult to separate.

1. Antennary exopod with four setae; maxilliped basis slender, long-oval, palmar margin not excavated and with its spinules in a single row (Fig. 110E).
    ....*Harpacticus flexus*

    Antennary exopod with six setae; maxilliped basis forming a short, broad-oval with palmar margin distinctly excavated and with spinules in several rows.
    ....**2**

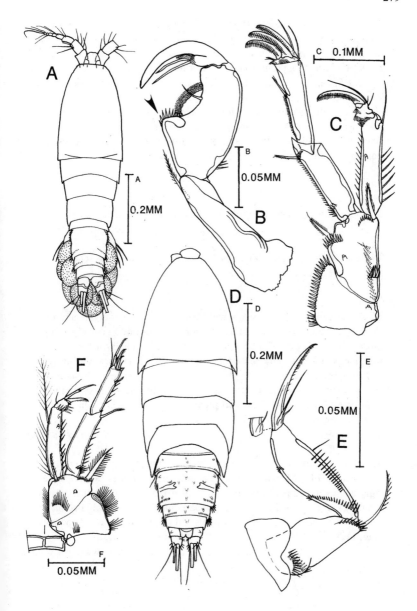

Fig. 110. *Harpacticus chelifer*: A, female body, dorsal; B, maxilliped; C, female P1. *Harpacticus flexus*: D, female body, dorsal; E, maxilliped; F, female P1.

2. Body laterally compressed (Fig. 110A); female antennule 8-segmented; maxilliped very strongly built, palmar margin of basis deeply excavated so that angle (arrowed in Fig. 110B) is acute, spinules longest around angle and becoming progressively shorter into excavation.
    ....*Harpacticus chelifer*

    Body not laterally compressed; female antennule 9-segmented; maxilliped less strongly built, palmar margin only moderately excavated with an obtuse angle (Fig. 113B,C), spinules shortest at angle and longest on palmar margin.
    ....**3**

3. P1 endopod 3-segmented (Fig. 111C); P2 endopod-2 with two setae.
    ....**4**

    P1 endopod 2-segmented (Fig. 104B); P2 endopod-2 with one seta.
    ....**5**

4. Maxillule exopod of both sexes with markedly convex margins and one lateral and three terminal setae all same length and each with long, closely-set limp pinnules on one edge only (Fig. 111B); P1 exopod-2 marginal spinules widely spaced and at an angle of 45° (arrowed in Fig. 111C), terminal claws almost straight (Fig. 111D); male P1 basis inner seta smooth or, at most, very slightly pinnate; female P5 baseoendopod with many surface pores and two proximal rows of spinules on anterior face (arrowed in Fig. 111E) .
    ....*Harpacticus uniremis*

    Maxillule exopod with parallel margins and four terminal naked setae (arrowed in Fig. 112B); P1 exopod-2 marginal spinules closely set at right-angles to segment margin (arrowed in Fig. 112A), terminal claws strongly curved (Fig. 112C); male P1 basis inner seta coarsely pectinate; female P5 baseoendopod with few pores and no proximal rows of spinules (Fig. 112D).
    ....*Harpacticus septentrionalis*

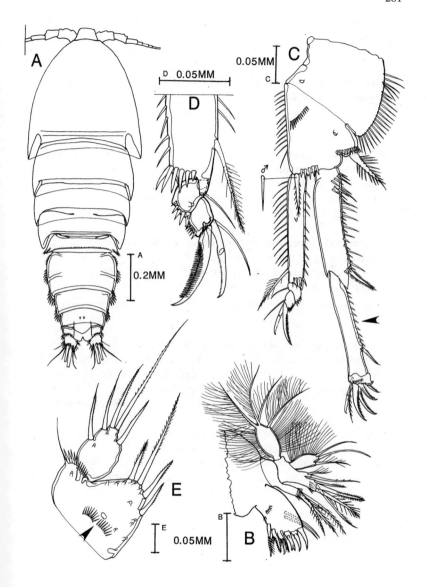

Fig. 111. *Harpacticus uniremis*: A, female body, dorsal; B, maxillule; C, female P1; D, distal endopod segments of P1; E, female P5.

5. P2 exopod-3 with one inner seta; P2 endopod-3 with only three setae; P3
    exopod-3 with two inner setae.
    ....*Harpacticus compsonyx*

    P2 exopod-3 with two inner setae; P2 endopod-3 with five setae; P3
    exopod-3 with three inner setae.
    ....**6**

6. P1 endopod-1 inner seta (arrowed in Fig. 114A) moderately-densely
    tripinnate, reaching only slightly beyond distal margin of endopod-2; P5
    baseoendopod with small pore near inner margin (arrowed in Fig. 113D);
    male urosomite-2 without frontolateral spinular row (see Fig. 114G).
    ....*Harpacticus obscurus*

    P1 endopod-1 inner seta (arrowed in Fig. 114B) sparsely bipinnate and
    reaching to tip of claws on endopod-2; P5 baseoendopod without small
    pore near inner margin (Fig. 114E); male urosomite-2 with frontolateral
    spinlar row (arrowed in Fig. 114G).
    ....**7**

7. Female urosomites-3 and -4 with row of spinules on ventral posterior
    margin (arrowed in Fig. 114D); in male, apophysis on P2 endopod-2
    usually short (Fig. 114F); in both sexes, endopod of maxilla with a
    densely pinnate outer seta (arrowed in Fig. 114C).
    ....*Harpacticus littoralis*

    Female urosomites-3 and -4 without row of spinules on ventral posterior
    margin; in male, apophysis on P2 endopod-2 usually long (Fig. 114I); in
    both sexes, endopod of maxilla with a naked outer seta (Fig. 114H).
    ....*Harpacticus giesbrechti*

283

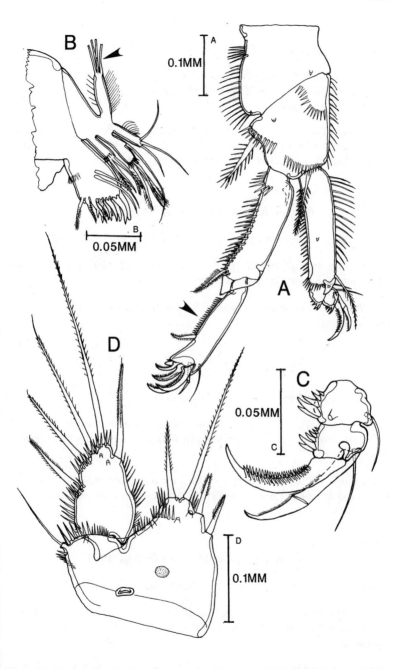

Fig. 112. *Harpacticus septentrionalis*: A, female P1; B, maxillule; C, distal endopod segments of P1; D, female P5.

Harpacticus chelifer (O. F. Müller, 1776)

Morphological descriptions: Sars (1911), Pallares (1973).

Habitat: Among algae and other organisms on rocks, from slightly above low-water spring tides to about 10m depth close inshore in full salinity seawater, occasionally in sediments close to weeds. Often abundant.

Distribution: On all north-west European mainland and island coasts except for the east coast of England from the Thames estuary to Flamborough Head. In this region it has only been recorded (as rare) intertidally and offshore near Cromer.

Harpacticus flexus Brady & Robertson, 1873

Morphological descriptions: Sars (1911), Bodin (1970), Mielke (1975).

Habitat: In clean or slightly silty sand from mid-tide level to 20m in full or nearly full salinity; sometimes in the plankton or among algae.

Distribution: All around the coasts of Britain, Ireland and the continent from Brest to Bergen.

Harpacticus uniremis Krøyer, 1842

Morphological descriptions: Sars (1911), Lang (1948).

Habitat: Fairly eurytopic, being found among algae or in sandy or muddy sediments from mid-tide level down to about 10-20m, very rarely to as deep as 500m. Frequent.

Distribution: All round the coasts of Britain (except north-west Scotland) and Ireland and the coast of north-west Europe; also throughout the sub-Arctic to the boreal Pacific.

Harpacticus septentrionalis Klie, 1939

Morphological descriptions: Klie (1939), Itô (1976).

Habitat: On algae from the lower intertidal down to 5-10m. Original British record from the filters of a fish hatchery at Bay of Nigg, Aberdeenshire. Occasional.

Distribution: Helgoland; the east coast of Scotland and northern England from Aberdeen to Robin Hood's Bay; also in the boreal Pacific.

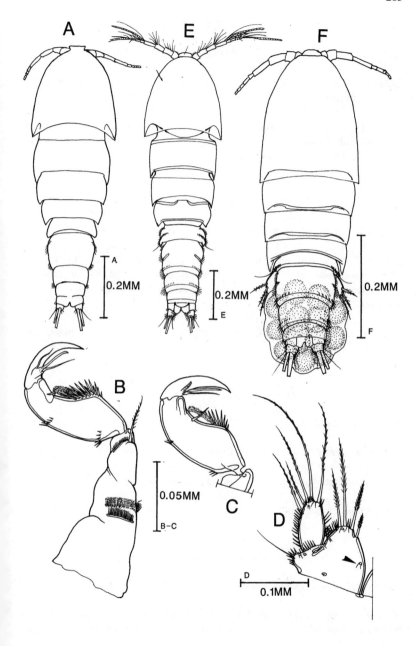

Fig. 113. *Harpacticus obscurus*: A, female body, dorsal; B, maxilliped, dorsal view; C, basis of maxilliped, posterior view; D, female P5. *Harpacticus littoralis*: E, female body, dorsal. *Harpacticus giesbrechti*: F, female body, dorsal.

Harpacticus compsonyx Monard, 1926

Morphological descriptions: Monard (1926, 1928), Lang (1948).

Habitat: Among algae on rocks or stable pebbles in clear full-salinity seawater from low-water neap-tide level to approximately 10m depth.

Distribution: Only in the extreme south-west of the region, in the Isles of Scilly and at Roscoff (France). Otherwise, in most of the Mediterranean and, as scattered records, world-wide in warm waters.

Harpacticus obscurus T. Scott, 1895

Morphological descriptions: Sars (1911) as *H. gracilis*, Lang (1948).

Habitat: Prefers small algae on stones on a bed of sand mixed with mud and plenty of suspended silt in the water. It is able to tolerate slightly varying salinities and moderately strong currents without wave action. Mainly intertidal and can be abundant.

Distribution: Throughout the region except, so far, the west coast of Ireland and north-west Scotland.

Harpacticus littoralis Sars, 1910

Morphological descriptions: Sars (1911), Lang (1948).

Habitat: Estuarine littoral species with marked preference for shallow water in flat sandy creeks and the channels draining salt-marshes. Occasional, but may be locally abundant, replacing *H. obscurus* in polyhaline lagoons..

Distribution: Throughout the area except north-west Scotland.

Harpacticus giesbrechti Klie, 1927

Morphological descriptions: Giesbrecht (1882) as *H. chelifer*, Klie (1927).

Habitat: Among algae (mainly but not exclusively red algae) on rocks or stable pebbles in clear, full-salinity seawater from low-water neap-tide levels to a depth of about 10m.

Distribution: Helgoland and south-west coasts of England and Ireland. Also throughout the western half of the Mediterranean.

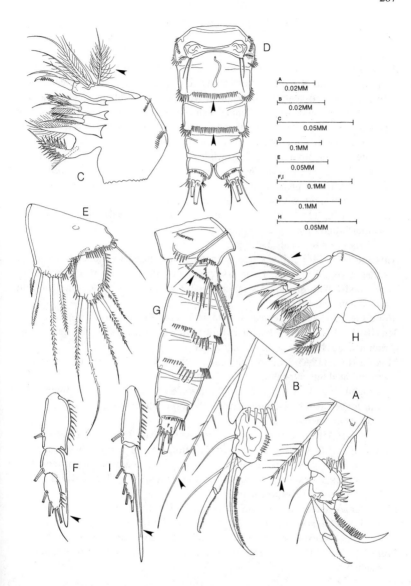

Fig. 114. *Harpacticus obscurus*: A, P1 endopod, distal portion. *Harpacticus littoralis*: B, P1 endopod, distal portion; C, maxilla; D, female urosome, ventral; E, female P5; F, male P2 endopod (with abbreviated setae); G, male urosome, lateral. *Harpacticus giesbrechti*: H, maxilla; I, male P2 endopod (with abbreviated setae).

Family TEGASTIDAE Sars, 1904

Diagnosis.

Body (Fig. 115A). Laterally compressed, amphipod-like, with integument strongly chitinised and pitted or sculptured to a variable degree. Cephalothorax deeply produced ventrolaterally, often with posterior chitinous stripe marking line of fusion of P1-bearing somite with cephalosome. Epimeral plates of free prosomites rudimentary. Genital and first abdominal somite fused in both sexes to form ventrally produced genital double-somite (Fig. 119C,D). P5-bearing somite also incorporated to form triple-somite in both sexes (except tropical genera *Feregastes* and *Arawella*). Remaining urosomites very reduced, often telescoped into triple-somite (Fig. 116D). Anal somite membranous dorsally. Caudal rami short, with seven setae.

Antennule (Fig. 115A). In female 6- to 8-segmented, with naked setae; aesthetasc on fourth and apical segments. In male 8-segmented, weakly haplocer with aesthetascs on segments 3, 4, and 8.

Antenna (Fig. 116B). Basis free or incompletely fused to endopod-1, without setae. Exopod minute, 1- or 2-segmented with maximum of four setae. Endopod-1 with one inner seta; endopod-2 without geniculate setae but with two slightly curved claws.

Mandible. Exopod represented by up to three setae. Endopod 1-segmented.

Maxillule (Fig. 115B). Coxal endite with one seta. Basis elongate; rami rudimentary, fully incorporated into basis.

Maxilla (Fig. 119A). Syncoxa elongate, with three endites. Endopod vestigial, incorporated into allobasis.

Maxilliped (Figs 116C, E; 119B). Subchelate. Syncoxa elongate, usually as long as or longer than basis, with one seta. Seta on palmar margin of basis usually modified as spinulose pad.

P1 (Fig. 115C). Basis elongate along dorso-ventral axis. Rami 1-segmented.

P2-P4 (Fig. 116A). Basis transversely elongate. P4 exopod 3-segmented, segmentation of other rami variable; distal exopod segment with at most two outer spines. P4 exopod-3 with modified inner spine (Fig. 115D) which can be slightly sexually dimorphic in male.

P5. In female endopodal lobe of baseoendopod enlarged, foliaceous, forming a brood-pouch (except in *Arawella*) (Figs 115E; 116D); exopod separate. In male baseoendopod extremely reduced, exopod elongate with four setae (Fig. 119E).

Male P6 (Fig. 119D). A large membranous flap, without ornamentation or armature.

Females with one egg-sac containing 3-4 eggs (Fig. 115E), males with one spermatophore (Fig. 119D).

Five genera known world-wide.

289

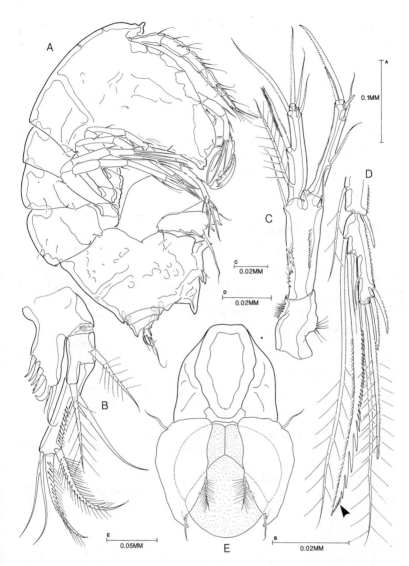

Fig. 115. *Parategastes sphaericus*: A, female body, lateral; B, maxillule; C, P1; D, P4 exopod-3 (modified inner spine arrowed); E, frontal view of female brood pouch showing enlarged endopodal lobes and egg-sac.

Key to world genera of Tegastidae

1. P2-P3 exopods 3-segmented.
  2

   P2-P3 exopods 2-segmented.
  4

2. P2-P3 endopods 3-segmented.
  3

   P2-P3 endopods 2-segmented.
   .... *Arawella* Cottarelli & Baldari, 1987

3. P4 endopod 3-segmented.
   ....*Tegastes* (p. 292)

   P4 endopod 2-segmented.
   ....*Feregastes* Fiers, 1986

4. P4 endopod 3-segmented, proximal segment normal.
   ....*Parategastes* (p. 298)

   P4 endopod 2-segmented, proximal segment swollen.
   ....*Syngastes* Monard, 1924

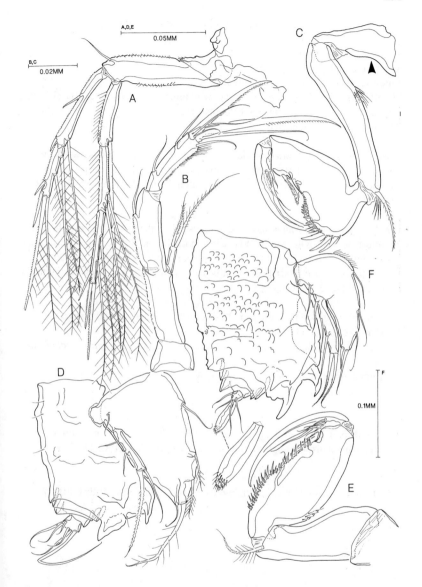

Fig. 116. *Parategastes sphaericus*: A, P2; B, antenna. *Tegastes longimanus*: C, maxilliped; D, female urosome, lateral. *Tegastes falcatus*: E, maxilliped; F, female urosome, lateral.

Genus TEGASTES Norman, 1903

Diagnosis: Tegastidae.
Antennule. In female 8-segmented.
Antenna. 1- or 2-segmented with three or four setae
Maxilla. Distal endite of syncoxa broad, with three articulating setae. Basal endite with three articulating setae on distal margin.
P2-P4. All rami 3-segmented.

Thirty-three species known world-wide. The above diagnosis is based on the European species but the only diagnostic feature exhibited by all species at present in this genus is the 3-segmented rami on P2 and P3. The genus is badly in need of revision.

Local species. Eight, which may be distinguished by the following key. However, this must be used with caution and any identification checked against original descriptions because it is known that there are several undescribed species in the area. The males are described for only four of the species. Setal formulae in Appendix Table 5 (p.344).

1. Genital triple-somite with paired posteriorly directed spur-like processes (arrowed in Fig. 117A).
    ....*Tegastes calcaratus*

    Genital triple-somite not as in Fig. 117A.
    ....**2**

2. Maxilliped basis with distal part of palmar margin strongly concave producing a distinct angle at mid-point on margin (Figs 116C; 117C)
    ....**3**

    Maxilliped basis palmar margin more or less straight (Figs 116E; 118B,D).
    ....**4**

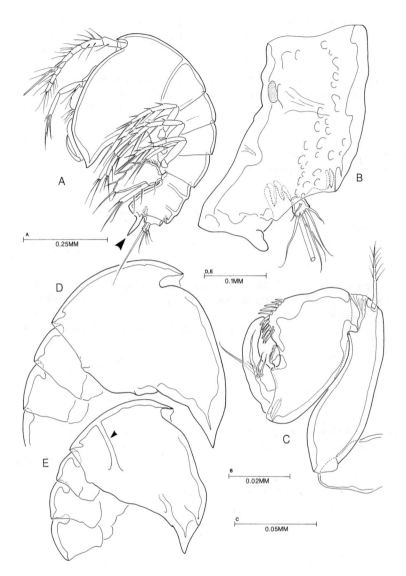

Fig. 117. *Tegastes calcaratus*: A, female body, lateral. *Tegastes grandimanus*: B, female urosome, lateral; C, maxilliped. *Tegastes flavidus*: D, cephalothorax, lateral: *Tegastes nanus* E, cephalothorax, lateral.

3. P3 exopod-1 without inner seta; maxilliped endopodal claw almost as long as basis (Fig. 116C); P5 exopod of female with four setae.
    ....*Tegastes longimanus*

    P3 exopod-1 with inner seta; maxilliped endopodal claw only half as long as basis (Fig. 117C); P5 exopod of female with five setae.
    ....*Tegastes grandimanus*

4. P3 and P4 endopod-3 with five and four setae / spines respectively; P4 endopod-1 without inner seta.
    .... *Tegastes satyrus*

    P3 and P4 endopod-3 with six and five setae / spines respectively; P4 endopod-1 with inner seta.
   5

5. Caudal ramus seta V lancet-shaped in female (Fig. 116F); posterior margin of triple-somite, in both sexes, produced into two hooked projections (Fig. 116F).
    .... *Tegastes falcatus*

    Caudal ramus seta V normal; posterior margin of triple-somite not as in Fig. 116F.
   6

6. Cephalothorax without transverse internal rib marking anterior boundary of P1- bearing somite (Fig. 117D).
    .... *Tegastes flavidus*

    Cephalothorax with distinct transverse internal rib (Fig. 117E).
   7

295

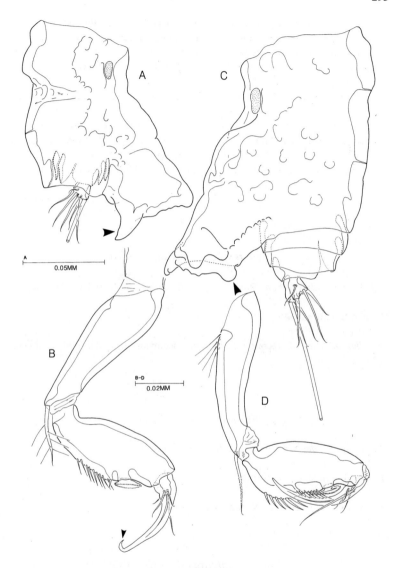

Fig. 118. *Tegastes nanus*: A, female urosome, lateral; B, maxilliped. *Tegastes clausi*: D, female urosome, lateral; D, maxilliped.

7. Posterior border of genital triple-somite, of both sexes, with one sharply pointed recurved process on ventro-lateral margin (arrowed in Fig. 118A); antennary exopod 2-segmented with four setae; maxilliped endopodal claw acutely recurved at tip (arrowed in Fig. 118B). P3 exopod-1 without inner seta.
.... *Tegastes nanus*

Posterior border of genital triple-somite of female (male unknown) with one bluntly rounded process on ventro-lateral margin (arrowed in Fig. 118C); antennary exopod 1-segmented with three setae; maxilliped endopodal claw not recurved at tip (Fig. 118D). P3 exopod-1 with inner seta.
.... *Tegastes clausi*

Tegastes satyrus (Claus, 1860)

Morphological description: Sars (1911) (as *T. harpacticoides* (Claus, 1863)).

Habitat: Sublittoral, 40m.

Distribution: The only record is of "several specimens" from the south-west coast of Norway.

Tegastes longimanus (Claus, 1863)

Morphological descriptions: Sars (1911), Klie (1949).

Habitat: Intertidal down to 30m.

Distribution: West coast of Norway, Helgoland.

Tegastes falcatus (Norman, 1868)

Morphological descriptions: Sars (1911), Chislenko (1967).

Habitat: Sandy sediments, 6-70m.

Distribution: West coast of Norway, all around Britain, Dublin Bay.

Tegastes flavidus Sars, 1904

Morphological description: Sars (1911).

Habitat: Muddy sand, 6m. Rare.

Distribution: The only record is from the west coast of Norway.

Tegastes grandimanus Sars, 1904

Morphological description: Sars (1911).

Habitat: Muddy sand, 6-54m.

Distribution: North-east coast of England, Isle of Man, west coast of Norway.

Tegastes nanus Sars, 1904

Morphological descriptions: Sars (1911), Chislenko (1967).

Habitat: Intertidal pools and algal holdfasts to "moderate depths".

Distribution: Ireland (Dublin Bay and Co. Mayo), west coast of Norway.

Tegastes clausi Sars, 1904

Synonym: T. longimanus (Claus, 1863) *sensu* Sars (1904).

Morphological descriptions: Sars (1911), Klie (1949).

Habitat: Muddy sand, 6m. on intertidal algae; intertidal and down to 15-20m in Norfolk waters, almost always found together with *Parategastes sphaericus*.

Distribution: West coast of Norway, Helgoland, St. Abbs Head, Robin Hood's Bay.

Tegastes calcaratus Sars, 1910

Morphological description: Sars (1911).

Habitat: Subtidal, 40m. Rare.

Distribution: The only record is of a single specimen from the west coast of Norway.

Genus PARATEGASTES Sars, 1904

Diagnosis: Tegastidae.
Antennule (Fig. 115A). In female 6- or 7- segmented.
Antenna (Fig. 116B). Exopod 1-segmented with up to three setae.
Maxilla (Fig. 119A). Distal syncoxal endite with two setae and a fused spine; allobasal endite slender, terminating in a fused recurved spine.
P2-P4. P2-P3 exopod 2-segmented, all other rami 3-segmented.

Five species known world-wide. The above diagnosis is based primarily on the European species but the only diagnostic feature exhibited by all species at present in this genus is the 2-segmented exopod of P2 and P3. The genus is in need of revision.

Local species. One. Setal formula in Appendix Table 5 (p.344).

Parategastes sphaericus (Claus, 1863)

Morphological description: Sars (1911).

Habitat: Intertidal algae.

Distribution: All around Britain, Helgoland, west coast of Norway.

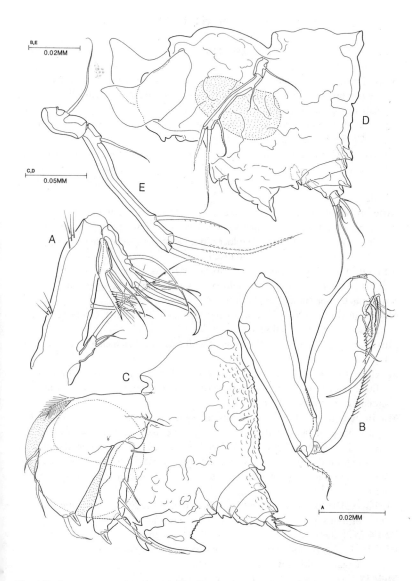

Fig. 119. *Parategastes sphaericus*: A, maxilla; B, maxilliped; C, female urosome, lateral; D, male urosome, lateral; E, male P5.

Family CLYTEMNESTRIDAE A. Scott, 1909

Synonym. Pseudo-Peltidiidae Poppe, 1891.

Diagnosis.

Body (Fig. 120A). Slender and dorso-ventrally flattened with marked distinction between prosome and urosome. Cephalothorax characteristically bell-shaped. Rostrum large, triangular, not defined at base. Epimeral plates laterally produced. Female genital double-somite with internal chitinous rib; female genital field (Fig. 120B) with large copulatory pore posterior to genital apertures. Caudal rami (Fig. 120C, H) noticeably convergent, at least as long as broad, with conical or obliquely truncate distal margin and a large terminal pore; setae IV and V short and stout in female, more elongate and slender in male.

Antennule. In female, 6- or 7-segmented, terminal segment elongate; five aesthetascs; all setae small and naked except for a few sparsely bipinnate setae on proximal two segments. Haplocer in male, 6- or 7-segmented with pairs of aesthetascs on segments 4, 5 and distal.

Antenna (Fig. 120D). Basis with no abexopodal seta. Exopod represented by one or two setae. Endopod-1 bare, endopod-2 with five or six non-geniculate setae.

Mouthparts. Very reduced in both sexes.

Mandible (Fig. 120E). Coxa long and slender with minute gnathobase; palp represented by one small seta.

Maxillule (Fig. 120F). A single segment with two apical elements (one missing in Fig. 120F).

Maxilla (Fig. 120G). Syncoxa with one endite bearing two or three setae. Allobasis distinct, with a terminal articulating spine and one seta. Endopod probably represented by one seta.

Maxilliped (Fig. 121A, D). Subchelate. Syncoxa (only partially illustrated in figure) long, slender, with one seta. In female, basis elongate with one small seta and a roughened pad at distal end of palmar margin; endopodal claw at most one third length of basis. In male, basis much larger than in female and with spinular rows on palmar margin; endopodal claw at least half as long as basis.

P1 (Fig. 121B). Basis almost square without inner seta. Exopod 1-segmented with three or four setae. Endopod indistinctly 3-segmented.

P2-P4. With transversely elongate basis. Rami 3-segmented.

P5 (Fig. 121C). In both sexes baseoendopod without endopodal lobe, exopod of one elongate segment with five or six setae.

Male P6. Symmetrical. Represented by one seta.

Females with a single discoid egg-sac, males with one spermatophore.

Monogeneric.

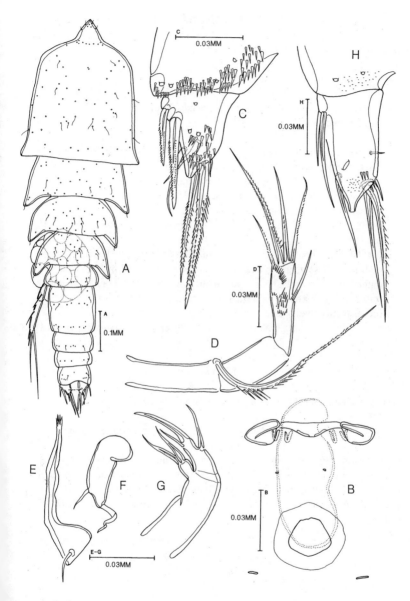

Fig. 120. *Clytemnestra rostrata* female: A, body, dorsal; B, genital field; C, caudal ramus (ventral view); D, antenna; E, mandible; F, maxillule; G, maxilla. *Clytemnestra scutellata* female: H, caudal ramus, ventral view.

Genus CLYTEMNESTRA Dana, 1848

Diagnosis: As for family (p. 300).

Two species known world-wide.

Local species. Two. Setal formulae in Appendix Table 5 (p.344). The species can be distinguished as follows.

1. Caudal rami about as long as broad (Fig. 120C); antennule of both sexes 6-segmented; antennary exopod represented by one seta (Fig. 120D); P1 (Fig. 121B) outer basal seta absent, exopod with three setae; P2 exopod-1 with outer spine, exopod-3 with 6 setae; P5 (Fig. 121C) exopod with five (occasionally four) setae.
    .... ***Clytemnestra rostrata*** (Brady, 1883)

    Caudal rami about 1.8 times longer than broad (Fig. 120H); antennule of both sexes 7-segmented; antennary exopod represented by two setae; P1 outer basal seta present, exopod with four setae; P2 exopod-1 without outer spine, exopod-3 with seven elements; P5 exopod with six (occasionally five) setae.
    .... ***Clytemnestra scutellata*** Dana, 1848

Both species

Morphological descriptions: Lang (1948), Boxshall (1979).

Habitat: Planktonic, from surface down to 60m. Rare, occasionally frequent.

Distribution: Both species are widespread throughout tropical and temperate oceanic waters but infrequent in inshore waters. *C. rostrata* has been recorded from near the Eddystone Lighthouse, Plymouth, and from off Roscoff (France) and Cork. A single specimen of *C. scutellata* was recorded by Sars (1921) from Oslofjord.

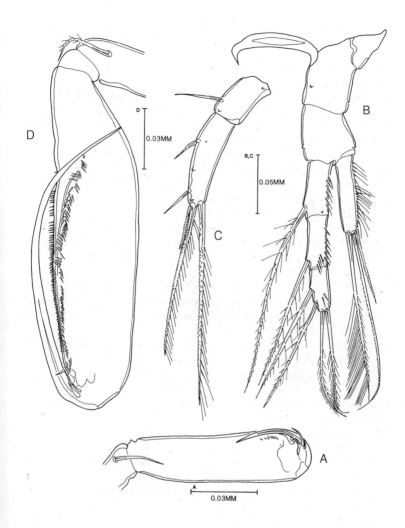

Fig. 121. *Clytemnestra rostrata*: A, female maxilliped basis and endopod; B, P1; C, P5; D, male maxilliped basis and endopod.

Family PORCELLIDIIDAE Brady, 1880

Diagnosis.

Body (Fig. 122A,B). Dorso-ventrally flattened, shield-shaped, with very large prosome and small urosome. Integument usually strongly chitinised and pitted or sculptured to variable degree. P1-bearing somite incorporated in large, expanded cephalothorax. Rostrum not defined at base; broad and lamellar in female, vestigial in male. Epimeral plates of first two free prosomites well developed, those of third rudimentary in female (Fig. 122A), well-developed in male (Fig. 122B). Urosome of only three somites, short and flattened in both sexes. P5-bearing somite separate in male, largely fused to genital double-somite in female. Anal somite deeply cleft medially, often telescoped into preceding somite. Caudal rami lamelliform, with 7 setae; apical setae very short (Figs 122E, 123B-F); sexually dimorphic.

Antennule (Fig. 122C). Short; majority of setae annulated. In female 6-segmented; distal segment indistinctly subdivided; aesthetascs on segments 4 and 6. In male 5-segmented, haplocer; segment 1 laterally expanded; with aesthetasc on segment 4.

Antenna. Basis without abexopodal seta. Exopod elongate, 1-segmented; with three lateral and three distal setae. Endopod 2-segmented, endopod-1 without setae, endopod-2 with three lateral setae and two setae plus four spines (three geniculate) distally.

Mandible (Fig. 122C). Coxa with narrow gnathobase. Basis and endopod fused to form elongate foliaceous segment; anterior lobe derived from basis, with four swollen fringed setae; posterior lobe derived from endopod, with one elongate and five swollen setae. Exopod with six swollen and five slender setae. Mandibular palp and P1 forming a ventral sucker (Tiemann, 1986).

Maxillule. Arthrite with several fringed spines. Coxa with five setae. Basis with two distinct endites, each with four setae. Exopod with two setae. Endopod arising from pedestal, with six setae.

Maxilla. Syncoxa with three endites; proximal and middle endites closely set; with three, two and two setae, respectively. Allobasis not drawn out into claw; with one short and two long setae, and one short articulated claw. Endopod indistinctly 2-segmented, with four setae.

Maxilliped (Fig. 123A). Weakly subchelate. Syncoxa broad, with one seta. Basis produced into distal rounded process fringed with hairs along inner margins of basis and syncoxa. Endopod indistinctly 2-segmented, with one geniculate seta and one simple seta on endopod-1 and two geniculate setae on endopod-2.

P1 (Fig. 122C). Very distinctive. Intercoxal sclerite broad. Outer basal seta extremely swollen and plumose. Endopod 2-segmented, endopod-1 a wide trapezoidal plate, with long plumose seta; endopod-2 distal segment small with two terminal, densely unipinnate claws. Exopod 3-segmented, somewhat broad and delicate, with basally expanded soft setae on outer margin.

P2-P4. Basis transversely elongate. Rami 3-segmented, with three outer spines on exopod-3. P2 endopod sexually dimorphic, endopod-3 with four setae in female, with two in male.

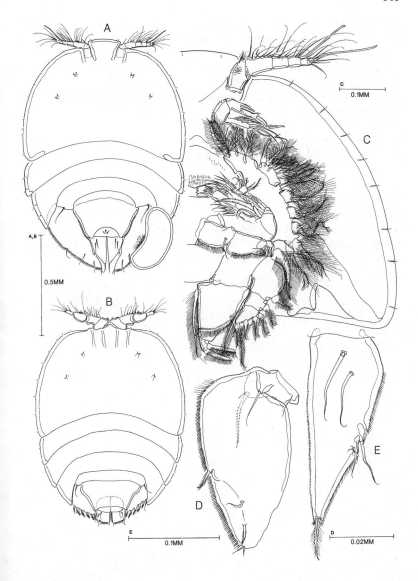

Fig. 122. *Porcellidium tenuicauda*: A, female body, dorsal, with spermatophore attached; B, male body, dorsal; C, cephalothorax, left half, ventral; D, female P5; E, female caudal ramus, dorsal.

P5 (Figs 122D, 123C) very characteristic, exopod and baseoendopod largely fused. Baseoendopod reduced, with one or two setae on weakly-developed endopodal lobe. In female exopod a large keeled plate tapering distally and embracing genital double-somite and anal somite, with five setae; in male much smaller, with oblique distal margin bearing six short spines.

Male P6. Asymmetrical. A large membranous flap on one side, without any armature or ornamentation.

Females with one egg-sac, males with one spermatophore. Precopulatory clasping around genital double-somite. Spermatophores deposited dorsally (Fig. 122A).

In two recent papers on Australian Porcellidiidae, Harris (1994) and Harris & Robertson (1994) established five new genera:- *Brevifrons, Tectacingulum, Kioloaria, Murramia* and *Acutiramus*. Almost all these genera were proposed to accommodate new species. Without any prior revision of the, highly speciose, type-genus *Porcellidium*, it does not seem justified to maintain these Australian genera - particularly as they are based on dubious grounds.

Genus PORCELLIDIUM Claus, 1860

Diagnosis: As for family (p. 304).

Twenty-six species known world-wide.

Local species. Five. Setal formula in Appendix Table 5 (p.344). Bocquet (1948) and Battaglia (1954) have demonstrated that *Porcellidium viride* (Philippi, 1840) *sensu* Lang (1948) is an amalgam of at least three species viz. *P. sarsi* Bocquet, 1948, *P. fimbriatum* Claus, 1863 and *P. lecanoides* Claus, 1889. All three species occur in north-west Europe together with *P. tenuicauda* Claus, 1860. *P. ovatum* Haller, 1879, a Mediterranean and Indo-pacific species, has recently been recorded from Ireland (Holmes & O'Connor, 1990). Males are insufficiently described to allow their easy identification, but females can be separated on the basis of the caudal ramus (Figs 122E, 123B, D-F).

1. Caudal ramus trapezoidal (Fig. 122E).
    .... *Porcellidium tenuicauda*

    Caudal ramus not trapezoidal (Fig. 123B, D-F).
    ....**2**

2. Posterior border of caudal ramus oblique (Fig. 123B).
    .... *Porcellidium ovatum*

    Posterior border of caudal ramus square (Fig. 123D-F).
    ....**3**

3. Both proximal and distal dorsal setae of caudal ramus situated in proximal half of ramus (Fig. 123D).
    .... *Porcellidium sarsi*

    Distal dorsal seta of caudal ramus situated in distal half of ramus (Fig. 123E-F).
    ....**4**

4. Four of terminal setae of caudal ramus swollen at base (Fig. 123E).
    .... *Porcellidium fimbriatum*

    None of terminal setae of caudal ramus swollen at base (Fig. 123F).
    .... *Porcellidium lecanoides*

Porcellidium sarsi Bocquet, 1948

Synonym: P. fimbriatum Claus, 1863 *sensu* Sars (1911).

Morphological descriptions: Sars (1911), Bocquet (1948).

Habitat: On surface of algae, particularly *Laminaria*.

Distribution: On all British coasts if most records of *P. viride* are assumed to refer to this species; west coast of Norway; Roscoff (France).

Porcellidium fimbriatum Claus, 1863

Morphological description: Bocquet (1948).

Habitat: On surface of algae (*Saccorhiza, Ulva, Chondrus*).

Distribution: Isles of Scilly, Roscoff (France).

Porcellidium lecanoides Claus, 1889

Morphological description: Bocquet (1948) (as *P. lecanoides* var. *roscoffensis*).

Habitat: On surface of algae (*Bifurcaria*).

Distribution: Devon, Roscoff (France), Mayo (Ireland).

Porcellidium tenuicauda Claus, 1860

Morphological description: Bocquet (1948).

Habitat: On surface of algae (*Saccorhiza, Laminaria, Ulva*).

Distribution: West coast of Ireland, Isles of Scilly, Isle of Man, Roscoff (France).

Porcellidium ovatum Haller, 1879

Morphological description: Lang (1948).

Habitat: On surface of algae.

Distribution: Lough Hyne (south-west Ireland).

Note: Harris & Robertson (1994) transfer *P. ovatum* Haller, 1879 *sensu* Geddes (1968) to their new genus *Acutiramus* and, erroneously, rename it *A. ovatus* (Geddes, 1968) without making any reference to the original description of *P. ovatum*. Since *Acutiramus* was proposed on dubious grounds, this new combination is not adopted here.

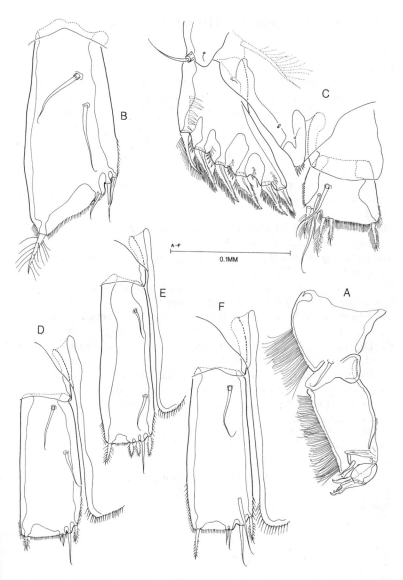

Fig. 123. *Porcellidium ovatum*: A, maxilliped; B, female caudal ramus, dorsal; C, male P5 and caudal ramus, dorsal. *Porcellidium sarsi*: D, female caudal ramus, dorsal. *Porcellidium fimbriatum*: E, female caudal ramus, dorsal. *Porcellidium lecanoides*: E, female caudal ramus, dorsal.

Family PELTIDIIDAE Sars, 1904

Diagnosis.

Body (Fig. 124A, B). Distinctive, broad, dorso-ventrally flattened with strongly-developed integument which may be strengthened by anastomosing struts, sometimes forming a conspicuous pattern (Fig. 127A, E). P1-bearing somite incorporated into large and more or less flattened cephalothorax. Rostrum usually broad, not defined at base. Epimeral plates of free prosomites, and sometimes first urosomite, laterally expanded. Urosome much shorter than prosome; female genital double-somite often backwardly produced and embracing rest of urosome.

Antennule. 5- to 9-segmented in female; haplocer in male.

Antenna (Fig. 124E). Basis and endopod-1 with one abexopodal seta. Exopod 1- or 2-segmented.

Mandible (Fig. 124F). Gnathobase elongate. Basis usually with three setae. Rami minute, 1-segmented or exopod absent.

Maxillule (Fig. 124G) with elongate basis. Distinct exopod and rudimentary endopod each with three setae.

Maxilla (Fig. 124H). Syncoxa with three widely separated endites. Endopod a small segment or largely incorporated into allobasis.

Maxilliped (Fig. 125). Subchelate. Basis with distal seta modified into spinulose pad.

P1 (Figs 124C, 127G). Exopod prehensile; consisting of two elongate segments and one small terminal segment with variable number of recurved spines (claws) and usually a more slender geniculate spine or seta. Exopod always more strongly-developed than 2- or 3-segmented endopod.

P2-P4 (Fig. 124D). Basis transversely elongated. Rami 3-segmented. Rarely sexually dimorphic.

P5 (Fig. 126) in both sexes with poorly developed baseoendopod, sometimes fused with elongate exopod.

Females with one egg-sac. Male with one spermatophore.

Eight genera known world-wide.

Key to world genera of Peltidiidae

1. P1 endopod 3-segmented.
   2

   P1 endopod 2-segmented.
   ....**.4**

2. P5 baseoendopod and exopod fused.
   .... *Alteuthella* A. Scott, 1909

   P5 baseoendopod and exopod separate.
   ....**.3**

3. P1 exopod-3 with four claws.
   .... *Alteutha* (p. 314)

   P1 exopod-3 with one stout claw only.
   .... *Alteuthoides* Hicks, 1986

4. P5 baseoendopod and exopod fused.
   ....**.5**

   P5 baseoendopod and exopod separate.
   ....**.6**

5. Integument strengthened with conspicuous anastomosing struts.
   .... *Parapeltidium* A. Scott, 1909

   Integument without conspicuous anastomosing struts.
   .... *Alteuthellopsis* Lang, 1944

6. Caudal rami slender and cylindrical; P1 endopod segments broad; integument strengthened with conspicuous anastomosing struts.
    .... *Peltidium* (p. 318)

    Caudal rami wide, lamellar; P1 endopod segments narrow; integument without conspicuous anastomosing struts.
   7

7. Posterior urosomites fused medially and partially embracing caudal rami.
    .... *Neopeltopsis* Hicks, 1976

    Posterior urosomites not as above.
    .... *Eupelte* (p.320)

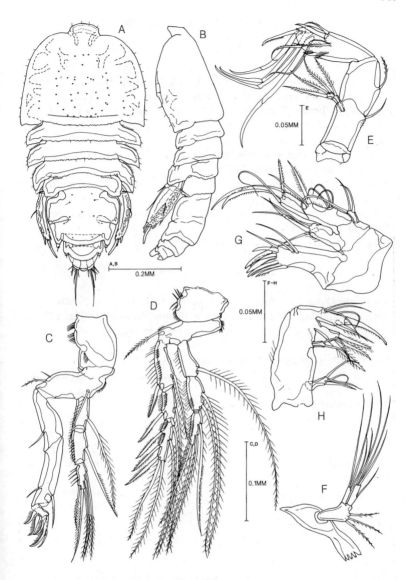

Fig. 124. *Alteutha depressa*: female A, body, dorsal; B, body lateral; C, P1; D, P2. *Alteutha oblonga*: E, antenna, F, mandible; G, maxillule; H, maxilla.

Genus ALTEUTHA Baird, 1845

Diagnosis: Peltidiidae.

Body. Lateral margins of cephalothorax turned in ventrally; skeletal strut pattern weak, only developed at ventro-lateral margins of cephalothorax. Rostrum usually large and broad. Epimeral plates of free prosomites well developed; those of the first urosomite smaller and more rounded (Fig. 124A, B). Caudal rami short and broad, lamellar; with setae IV and V distinct.

Antennule. 7- to 9-segmented in female.

Antenna. Exopod 2- (or 3-?) segmented (Fig. 124E).

Mandible. Exopod present (Fig. 124F).

Maxilliped (Fig. 125). Basis inflated or elongate with convex palmar margin; endopodal claw elongate.

P1. Exopod-3 (Fig. 124C) with four claw setae and usually one geniculate seta. Endopod 3-segmented.

P5. Baseoendopod and exopod separate in both sexes (Fig. 126).

Thirteen species known world-wide.

Local species. Four. Setal formulae in Appendix Table 5 (p.344). Adults of both sexes may be distinguished by the shape of the maxilliped basis (Fig. 125) and females may also be distinguished by the form of the P5 (Fig. 126).

1. P1-P4 endopod-3 with 4 setae; maxilliped as in Fig. 125C.
   .... *Alteutha roeae*

   P1-P4 endopod-3 with 5,5,6,5 setae.
   ....**2**

2. P2-P4 exopod-1 and P1 endopod-2 without inner seta; maxilliped as in Fig. 125B.
   .... *Alteutha oblonga*

   P2-P4 exopod-1 and P1 endopod-2 with inner seta.
   ....**3**

3. Maxilliped basis short, length less than twice width (Fig. 125D).
   .... *Alteutha depressa*

   Maxilliped basis elongate, length at least twice width (Fig. 125A).
   .... *Alteutha interrupta*

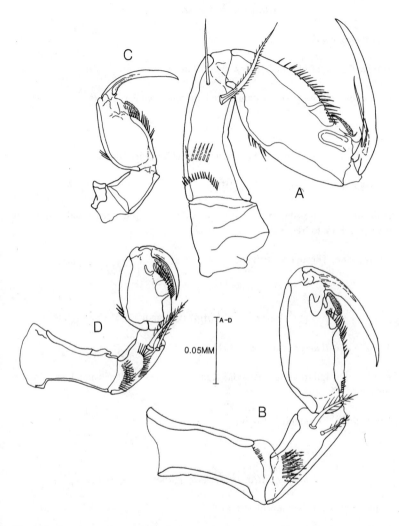

Fig. 125. *Alteutha* species, maxilliped: A, *A. interrupta*; B, *A. oblonga*; C, *A. roeae*; D, *A. depressa*.

Alteutha depressa (Baird, 1837)

Morphological description: Lang (1948).

Habitat: On intertidal and shallow subtidal algae. Frequent.

Distribution: Throughout Britain, except on south and east coasts.

Alteutha interrupta (Goodsir, 1845)

Morphological description: Sars (1911).

Habitat: On intertidal and shallow subtidal algae but occasionally found in plankton. Rare to frequent.

Distribution: Throughout Britain.

Alteutha oblonga (Goodsir, 1845)

Morphological description: Sars (1911).

Habitat: On intertidal and subtidal algae and occasionally in plankton. Rare to frequent.

Distribution: Throughout Britain.

Alteutha roeae Hicks, 1982

Synonym: Alteutha sp. in Roe (1958).

Morphological descriptions: Roe (1958), Hicks (1982; based on S. African material). It is possible that the Irish and S. African populations represent distinct species.

Habitat: Laminaria holdfasts. Rare.

Distribution: Dublin Bay, Ireland, is the only record from the British Isles.

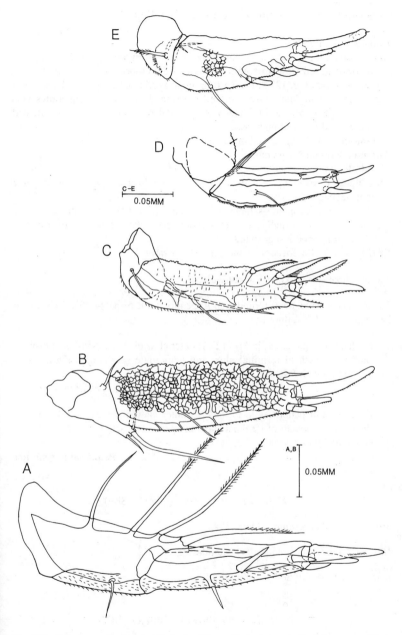

Fig. 126. *Alteutha species* female P5: A, *A. oblonga*; B, *A. depressa*; C, *A. interrupta*; D, *A. roeae*. E, male P5 of *A. depressa*.

Genus PELTIDIUM Philippi, 1839

Diagnosis: Peltidiidae.

Body. Lateral margin of cephalothorax not inflexed ventrally; cephalothorax, free prosomites and first urosomite with well developed, complex network of skeletal struts (Fig. 127A, E). Rostrum large and broad. Epimeral plates of free prosomites and first urosomite well developed; remaining urosomites very small, scarcely visible in dorsal view. Caudal rami slender, cylindrical, with setae IV and V not fused at base.

Antennule. 6- to 8-segmented in female.

Antenna. Exopod 2-segmented.

Mandible. Exopod absent.

Maxilliped. Basis elongate with slightly convex palmar margin; endopodal claw elongate, narrow.

P1 (Fig. 127G). Exopod 3-segmented; exopod-3 (Fig. 127C, H) with one or two stout claws and, usually, a more slender, geniculate claw; rest of armature reduced. Endopod 2-segmented.

P5 (Fig. 127D). Baseoendopod and exopod separate.

Twenty-three species known world-wide.

Local species. Two. Setal formulae in Appendix Table 5 (p.344). The species can be distinguished as follows.

1. Skeletal strut pattern as in Fig. 127A; outer claw of P1 exopod-3 less than half the length of terminal claw and geniculate seta (Fig. 127C); P3 endopod-3 with 5 setae.
    .... ***Peltidium robustum***

    Skeletal strut pattern as in Fig. 127E; outer claw of P1 exopod-3 more than half the length of terminal claw and geniculate seta (Fig. 127H); P3 endopod-3 with 6 setae.
    .... ***Peltidium purpureum***

Peltidium robustum (Claus, 1889)

Morphological description: Lang (1948).

Habitat: On intertidal and shallow subtidal algae.

Distribution: Isles of Scilly, Dublin Bay.

Peltidium purpureum Philippi, 1839

Morphological description: Sars (1911).

Habitat: On intertidal and shallow subtidal algae.

Distribution: Devon, west coasts of Scotland, Ireland and Norway.

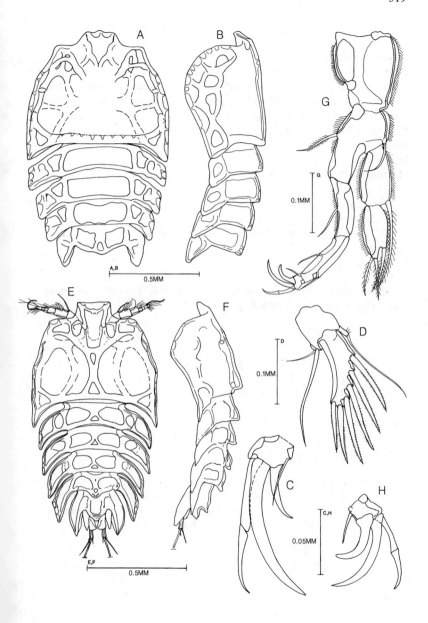

Fig. 127. *Peltidium robustum* female: A, prosome and first urosomite (dorsal view); B, prosome and first urosomite, lateral view; C, armature of P1 exopod-3; D, P5. *Peltidium purpureum* female: E, body (dorsal view); F, body (lateral view); G, P1; H, armature of P1 exopod-3.

Genus EUPELTE Claus, 1860

Diagnosis: Peltidiidae.

Body. Skeletal strut pattern virtually absent, cephalothorax sometimes with transverse chitinous ridge (Fig. 128A). Rostrum large and broad. Epimeral plates of free prosomites well-developed. Caudal rami short and broad, lamellar; with setae IV and V distinct.

Antennule. 9-Segmented in female.

Antenna. Exopod 2-segmented.

Mandible. Exopod present.

Maxilliped. Basis inflated or elongate with convex palmar margin; endopodal claw elongate.

P1 (Fig. 128B). Exopod-3 with four claw setae and one geniculate seta. Endopod 2-segmented.

P5 (Fig. 128C, D). Baseoendopod and exopod separate in both sexes.

Nine species known world-wide.

Local species. One, as yet unnamed, species has been recorded from Cornwall. Setal formula in Appendix Table 5 (p. 344).

Eupelte sp.

Morphological description: Undescribed (see Fig. 128).

Habitat: On shallow subtidal algae.

Distribution: Penwith Peninsula, Cornwall.

Note. There is a single, unconfirmed, record of *Eupelte gracilis* Claus, 1860, from the Isles of Scilly (Wells, 1970). Since all other northern hemisphere records of this species are from the Mediterranean, and the published descriptions are poor, it is omitted from the British fauna pending the discovery of new material.

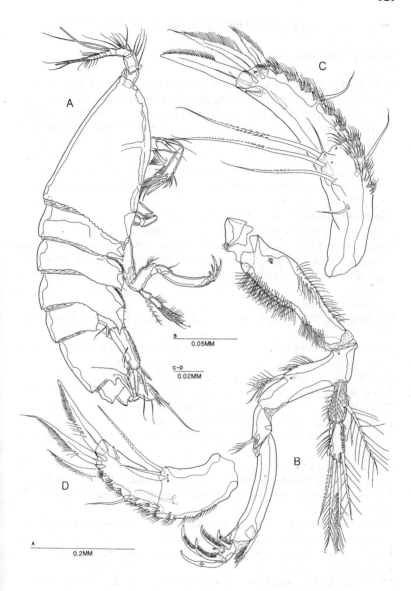

Fig. 128. *Eupelte* sp: A, habitus, female, lateral; B, P1; C, P5 female; D, P5 male.

Family MIRACIIDAE Dana, 1846

Synonym. Macrosetellidae A. Scott, 1909.

Diagnosis.

Body. Body cyclopiform or fusiform. Cephalothorax (Fig. 129A) with paired cuticular lenses anteriorly (secondarily reduced in *Macrosetella*: Fig. 130A). Dorsal surface of thoracic and abdominal somites without spinular ornamentation. Female genital double-somite without internal chitinous rib; P6 with one long and one or two short setae; genital pores located close to anterior margin; seminal receptacle median, trilobate. Anal operculum weakly developed; no pseudoperculum. Caudal rami parallel, as long or longer than last two urosomites combined; with seven setae; setae I-III closely set together; setae IV and V spinulose.

Antennule. Slender; 7- or 8-segmented in female; haplocer and 10-segmented in male, geniculation located between segments 7 and 8.

Antenna (Fig. 130B). Partial or complete allobasis without setae on abexopodal margin. Endopod 1-segmented, with one or two lateral spines, and three to five non-geniculate setae distally. Exopod absent or at most represented by bisetose segment.

Mouthparts reduced.

Mandible (Fig. 129B). Gnathobase reduced. Palp small, 1-segmented, with one or two setae.

Maxillule (Fig. 129C). Praecoxal arthrite with stubby armature elements. Palp reduced, with up to four setae; rami incorporated into palp.

Maxilla (Fig. 129D). Syncoxa with two endites, each with one or two setae. Allobasis drawn out into short strong claw; endopod completely incorporated.

Maxilliped (Fig. 129E) powerful, subchelate. Syncoxa and basis elongate. Basis with two vestigial setae and distal concavity delineated by anterior chitinous ridge. Endopod represented by anteriorly recurved claw and two to three accessory setae.

P1. Exopod 3-segmented, exopod-1 without inner seta, exopod-3 with three or four setae. Endopod 2-segmented; endopod-1 elongate, twice as long as endopod-2. In male inner margin of basis with raised spinular comb or distally produced process.

P2-P4. Protopods without surface ornamentation. Rami 3-segmented. Male P2 endopod (Fig. 129F) 2-segmented; endopod-2 a compound segment with one seta less than in female (outer terminal seta transformed into spinous process; outer spine modified).

P5. Exopod and baseoendopod separate in both sexes. Baseoendopods fused medially in male. Exopod with five to six setae / spines in female and four to six in male. Endopodal lobe with three to five setae / spines in female and two to three in male.

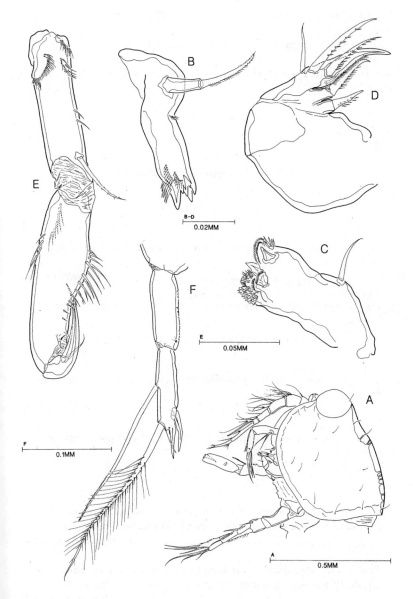

Fig. 129. *Miracia efferata* female: A, cephalothorax, lateral. *Macrosetella gracilis*: B, mandible; C, maxillule; D, maxilla; E, maxilliped; F, P2 endopod male.

Male P6. Plates symmetrical, slightly fused medially; with one to three setae.

Females with paired egg-sacs; males with one spermatophore.

Four genera known world-wide. Latest revision in Huys & Böttger-Schnack (1994).

Key to world genera of Miraciidae

1. Paired cephalic cuticular lenses absent; P1 exopod-3 with three setae / spines.
   .... *Macrosetella* (p. 326)

   Paired cephalic cuticular lenses present; P1 exopod-3 with four setae / spines.
   ....**2**

2. Cephalic cuticular lenses not touching mid-dorsally; P1 endopod-2 with two setae.
   ....*Distioculus* Huys & Böttger-Schnack, 1994

   Cephalic cuticular lenses touching mid-dorsally; P1 endopod-2 with three setae / spines.
   ....**3**

3. Rostrum well developed, defined at base; antennule 7-segmented in female; P5 baseoendopod with three setae in female, two setae in male.
   ....*Oculosetella* Dahl, 1895

   Rostrum minute, fused to cephalothorax; antennule 8-segmented in female; P5 baseoendopod with five setae in female, three setae in male.
   ....*Miracia* Dana, 1846

325

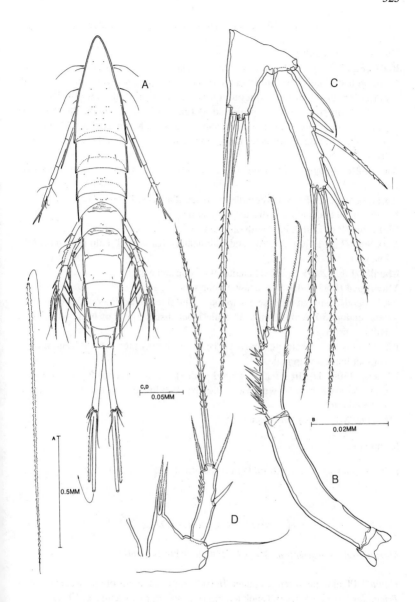

Fig. 130. *Macrosetella gracilis*: A, female body, dorsal; B, antenna; C, P5 female; D, P5 male.

326

Genus MACROSETELLA A. Scott, 1909

Diagnosis: Miraciidae.

Body (Fig. 130A). Fusiform, elongate; boundary between prosome and urosome not well defined. Cephalothorax pointed anteriorly, not ventrally deflected; cuticular lenses absent. Integument weakly chitinised, smooth. Rostrum moderate in size, ventrally projected, defined at base. Vestigial P6 of female genital field with one long and one short seta. Caudal ramus about 11 times as long as wide; seta V distinctly longer than entire body; setae IV and V fused at base.

Antennule. 8-segmented in female; aesthetascs on segments 4 and 8; seta on segment 1 absent.

Antenna (Fig. 130B). With completely fused allobasis. Exopod absent. Endopod with one lateral and three distal setae / spines.

Mandible (Fig. 129B). Palp with one seta.

Maxillule (Fig. 129C). Arthrite and rudimentary palp fused. Palp represented by one seta.

Maxilla (Fig. 129D). Syncoxal endites with one spine each.

Maxilliped (Fig. 129E). Syncoxa with one seta.

P1. Exopod-2 without inner seta, exopod-3 with three setae. Endopod-1 with inner seta, endopod-2 with 3 setae. In male inner distal corner of basis with large, bulbous process.

P2-P4. Intercoxal sclerites narrow. Basis without outer seta. P2 endopod-1 without inner seta in male.

P5 (Fig. 130C, D). In female, exopod with six setae, baseoendopod with four setae. In male, exopod with four setae, baseoendopod with two setae fused to endopodal lobe.

Male P6. With one or two short setae.

Monotypic.

Local species. One. Setal formula in Appendix Table 5 (p.344).

Macrosetella gracilis (Dana, 1847)

Morphological description: Huys & Böttger-Schnack (1994).

Habitat: Planktonic, often abundant. In (sub)tropical regions often associated with *Trichodesmium* colonies (Cyanobacteria) (Huys & Böttger-Schnack, 1994).

Distribution: World-wide in tropical and subtropical waters within the 15°C mean annual sea temperature isotherms (Steuer, 1935), but occasionally found further north in the Atlantic Ocean. Thompson (1903) recorded the species as plentiful in two samples from around 2000m depth off the west coast of Ireland (52°27'N; 15°40'W).

Acknowledgements

We would like to express our special thanks to Dr D. C. Geddes, formerly of the Department of Biology, Paisley College of Technology, for his assistance in the initiation of this volume, his valuable contribution to the first draft of the Darcythompsoniidae, Tegastidae, Porcellidiidae and Peltidiidae and for providing figures 124-127.

We are most grateful to Miss Sophie Conroy-Dalton (Zoology Department, The Natural History Museum) for compiling reference lists, organising material and helping in the preparation and proof-reading of this volume.

For the loan of material we wish to thank Prof. M. E. Christiansen (Zoologisk Museum, Oslo, Norway). Dr Ph. Bodin (Université de Bretagne Occidentale, Brest, France), Dr W. Mielke (Universität Göttingen, Germany), Dr J. M. C. Holmes (National Museum of Ireland), Dr A. Lindley (Sir Alister Hardy Foundation for Ocean Science and Plymouth Marine Laboratory), Dr P. G. Moore (University Marine Biological Station, Millport) and Mr R. Millward (University of East Anglia, Norwich).

Finally, we acknowledge the support and encouragement of Dr Doris M. Kermack, Dr Richard S. K. Barnes and Dr John H. Crothers, the editors involved with this book since its inception.

References

Battaglia, B., 1954. Microsistematica e analisi di popolazioni del genere *Porcellidium* (Copepoda Harpacticoida) - Le popolazioni del Golfe di Napoli. *Pubblicazioni della Stazione zoologica di Napoli*, **25**, 112-134.

Becker, K.-H., 1974. Eidonomie und Taxonomie abyssaler Harpacticoidea (Crustacea, Copepoda). Teil I. Cerviniidae - Ameiridae. *"Meteor" Forschungs-Ergebnisse*, **18**, 1-28.

Bocquet, C., 1948. Recherches sur les *Porcellidium* (Copépodes) de Roscoff. *Archives de Zoologie expérimentale et générale*, **85**, 237-259.

Bodin, P., 1968. Copépodes Harpacticoïdes des étages bathyal et abyssal du Golfe de Gascogne. *Mémoires du Museum nationale d'Histoire naturelle*, Sér. A, **55**, 1-107.

Bodin, P., 1970. Copépodes Harpacticoïdes marins des environs de La Rochelle, 1. Espèces de la vase intertidale de Châtelaillon. *Téthys*, **2**(2), 385-436.

Bodin, P., 1973. Copépodes Harpacticoïdes marins des environs de La Rochelle, 4. Espèces de la zone intertidale des Nauteries. *Téthys*, **4**(3), 651-682.

Bodin, P., 1979. Copépodes Harpacticoïdes marins des environs de La Rochelle, 5. Espèces nouvelles ou incertaines. *Vie et Milieu*, (A) **27** (3), 311-357.

Bodin, P., 1988. *Catalogue des nouveaux Copépodes Harpacticoïdes marins (Nouvelle édition)*. Université de Bretagne Occidentale, Laboratoire d'Océanographie Biologique. Brest, France. 288pp.

Bowman, T. E. &. Abele, L. G., 1982. Classification of the Recent Crustacea. In L. G. Abele (Ed.) *The Biology of Crustacea Volume 1. Systematics, the Fossil Record and Biogeography*. pp. 1-27. Academic Press. New York.

Boxshall, G. A., 1979. The planktonic copepods of the northeastern Atlantic Ocean: Harpacticoida, Siphonostomatoida and Mormonilloida. *Bulletin of the British Museum (Natural History). Zoology.*, **35**(3), 201-264.

Boxshall, G. A. & Huys, R., 1989. A new tantulocaridan (Crustacea: Tantulocarida) parasitic on harpacticoid copepods from an anchialine cave, with an analysis of the phylogenetic relationships of the Tantulocarida. *Journal of Crustacean Biology*, **9**, 126-140.

Božić, B., 1960. Le genre *Tigriopus* Norman (Copépodes Harpacticoïdes) et ses formes européennes; Recherches morphologiques et expérimentales. *Archives de Zoologie expérimentale et générale*, **98**, 167-269.

Bradford, J. M., 1967. The genus *Tigriopus* Norman (Copepoda, Harpacticoida) in New Zealand with a description of a new species. *Transactions of the Royal Society of New Zealand (Zoology)*, **10**(6), 51-59.

Brady, G. S., 1878. *A monograph of the free and semi-parasitic Copepoda of the British Islands 1*. The Ray Society, London, 148pp.

Brotskaya, V. A., 1963. A survey of the family Cerviniidae (Crustacea, Copepoda). *Zoologicheskij Zhurnal*, **42**(12), 1785-1803. (In Russian with English summary).

Campbell, M. H., 1929. Some free-swimming copepods of the Vancouver Island region. *Transactions of the Royal Society of Canada*, (3)**23**(5), 303-332.

Carli, A. & Fiori, A., 1977. Morphological analysis of the two *Tigriopus* species found along the European coasts (Copepoda, Harpacticoida). *Natura. Milano*, **68**, 101-110.

Ceccherelli, V. U. & Rossin, F., 1979. Contributo alla conoscenza degli arpacticoidi (Crustacea, Copepoda) delle "Valli di Comacchio", lagune polialine dell'alto Adriatico. *Bolletino del Museo Civico Storia Naturale di Verona*, **6**, 95-125.

Chappuis, P. A., 1936. Brasilianische Ruderfusskrebse (Crustacea, Copepoda) gesammelt von Herrn Dr. Otto Schubart. IV. Mitteilung. *Buletinul Societatii de stiinte din Cluj*, **8**, 450-461.

Chislenko, L. L., 1967. Copepoda Harpacticoida of the Karelian coast of the White Sea. *Gidrobiologicheskie issledovaniya na Karel'skom poberezh'e Belogo morya, Issled Fauny Morei*, **7**, 48-196.

Clément, M. & Moore, C. G., 1995. A revision of the genus *Halectinosoma* (Harpacticoida: Ectinosomatidae): a reappraisal of *H. sarsi* (Boeck) and related species. *Zoological Journal of the Linnean Society*, **114**, 247-306.

Codreanu, R. & Mack-Fira, V., 1961. Sur un Copépode, *Sunaristes paguri* Hesse 1867 et un Polychète, *Polydora ciliata* (Johnston) 1838, associés au Pagure, *Diogenes pugilator* (Roux) dans la mer Noire et de Méditerranée. La notion de cryptotropisme. *Rapport et Procès-Verbaux des Réunions de la Commission Internationale pour l'Exploration Scientifique de la Mer Méditerranée*, **16**(2), 471-494.

Coull, B. C., 1977. Marine flora and fauna of the northeastern United States. Copepoda: Harpacticoida. *NOAA Technical Report. NHFS Circular*, **399**, 1-48.

Dahms, H-U., 1990a. Naupliar development of Harpacticoida (Crustacea, Copepoda) and its significance for phylogenetic systematics. *Microfauna Marina*, **6**, 169-272.

Dahms, H-U., 1990b. The first nauplius and the copepodite stages of *Thalestris longimana* Claus, 1863 (Copepoda, Harpacticoida, Thalestridae) and their bearing on the reconstruction of phylogenetic relationships. *Hydrobiologia*, **202**, 33-60.

Dinet, A., 1974. Espèces nouvelles de Copépodes Harpacticoïdes (Crustacea) des sédiments profonds de la dorsale de Walvis. *Archives de Zoologie experiméntale et générale*, **115**, 549-576.

Drzycimski, I., 1968. Drei neue Harpacticoida (Copepoda) aus Westnorwegen. *Sarsia*, **36**, 55-64.

Drzycimski, I., 1969. Harpacticoida (Copepoda) of sea waters in Bergen region (West Coast of Norway) and their ecology. *Wyższa Szkola Rotnicza w Szczecinie Rozprawy*, **17**, 1-72. (In Polish with English and Russian summaries).

Dumont, H. J. & Maas, S., 1988. Five new species of leaf litter harpacticoids (Crustacea, Copepoda) from Nepal. *Zoologica Scripta*, **17**, 55-68.

Fiers, F., 1990. *Abscondicola humesi* n.gen., n.sp. from the gill chamber of land crabs and the definition of the Cancrincolidae n. fam. (Copepoda, Harpacticoida). *Bulletin de l'Institut Royal des Sciences naturelles de Belgique. Biologie*, **60**, 69-103.

Fleeger, J. W. & Clark, D. R., 1980. A revised key to *Leptocaris* (Copepoda, Harpacticoida), including a new species from a shallow estuarine lake in Louisiana, U.S.A. *Northeast Gulf Science*, **3**(2), 53-59.

Fleeger, J. W., Thistle, D. & Thiel, H., 1988. Sampling equipment. In Higgins, R.P. & Thiel, H. Eds. *Introduction to the study of meiofauna*. Smithsonian Institution Press, Washington D.C., London.

Geddes, D. C., 1968. Marine biological investigations in the Bahamas. 7. Harpacticoid copepods belonging to the families Porcellidiidae Sars, Peltidiidae Sars, and Tegastidae Sars. *Sarsia*, **35**, 9-56.

Gee, J. M., 1988a. Taxonomic studies on *Danielssenia* (Crustacea, Copepoda, Harpacticoida) with descriptions of two new species from Norway and Alaska. *Zoologica Scripta*, **17**, 39-53.

Gee, J. M., 1988b. Some harpacticoid copepods (Crustacea) of the family Tachidiidae from sublittoral soft sediments in Norway, the Celtic Sea and Gulf of Mexico. *Zoologica Scripta*, **17**, 181-194.

Gee, J. M. & Huys, R., 1990. The rediscovery of *Danielssenia intermedia* Wells, 1965 (Copepoda, Harpacticoida): a missing link between the 'danielsseniid' genera and *Paranannopus* Lang, 1936 (Paranannopidae). *Journal of Natural History*, **24**, 1549-1571.

Gee, J. M. & Huys, R., 1994. Paranannopidae (Copepoda: Harpacticoida) from sublittoral soft sediments in Spitsbergen. *Journal of Natural History*, **28**, 1007-1046.

Giesbrecht, W., 1882. Die freilebenden Copepoden der Kieler Foehrde. *VI. Jahresbericht der Commission zur Wissenschaftlichen Untersuchung der Deutschen Meere in Kiel*, Abt. 1, 87-168.

Glatzel, T., 1989. Comparative morphology of *Chappuisius inopinus* Kiefer and *C. singeri* Chappuis (Copepoda, Harpacticoida). *Zoologica Scripta*, **18**, 411-422.

Gotto, V., 1993. *Commensal and parasitic copepods associated with marine invertebrates (and whales)*. Synopses of the British Fauna (New Series) No 46 published for the Linnean Society of London and the Estuarine and Coastal Sciences Association by Universal Book Services/ Dr W. Backhuys. Oegstgeest, The Netherlands.

Gurney, R., 1920. A description of the copepod *Cylindropsyllus brevicornis* van Douwe, and of a new species of *D'Arcythompsonia* Scott. *Annals and Magazine of Natural History*, Ser. 9, **5**, 134-140.

Gurney, R., 1932. *British Fresh-water Copepoda*, 2. The Ray Society, London, i-ix, 1-336.

Hamond, R., 1969. Methods of studying the copepods. *Journal of the Quekett Microscopical Club*, **31**, 137-149.

Hamond, R., 1973. Four new copepods (Crustacea: Harpacticoida, Canuellidae) simultaneously occurring with *Diogenes senex* (Crustacea: Paguridae) near Sydney. *Proceedings of the Linnean Society of New South Wales*, **97**(3), 165-201.

Hamond, R., 1988. Non-marine harpacticoid copepods of Australia 1. Canthocamptidae of the genus *Canthocamptus* Westwood s.lat. and *Fibulacamptus*, gen. nov., and including the description of a related new species of *Canthocamptus* from New Caledonia. *Invertebrate Taxonomy*, **1**, 1023-1247.

Haq, S. M., 1965. Development of the copepod *Euterpina acutifrons* with special reference to dimorphism in the male. *Proceedings of the Zoological Society, London*, **144**, 175-201.

Harris, V. A. P., 1994. New species belonging to the family Porcellidiidae (Harpacticoida: Copepoda) from Kioloa, New South Wales, Australia. *Records of the Australian Museum*, **46**, 303-340.

Harris, V. A. P., & Robertson, H. M., 1994. New species belonging to the family Porcellidiidae (Harpacticoida: Copepoda) from the southern coast of New South Wales, Australia. *Records of the Australian Museum*, **46**, 257-301.

Heip, C., Warwick, R. M., Carr, M. R., Herman, P. M. J., Huys, R., Smol, N., & Van Holsbeke, K., 1988. Analysis of community attributes of the benthic meiofauna of Frierfjord/Langesundfjord. *Marine Ecology Progress Series*, **46**, 171-180.

Hicks, G. R. F., 1982. Porcellidiidae and Peltidiidae (Copepoda Harpacticoida) from the marine algae of St. Croix Island, Algoa Bay, South Africa. *Zoological Journal of the Linnean Society*, **75**, 49-90.

Hicks, G. R. F., 1986. Phylogenetic relationships within the harpacticoid copepod family Peltidiidae Sars, including the description of a new genus. *Zoological Journal of the Linnean Society*, **86**, 349-362.

Hicks, G. R. F., 1988. Systematics of the Donsiellinae Lang (Copepoda, Harpacticoida). *Journal of Natural History*, **22**, 639-684.

Hicks, G. R. F. & Coull, B. C., 1983. The ecology of marine meiobenthic harpacticoid copepods. *Oceanography and Marine Biology. Annual Review*, **21**, 67-175.

Hicks, G. R. F. & Schriever, G., 1983. A new genus and species of Ectinosomatidae (Copepoda, Harpacticoida) based on the original material of Dr. h.c. Walter Klie. *Mitteilungen aus dem Zoologischen Museum, Universität Kiel*, **2**(1), 1-7.

Holmes, J. M. C. & O'Connor, J. P., 1990. A provisional list of the Harpacticoida (Crustacea: Copepoda) of Ireland. *Bulletin of the Irish Biogeographical Society*, **13**, 44-130.

Huys, R., 1987. Some morphological observations on the Neobradyidae Olofsson, 1917 (Copepoda, Harpacticoida) including the redescription of *Antarcticobradya tenuis* (Brady 1910) comb. nov. *Bulletin de l'Institut Royal des Sciences naturelles de Belgique. Biologie*, **57**, 133-148.

Huys, R., 1988a. Sexual dimorphism in aegisthid cephalosomic appendages (Copepoda, Harpacticoida): a reappraisal. *Bijdragen tot de Dierkunde*, **58**, 114-136.

Huys, R., 1988b. Rotundiclipeidae fam. nov. (Copepoda, Harpacticoida) from an anchihaline cave on Tenerife, Canary Islands. *Stygologia*, **4**, 42-63.

Huys, R., 1990a. A new family of harpacticoid copepods and an analysis of the phylogenetic relationships within the Laophontoidea T. Scott. *Bijdragen tot de Dierkunde*, **60**(2), 79-120.

Huys, R., 1990b. A new harpacticoid copepod family collected from Australian sponges and the status of the sub-family Rhynchothalestrinae Lang. *Zoological Journal of the Linnean Society*, **99**, 51-115.

Huys, R., 1992. The amphiatlantic distribution of *Leptastacus macronyx* (T. Scott, 1892) (Copepoda: Harpacticoida): a paradigm of taxonomic confusion; and a cladistic approach to the classification of the Leptastacidae Lang, 1948. *Mededelingen van de Koninklijke Academie voor Wetenschappen, Letteren en Schone Kunsten van België*, **54**(4), 21-196.

Huys, R., 1993. Styracothoracidae (Copepoda: Harpacticoida), a new family from the Philippine deep sea. *Journal of Crustacean Biology*, **13**, 769-783.

Huys, R., 1995. A new genus of Canuellidae (Copepoda: Harpacticoida) associated with Atlantic bathyal sea-urchins. *Zoologica Scripta*, **24**(3), 225-243.

Huys, R., 1996. A revision of the Tachidiidae Boeck (Copepoda, Harpacticoida). *Zoological Journal of the Linnean Society*, In press.

Huys, R. & Böttger-Schnack, R., 1995. Taxonomy, biology and phylogeny of Miraciidae (Copepoda: Harpacticoida). *Sarsia*, **79**, 207-283.

Huys, R. & Boxshall, G. A., 1991. *Copepod Evolution*. Ray Society, London. No. 159, 468pp.

Huys, R. &. Gee, J. M., 1990. A revision of the family Thompsonulidae Lang grad. nov. (Copepoda Harpacticoida). *Zoological Journal of the Linnean Society*, **99**, 1-49.

Huys, R. &. Gee, J. M., 1992. A revision of *Danielssenia perezi* Monard, *D. paraperezi* Soyer, *D. eastwardae* Coull (Harpacticoida; Paranannopidae) and their transfer to a new genus. *Zoological Journal of the Linnean Society*, **104**, 31-56.

Huys, R. &. Gee, J. M., 1993. A revision of *Danielssenia* Boeck and *Psammis* Sars with the establishment of two new genera *Archisenia* and *Bathypsammis* (Harpacticoida: Paranannopidae). *Bulletin of the Natural History Museum (Zoology)*, **59**, 45-81.

Huys, R., Herman, P. M. J., Heip, C. H. R., & Soetaert, K., 1992. The meiobenthos of the North Sea: density, biomass trends and distribution of copepod communities. *ICES Journal of Marine Science*, **49**(1), 23-44.

Huys, R. & Willems, K., 1989. *Laophontopsis* Sars and the taxonomic concept of the Normanellinae (Copepoda: Harpacticoida): a revision. *Bijdragen tot de Dierkunde*, **59**(4), 203-227.

332

Itô, T., 1974. Descriptions and records of marine harpacticoid copepods from Hokkaido, V. *Journal of the Faculty of Science, Hokkaido University.* Ser. VI, Zoology, **19**, 546-640.

Itô, T., 1976. Descriptions and records of marine harpacticoid copepods from Hokkaido, VI. *Journal of the Faculty of Science, Hokkaido University.* Ser. VI, Zoology, **20**, 448-567.

Itô, T., 1982. Harpacticoid copepods from the Pacific abyssal off Mindanao 1. Cerviniidae. *Journal of the Faculty of Science, Hokkaido University.* Ser. VI, Zoology, **23**, 63-127.

Jakobi, H., 1972. Trends (Enp. P4 ♂) innerhalb der Parastenocariden (Copepoda, Harpacticoidea). *Crustaceana*, **22**, 127-146.

Kabata, Z., 1993. *Copepods parasitic on fishes.* Synopses of the British Fauna (New Series) No 47 published for the Linnean Society of London and the Estuarine and Coastal Sciences Association by Universal Book Services/ Dr W. Backhuys. Oegstgeest, The Netherlands.

Kiefer, F., 1967. Neue Copepoda Harpacticoida aus dem Amazonasgebiet. *Crustaceana*, **13**, 114-122.

Kikuchi, Y. & Yokota, K., 1984. New records of two freshwater harpacticoid copepods, *Nannopus palustris* Brady and *Leptocaris brevicornis* (van Douwe), in Lake Hinuma. *Publications of the Itako Hydrobiological Station*, **1**(1), 1-9.

Klie, W., 1927. Die Copepoda Harpacticoida von Helgoland. *Wissenschaftliche Meeresuntersuchungen der Kommission zur Wissenschaftlichen Untersuchung der Deutschen Meere. Abteilung Helgoland*, **16**(9), 1-20.

Klie, W., 1939. Diagnosen neuer Harpacticoiden aus den Gewässern um Island. *Zoologische Anzeiger*, **126**, 223-226.

Klie, W., 1949. Harpacticoida (Cop.) aus dem Bereich von Helgoland und der Kieler Bucht. I. *Kieler Meeresforschungen*, **6**, 90-128.

Krishnaswamy, S., 1957. *Studies on the Copepoda of Madras.* Thesis, University of Madras, 168 pp.

Kunz, H., 1935. Zur Oekologie der Copepoden Schleswig-Holsteins und der Kieler Bucht. *Schriften des Naturwissenschaftlichen Vereins für Schleswig-Holstein*, **21**, 84-132.

Kunz, H., 1974. Harpacticoiden (Crustacea, Copepoda) aus dem Küstengrundwasser der französischen Mittelmeerküste. *Zoologica Scripta*, **3**, 257-282.

Kunz, H., 1975. Copepoda Harpacticoidea aus dem Litoral des südlichen Afrika. I. Teil. *Kieler Meeresforschungen*, **31**, 179-212.

Lang, K., 1935. Beitrage zur Kenntnis der Harpacticiden 1. *Hemicervinia ryforsi* n.g. n.sp.. *Zoologischer Anzeiger*, **112**, 262-264.

Lang, K., 1944. *Monographie der Harpacticiden (Vorläufige Mitteilung)*, Uppsala: Almqvist & Wiksell. 39pp

Lang, K., 1948. *Monographie der Harpacticiden* 2 vols. Lund, Håkan Ohlsson's Bøktryckeri. Stockholm, Nordiska Bøkhandeln. 1682pp.

Lang, K., 1965. Copepoda Harpacticoidea from the Californian Pacific coast. *Kungliga Svenska Vetenskapsakademiens Handlingar*, (4)**10**(2), 1-560.

Lorenzen, S., 1969. Harpacticoiden aus dem lenitischen Watt und den Salzwiesen der Nordseeküste. *Kieler Meeresforschungen*, **25**, 215-223.

McIntyre, A. D. & Warwick, R. M., 1984. Meiofauna techniques. In Holme, N. A. & McIntyre, A. D. (Eds.) *Methods for the study of marine benthos.* 2nd Edition. I.B.P. Handbook No. 16. Blackwell Scientific Publications. Oxford.

McLachlan, A. & Moore, C. G., 1978. Three new species of Harpacticoida (Crustacea, Copepoda) from sandy beaches in Algoa Bay, South Africa, with keys to the genera *Arenosetella, Hastigerella, Leptastacus* and *Psammastacus. Annals of the South African Museum*, **76**, 191-211.

Mielke, W., 1975. Systematik der Copepoden eines Sandstrandes der Nordseeinsel Sylt. *Mikrofauna Meeresboden*, **52**, 1-134.

333

Mielke, W., 1979. Interstitielle Fauna von Galapagos. XXV - Longipediidae, Canuellidae, Ectinosomatidae (Harpacticoida). *Mikrofauna Meeresboden*, **77**, 1-106.

Mielke, W., 1981. Interstitielle Ectinosomatidae (Copepoda) von Panama. *Mikrofauna Meeresboden*, **85**, 1-45.

Mielke, W., 1986. Copepodos de la meiofauna de Chile, con descripcion de dos nuevas especies. *Revista Chilena de Historia Natural*, **59**, 73-86.

Mielke, W., 1994. Two co-occuring new *Karllangia* species (Copepoda: Ameiridae) from the Caribbean coast of Costa Rica. *Revista de Biologia Tropical*, **42**(1/2), 141-153.

Monard, A., 1926. Sur les *Harpacticus* de Banyuls. *Bulletin de la Société zoologique de France*, **51**, 419-434.

Monard, A., 1928. Les Harpacticoïdes marins de Banyuls. *Archives de zoologie expérimentale et générale*, **67**, 259-443.

Monard, A., 1935. Étude sur la faune des Harpacticoïdes marins de Roscoff. *Travaux de la Station biologique de Roscoff*, **13**, 5-88.

Montagna, P. A., 1981. A new species and a new genus of Cerviniidae (Copepoda: Harpacticoida) from the Beaufort Sea, with a revision of the family. *Proceedings of the Biological Society of Washington*, **93**, 1204-1219.

Moore, C. G., 1976. The harpacticoid families Ectinosomatidae and Diosaccidae (Crustacea, Copepoda) from the Isle of Man. *Journal of Natural History*, **10**, 131-155.

Moore, P. G., 1973. The kelp fauna of northeast Britain. II. Multivariate classification: turbidity as an ecological factor. *Journal of Experimental Marine Biology and Ecology*, **13**, 127-164. •

Noodt, W., 1955. Copepoda Harpacticoida von Teneriffa (Kanarische Inseln). *Zoologischer Anzeiger*, **154**, 200-222.

Noodt, W., 1964. Copepoda Harpacticoidea aus dem Litoral des Roten Meeres. *Kieler Meeresforschungen*, **20**, Sonderheft: 128-154.

Pallares, R., 1973. El genero *Harpacticus* en la Ria Deseado (Crustacea, Copepoda). *Physis*, (A), **32**(85), 275-288.

Perkins, E. J., 1956. The harpacticoid genus *Tetanopsis* Brady, with a description of *Tetanopsis smithi* sp. nov. and *Tetanopsis medius* sp. nov. *Annals and Magazine of Natural History*, (12) **9**, 497-504.

Pfannkuche, O. & Thiel, H. 1988. 9. Sample processing. In Higgins, R. P. & Thiel, H., Eds. *Introduction to the study of meiofauna*. Smithsonian Institution Press, Washington D.C., London.

Por, F. D., 1964a. A study of the Levantine and Pontic Harpacticoida (Crustacea, Copepoda). *Zoologische Verhandelingen. Rijksmuseum van Natuurlijke Historie te Leiden*, **64**, 1-128.

Por, F. D., 1964b. Les Harpacticoïdes (Crustacea, Copepoda) des fonds meubles du Skagerak. *Cahiers de Biologie marine*, **5**(3), 233-270.

Por, F. D., 1967. Level bottom Harpacticoida (Crustacea, Copepoda) from Elat (Red Sea) Part 1. *Israel Journal of Zoology*, **16**, 101-165.

Por, F. D., 1969. Deep sea Cerviniidae (Copepoda, Harpacticoida) from the western Indian Ocean collected with R/V Anton Bruun in 1964. *Smithsonian Contributions to Zoology*, **29**, 1-60.

Por, F. D., 1984. Canuellidae Lang (Harpacticoida, Polyarthra) and the ancestry of the Copepoda. In: Studies on Copepoda II. Proceedings of the First International Conference on Copepoda, Amsterdam, The Netherlands. *Crustaceana*, **suppl. 7**, 1-24.

Por, F. D., 1986. A re-evaluation of the family Cletodidae Sars, Lang (Copepoda, Harpacticoida). *Syllogeus*, **58**, 420-425.

Rao, G. Chandrasekhara & Ganapati, P. N., 1969. Some new interstitial copepods from Waltair coast. *Proceedings of the Indian Academy of Sciences*, (B) **69**(1), 1-14.

334

Redeke, H. C., 1953. On *D'Arcythompsonia neglecta*, a new harpacticid copepod from brackish water in Holland. *Beaufortia*, **26**, 1-8.

Reyne, A., 1950. Faure's vloeistof als insluitmiddel voor microscopische preparaten van kleine insecten. *Entomologische Berichten*, **13**(297), 37-42.

Roe, K., 1958. The littoral harpacticids of the Dalkey (Co.Dublin) area with descriptions of six new species. *Proceedings of the Royal Irish Academy*, **59**(B) (12), 221-255.

Sars, G. O., 1909. Crustacea. *Report of 2nd Norwegian Arctic Expedition "Fram" 1892-1902*, **18**, 1-42.

Sars, G. O., 1911. *An Account of the Crustacea of Norway*. Volume 5. Copepoda, Harpacticoida. Bergen Museum. Bergen. 449pp.

Sars, G. O., 1921. *An Account of the Crustacea of Norway*. Volume 7. Copepoda supplement. Bergen Museum. Bergen. 121pp.

Scott, T., 1899. Notes on recent gatherings of micro-Crustacea from the Clyde and the Moray Firth. *17th Annual Report of the Fishery Board for Scotland*, Part 3, 248-273.

Scott, T., 1900. Notes on gatherings of Crustacea, collected for the most part by the fishery steamer "Garland" and the steam trawler "St. Andrew" of Aberdeen, and examined during the year 1900. *19th Annual Report of the Fishery Board for Scotland*, Part 3, 235-281.

Scott, T., 1912. The Entomostraca of the Scottish National Antarctic Expedition, 1902-1904. *Transactions of the Royal Society of Edinburgh*, **48**(3), 521-599.

Scott, T. & Scott, A., 1893. Notes on Copepoda from the Firth of Forth: *Longipedia coronata*, Claus; and a preliminary description of an apparently new genus and species. *Annals of Scottish Natural History*, 1893, 89-94.

Shen, C. j. & Tai, A. y., 1963. On five new species, a new subgenus and a new genus of freshwater Copepoda (Harpacticoida) from the delta of the Pearl River, South China. *Acta Zoologica Sinica*, **15**, 417-432.

Soyer, J., 1970. Contribution a l'étude des Copépodes Harpacticoïdes de Méditerranée occidentale. 1, Cerviniidae Sars, Lang. *Vie et Milieu*, (B) **20**(2), 367-386.

Soyer, J., 1974. Contribution a l'étude des Copépodes Harpacticoïdes de Méditerranée Occidentale. 9. Le genre *Hastigerella* Nicholls (Ectinosomidae Sars, Olofsson). Systématique, écologie. *Vie et Milieu*, (A) **24**(1), 175-192.

Steuer, A., 1935. Die Copepodenfamilie der Macrosetellidae. *Sitzungsberichte der Akademie der Wissenschaften, Mathematisch-Naturwissenschaftliche Klasse. Wien*, **144**, Abteilung I: 391-399.

Stitt, E. R., Clough P. W., & Branham, S. E., 1948. *Practical bacteriology, hematology and parasitology*. 10th Edition. New York; Blakiston.

Thompson, I. C., 1893. Revised report on the Copepoda of Liverpool Bay. *Transactions of the Liverpool Biological Society*, **7**, 175-230.

Thompson, I. C., 1903. Report on the Copepoda obtained by Mr. George Murray F.R.S., during the cruise of the "Oceana" in 1898. *Annals and Magazine of Natural History*, (7)**12**, 1-36.

Tiemann, H., 1986. The functional morphology and histology of the genus *Porcellidium* (Copepoda Harpacticoida). *Syllogeus*, **58**, 487-493.

Vervoort, W., 1964. Free-living Copepoda from Ifaluk Atoll in the Caroline Islands. *Bulletin of the U.S. National Museum*, **236**, 1-431.

Warwick, R. M., 1988. The level of taxonomic discrimination required to detect pollution effects on marine benthic communities. *Marine Pollution Bulletin*, **19**, 259-268.

Watkins, R .L., 1987. Descriptions of new species of *Bradyellopsis* and *Perissocope* (Copepoda: Harpacticoida) from the California coast with revised keys to the genera. *Journal of Crustacean Biology*, **7**, 380-393.

335

Wells, J. B. J., 1965a. Two new genera of harpacticoid Copepods of the family Ectinosomidae. *Revista de Biologia*, **5**, 30-35.

Wells, J. B. J., 1965b. Copepoda (Crustacea) from the meiobenthos of some Scottish marine sub-littoral muds. *Proceedings of the Royal Society of Edinburgh*, (B) **69**(1), 1-33.

Wells, J. B. J., 1967. The littoral Copepoda (Crustacea) of Inhaca Island, Mozambique. *Transactions of the Royal Society of Edinburgh*, **67**(7), 189-358.

Wells, J. B. J., 1968. New and rare Copepoda Harpacticoida from the Isles of Scilly. *Journal of Natural History*, **2**, 397-424.

Wells, J. B. J., 1970. The marine flora and fauna of the Isles of Scilly. Crustacea: Copepoda: Harpacticoida. *Journal of Natural History*, **4**, 255-268.

Wells, J. B. J., 1976. *Keys to aid in the identification of marine harpacticoid copepods.* Department of Zoology, University of Aberdeen pp. 215.

Wells, J. B. J., 1978. Keys to aid in the identification of marine harpacticoid copepods. Amendment Bulletin No. 1. *Zoology Publications from Victoria University of Wellington*, **70**, 1-11.

Wells, J. B. J., 1979. Keys to aid in the identification of marine harpacticoid copepods. Amendment Bulletin No. 2. *Zoology Publications from Victoria University of Wellington*, **73**, 1-8.

Wells, J. B. J., 1980. A revision of the genus *Longipedia* Claus (Crustacea, Copepoda, Harpacticoida). *Zoological Journal of the Linnean Society*, **70**, 103-189.

Wells, J. B. J., 1981. Keys to aid in the identification of marine harpacticoid copepods. Amendment Bulletin No. 3. *Zoology Publications from Victoria University of Wellington*, **75**, 1-13.

Wells, J. B. J., 1983. Keys to aid in the identification of marine harpacticoid copepods. Amendment Bulletin No. 4. *Zoology Publications from Victoria University of Wellington*, **77**, 1-9.

Wells, J. B. J., 1985. Keys to aid in the identification of marine harpacticoid copepods. Amendment Bulletin No. 5. *Zoology Publications from Victoria University of Wellington*, **80**, 1-19.

Wells, J. B. J. & Rao, G. Chandrasekhara, 1987. Littoral Harpacticoida (Crustacea: Copepoda) from Andaman and Nicobar Islands. *Memoirs of the Zoological Survey of India*, **16**(4): 1-385.

Wells, J. B. J., Hicks G. R. F., & Coull, B. C., 1982. Common harpacticoid copepods from New Zealand harbours and estuaries. *New Zealand Journal of Zoology*, **9**, 151-184.

Glossary

Abdomen. The postgenital region of the body including the four posterior somites without appendages (although some taxonomists refer to the five posterior somites as the abdomen).

Accessory nuchal organ. A lateral nuchal organ on the cephalothorax and free prosomites.

Aesthetasc. A simple, tubular, thin-walled, sensory filament found on the antennules (and rarely on the mouthparts).

Allobasis. A compound segment resulting from the fusion of the basis and proximal endopod segment(s). Often present on the antenna and the maxilla.

Anal somite. The terminal body somite bearing the anal opening either dorsally or terminally.

Antennae. The second pair of cephalic appendages.

Antennules. The first pair of cephalic appendages.

Apophysis. An elongate process formed from an outgrowth of a segment or by modification of an armature element.

Armature. The spines and setae present on a segment or appendage.

Arthrite. A praecoxal endite on the maxillule bearing spines and setae around its distal margin.

Arthrodial membrane. The flexible membrane connecting body somites or limb segments.

Baseoendopod. The basal segment of the fifth leg resulting from the fusion of the basis and endopod.

Basis. The distal segment of the protopod.

Biramous. Two-branched, i.e., having both an exopod and endopod.

Caudal rami. The paired posterior appendages of the anal somite, typically bearing seven setae.

Cephalic shield. The dorsal covering of the cephalosome, formed by the fusion of the tergites of the first six (or seven) body somites.

Cephalon. The anterior region of the body comprising the first five appendage-bearing somites (i.e., antennules, antennae, mandibles, maxillules, maxillae).

Cephalosome. The anterior six appendage-bearing somites of the body covered by the cephalic shield; comprises the five cephalic somites and the first thoracic (maxilliped-bearing) somite.

Cephalothorax. The anterior seven appendage-bearing somites covered by the cephalic shield; comprises the cephalosome and the second (P1-bearing) thoracic somite.

Chirocer. The condition of the male antennule with the geniculation located between one very swollen, thick-walled segment and the apical segment.

Copepodite (copepodid). A post-naupliar stage in copepod development; in harpacticoids there are five stages prior to the adult (designated CI - CV).

Copulatory pore. The median pore (or pair of pores) on the second urosomite of the female leading to the seminal receptacles into which the spermatophore discharges after copulation.

Coupler. An alternative name for the intercoxal sclerite.

Coxa. The middle segment of the protopod in postmandibular appendages; the proximal segment of the protopod in the antennae and mandibles.

Endite. A medially-directed projection arising from the protopodal segments of an appendage.

Endopod (endopodite). The inner ramus of an appendage.

Endopod-1 (-2,-3). Denotes the proximal (median, distal) segment of the endopod.

Endopodal lobe. The inner lobe of the baseoendopod representing the fused endopod.

Endopsammic. The habit of burrowing into sediment.

Epimeron (plural: epimera). The lateral projection of a tergite of the free prosomites.

Epipodite. An exite on the coxa of the maxillules.

Epipsammic. The habit of living on or above the sediment surface.

Exite. A lateral projection on the outer margin of protopodal segments of an appendage.

Exopod (exopodite). The outer ramus of an appendage.

Exopod-1 (-2,-3). Denotes the proximal (median, distal) segment of the exopod.

Free prosomites. The three (or four) posterior somites of the prosome not fused to the cephalothorax (cephalosome), bearing P2 to P4 (and P1 if not fused to cephalosome).

Furcal rami. An alternative name for the caudal rami.

Geniculate. Knee-shaped. A seta with a definite point of flexion somewhere along its length. Most frequently applied to setae on the terminal endopod segment of the antennae or the distal segment of P1.

Geniculation. Well-developed articulation between proximal and distal regions of male antennules.

Genital antrum (atrium). The chamber in which the eggs are fertilized by sperm stored in the seminal receptacles.

Genital aperture. The external pore of the genital antrum through which the eggs emerge before being united into an egg mass.

Genital double-somite. The compound somite resulting from the fusion of the genital somite and third urosomite (= first abdominal somite) in females (and in male Tegastidae).

Genital somite. The second urosomite (last thoracic somite) bearing the P6 and gonopores.

Gnathobase. An endite of the mandibular coxa bearing distally the toothed cutting edge.

Gonochoristic. Having the sexes separate, producing distinct females and males.

Haplocer. The condition of the male antennule where the middle segments are only slightly modified and there are a number of segments distal to these.

Head. See cephalon.

Hyaline frill. The transparent membrane on the posterior margin of the somite or segment covering the arthrodial membrane.

Integument. The external covering layer of the body and its appendages.

Intercoxal sclerite. The ventral plate connecting the protopods of each member of a pair of swimming legs (and rarely maxillipeds).

Interpodal bar, intercoxal plate. Alternative names for the intercoxal sclerite.

Labrum. A posteroventrally directed outgrowth of the antennary somite forming the anterior border of the oral opening.

338

Major articulation. The point at which the abdomen bends most readily up or down, relative to the prosome. In harpacticoids, it lies between the P4- and P5-bearing somites.

Mandibles. The third pair of cephalic appendages.

Mandibular palp. The portion of the mandible distal to the coxa, comprising the basis, exopod and endopod.

Maxillae. The fifth pair of cephalic appendages.

Maxillipeds. The first pair of thoracic appendages, always incorporated in the cephalosome under the cephalic shield.

Maxillules. The fourth pair of cephalic appendages.

Mesopsammic. The habit of occupying the interstices between sediment particles.

Metasome. An alternative name for the free prosomites.

Microsetule. An extremely small setule often formed into rows on the integument.

Microspinule. A rigid microsetule.

Mucroniform process. A projection formed by the elongation of part of the integument of a segment.

Nauplius. The first larval stage in copepod development; in harpacticoids there are six naupliar stages (denoted NI - NVI) prior to metamorphosis to copepodite I.

Nuchal organ. A dorsal, presumably sensory organ found medially on the cephalothorax.

Operculum. A posteriorly directed extension of the dorsal wall of the anal somite covering the anus.

Oral opening. The mouth.

Ornamentation. The sculpturing and superficial rows or patches of spinules and denticles on the surface of the body and appendages (i.e., those surface structure that do not penetrate the integument).

P1-P6. An abbreviation referring to the first to sixth pereiopods.

Paragnaths. Paired ventral postoral lobes forming the posterior face of the oral opening.

Pediger. A somite bearing a pair of pereiopods.

Pereiopod. A thoracic walking (swimming) leg, usually biramous in harpacticoids (except for the sixth which is very reduced).

Phyllopodial. Leaf-like limb, used to describe one form of non-subchelate maxilliped.

Pinnate. A spine or seta with a row of setules or spinules on the lateral border.

Plumose. The condition of a pinnate seta when the pinnules are long and very fine.

Praecoxa. The proximal segment of the protopod of an appendage.

Precopulatory coupling. The posture when an adult male clasps an immature female before spermatophore transfer.

Prehensile. Referring to the condition of the P1 where at least the proximal segment of a ramus is elongate and at least one of the distal segments is short and bears one or more recurved or geniculate setae, the whole structure suggesting a clinging or grasping function.

Principal terminal seta. A term often used to describe caudal rami seta V, the inner terminal seta.

Prosome. The region of the body anterior to the major articulation.

Prosomite. A somite of the prosome.

Protopod (protopodite). The three basal (proximal) segments of an appendage, bearing the exopod and endopod.

Pseudoperculum. An outgrowth of the posterior dorsal margin of the penultimate urosomite covering at least part of the anus; often present in species with a deeply divided anal somite.

Ramus (plural: rami). A branch of an appendage; either the exopod or the endopod.

Rostrum. A small plate, projecting from the anterodorsal margin of the cephalic shield between the antennules.

Segment. A section of a jointed appendage.

Seminal receptacle. Part of the female genital apparatus in which sperm are stored after insemination.

Sensillum (plural: sensilla). A fine hair-like sensory filament projecting through the integument.

Seta (plural: setae). A tapering, flexible structure which is inserted into a hole passing right through the integument and with a central axial, hollow core.

Setal formula. A numerical code denoting the arrangement of setae / spines on an appendage or ramus.

Setophore. A cylindrical extension, often articulated, of the P5 basis bearing the outer basal seta.

Setule. A small flexible structure which is borne on (often in a depression of) the surface of the integument

Sexual dimorphism. Differences in body characteristics between the sexes of a given species.

Somite. A "segment" of the body.

Spermatophore. The small, oval or elongate body in which sperm is transferred from the male to the female.

Spine. A rigid seta, with substantially thicker walls than normal.

Spinule. A rigid setule.

Stenopodial. A long and narrow limb, most often used to describe a form of non-subchelate maxilliped.

Subchelate. The condition of the maxillipeds in which the endopod, equipped with one or more claw-like elements, is flexed inwards and capable of opposing the inner margin of the basis.

Subchirocer. The condition of the male antennule with the geniculation located between a swollen thick walled segment and the penultimate segment.

Syncoxa. A compound segment resulting from the fusion of the praecoxa and the coxa.

Tagmosis. The division of the body into functional regions (tagmata); see prosome and urosome.

Tergite. The dorsal plate of a somite, completely fused to the pleurite forming a pleurotergite.

Thorax. The middle region of the body delineated anteriorly by the maxillipedal somite and posteriorly by the genital (P6-bearing) somite (many taxonomists use P5-bearing somite as the posterior limit).

Thorn. A small, pointed, outgrowth of the integument.

Uniramous. Having a single ramus.

Urosome. The region of the body posterior to the major articulation. In harpacticoids the posterior six body somites constitute the urosome.

Urosomite. A somite of the urosome.

Appendix

Setal formulae of local genera and/or species. For explanation of setal formulae see page 14.

Table 1.

	P1		P2		P3		P4	
LONGIPEDIIDAE								
Longipedia coronata	1.1.123	1.1.122	1.1.222	1.2.231	1.1.222	1.2.321	1.1.122	1.2.022
L. helgolandica/scotti (female)	1.1.123	1.1.122	1.1.222	1.2.231	1.1.222	1.2.321	1.1.122	1.2.022
L. helgolandica/scotti (male)	1.1.123	1.1.122	1.1.222	1.2.230	1.1.222	1.2.321	1.1.122	1.2.022
L. minor (female)	1.1.123	1.1.122	1.1.222	1.0-1.231	1.1.222	1.2.321	1.1.122	1.2.022
L. minor (male)	1.1.123	1.1.122	1.1.222	1.0-1.230	1.1.222	1.2.321	1.1.122	1.2.022
CANUELLIDAE								
Brianola sp.	0.1.5	1.1.4	0.1.4	1.1.5	0.1.4	1.1.4	0.0.4	1.0.4
Canuella spp.	0.1.7	1.1.6	0.1.7	1.1.5	0.1.5	1.1.4	0.1.5	1.0.4
Canuellopsis swedmarki	0.9	1.1.6	0.1.5	1.1.5	0.1.4	1.1.4	0.0.4	1.0.4
Sunaristes paguri	0.1.7	1.1.6	0.1.7	1.1.5	0.1.5	1.1.3	0.1.4	1.0.3
CERVINIIDAE								
Cervinia bradyi	1.1.123	1.1.221	1.1.223	1.2.221	1.1.223	1.2.321	1.1.223	1.2.221
Cervinia synarthra	1.1.123	1.1.221	1.1.223	1.321	1.1.223	1.421	1.1.223	1.321
Cerviniopsis spp.	1.1.023	1.1.121	1.1.223	1.2.221	1.1.223	1.2.321	1.1.223	1.2.221
Eucanuella spinifera	1.1.123	1.1.021	1.1.223	1.2.221	1.1.223	1.2.221	1.1.223	1.1.221
Hemicervinia stylifera	1.1.123	1.320	1.1.223	1.2.221	1.1.223	1.2.321	1.1.223	1.1.221

Table 2.

	P1		P2		P3		P4	

ECTINOSOMATIDAE

	P1		P2		P3		P4	
Arenosetella germanica	0.1.122	1.1.121	0-1.1.122	1.2.121	0-1.1.1-222	1.2.121	0-1.1.1-222	1.2.121
Arenosetella tenuissima	0.1.122	1.2.120	0.1.122	1.2.120	0.1.122	1.2.120	0.1.222	1.2.120
Bradya furcata	0.1.123	1.1.221	1.1.223	1.2.221	1.1.323	1.1.221	1.1.323	1.1.221
Bradya proxima	0.1.123	1.1.221	1.1.223	1.1.221	1.1.223	1.1.221	1.1.323	1.1.221
Bradya (other species)	0.1.123	1.1.221	1.1.223	1.1.221	1.1.323	1.1.321	1.1.323	1.1.221
Ectinosoma spp.	0.1.123	1.1.221	1.1.222-3	1.1.221	1.1.2-322-3	1.1.221	1.1.2-322-3	1.1.221
Ectinosomella nitidula	0.1.123	1.1.121	1.1.223	1.2.221	1.1.323	1.2.221	1.1.323	1.1.221
Halectinosoma spp.	0.1.122-3	1.1.221	1.1.222-3	1.1.221	1.1.2-322-3	1.1.221	1.1.2-322-3	1.1.221
Halophytophilus similis	0.1.123	1.020	1.1.223	1.1.221	1.1.323	1.1.221	1.1.323	1.1.221
Halophytophilus spinicornis	0.1.123	1.121	1.1.223	1.1.221	1.1.323	1.1.221	1.1.323	1.1.221
Hastigerella bozici	0.1.122	1.1.220	0.1.222	1.1.220	0.1.222	1.1.220	0.1.222	1.1.220
Hastigerella leptoderma	0.1.122	1.2.221	1.1.122	1.2.221	1.1.122	1.2.221	1.1.122	1.2.221
Hastigerella psammae	0.1.122	1.1.221	1.1.222	1.1.221	1.1.222	1.1.221	1.1.222	1.1.221
Hastigerella scheibeli	0.1.122	1.1.221	0-1.1.222	1.1.321	0-1.1.222	1.1.321	0-1.1.222	1.1.321
Klieosoma triarticulatum	0.1.123	1.1.121	1.1.223	1.1.221	1.1.323	1.1.221	1.1.322	1.1.221
Lineosoma iscensis	0.0.021	1.1.120	1.1.021	1.1.120	1.1.021	1.1.221	1.1.021	1.1.221
Microsetella spp.	0.1.122	1.1.221	1.1.222	1.1.221	1.1.322	1.1.221	1.1.322	1.1.221
Noodtiella gracile	0.1.021	1.120	1.1.021	1.121	1.1.021	1.121	1.121	1.120
Pseudectinosoma minor	0.1.122	1.221	0.1.222	1.221	0.1.322	1.221	0.1.322	1.221
Pseudobradya spp.	0.1.122-3	1.1.221	1.1.222-3	1.1-2.221	1.1.2-322-3	1.1-2.221	1.1.2-322-3	1.1.221
Sigmatidium difficile	0.1.022	1.321	0.1.422	1.1.121	0.1.422	1.1.121	0.1.422	1.1.121

Table 3.

	P1		P2		P3		P4	
NEOBRADYIDAE								
Marsteinia typica	0.1.122	1.1.121	0.1.223	1.1.221	0.1.223	1.1.221	0.1.223	1.1.221
Marsteinia similis	0.1.122	1.1.121	0.1.223	1.1.221	0.1.323	1.1.221	0.1.323	1.1.221
Neobradya pectinifera	0.0.122	0.1.021	0.0.112	0.211	0.0.112	0.211	0.0.122	0.111
DARCYTHOMPSONIIDAE								
Darcythompsonia fairliensis	0.0.022	0.111	0.1.122	0.121	0.1.222	0.121	0.1.222	1.121
Darcythompsonia neglecta	0.0.022	0.111	0.1.022	0.121	0.1.122	0.121	0.1.122	1.121
Leptocaris brevicornis	0.0.022	1.111	0.0.022	0.121	0.0.122	0.121	0.0.122	0.121
Leptocaris minutus (female)	0.0.211	1.120	0.0.022	0.120	0.0.022	0.120	0.0.022	0.120
Leptocaris minutus (male)	0.0.211	1.120	0.0.022	0.120	0.0.022	0.220	0.0.022	0.220
Leptocaris trisetosus	0.0.022	1.111	0.0.022	1.121	0.0.122	0.121	0.0.122	0.121
EUTERPINIDAE								
Euterpina acutifrons								
(female)	0.223	1.321	1.1.222	1.2.221	1.1.222	1.2.221	1.1.122	1.1.221
(Large male)	0.223	1.321	1.1.222	1.221	1.1.222	1.2.221	1.1.122	1.1.221
(Small male)	0.223	1.321	1.1.222	1.321	1.1.222	1.2.221	1.1.122	1.1.221
TACHIDIIDAE								
Geeopsis incisipes (female)	0.1.123	1.1.221	1.1.222	1.2.221	1.1.222	1.2.222	1.1.122	1.2.221
Geeopsis incisipes (male)	0.1.123	1.1.221	1.1.222	1.2.021	1.1.222	1.2.222	1.1.122	1.2.221
Microarthridion fallax	0.1.123	0.1.221	0.1.222	0.1.221	0.1.222	0.1.321	0.1.122	0.1.221
Microarthridion littorale	0.1.123	0.1.221	0.1.222	0.2.221	0.1.222	0.2.321	0.1.122	0.1.221
Microarthridion reductum	0.1.123	0.1.221	0.1.222	0.2.221	0.1.222	0.2.321	0.1.122	0.1.221
Tachidius discipes (female)	0.1.122	1.1.221	1.1.222	1.2.221	1.1.222	1.2.221	1.1.122	1.1.221
Tachidius discipes (male)	0.1.122	1.1.221	1.1.222	1.2.021	1.1.222	1.2.221	1.1.122	1.1.221
THOMPSONULIDAE								
Thompsonula hyaenae	0.1.022	1.1.121	1.1.223	1.1.221	1.1.223	1.1.321	1.1.323*	1.1.221

* distal inner seta minute

Table 4.

	P1		P2		P3		P4	

DANIELSSENIIDAE

	P1		P2		P3		P4	
Danielssenia typica	0.1.023	1.121	0.1.223	1.1.221	0.1.223	1.1.221	0.1.323	1.1.121
Fladenia robusta (female)	0.1.023	1.121	1.1.223	1.1.221	1.1.223	1.1.221	1.1.223	1.1.121
Fladenia robusta (male)	0.1.023	1.121	1.1.223	1.1.221	1.1.223	1.1.321	1.1.223	1.1.221
Jonesiella fusiformis	0.1.023	1.121	1.1.223	1.2.221	1.1.323	1.1.321	1.1.323	1.1.221
Micropsammis noodti	0.1.023	1.121	1.1.123	0.0.021*	1.1.123	0.1.021*	1.1.122	0.0.021*
Paradanielssenia biclavata	0.1.023	1.121	1.1.223	1.1.221	1.1.223	1.1.321	1.1.323	1.1.221
Paranannopus triarticulatus (female)	0.1.023	0.111	1.1.123	1.020	1.1.123	1.020	1.1.123	1.020
Paranannopus triarticulatus (male)	0.1.023	0.111	1.1.223	1.1.221	1.1.323	1.1.221	1.1.323	1.221
Paranannopus sp.	0.1.023	1.111	1.1.123	3	1.1.123	2	1.1.123	2
Psammis longisetosa	0.1.023	1.121	1.1.123	1.2.221	1.1.223	1.1.321*	1.1.223	1.1.221*
Telopsammis secunda	0.1.023	1.121	1.1.023	0.1.021*	1.1.022	0.0.011	1.1.022	0.0.011

HARPACTICIDAE P1 highly modified so not included.

	P1		P2		P3		P4	
Harpacticus chelifer			1.1.223	1.1.221	1.1.323	1.1.321	1.1.323	1.1.221
Harpacticus compsonyx			1.1.123	1.1.120	1.1.223	1.1.321	1.1.323	1.1.221
Harpacticus flexus			1.1.223	1.1.221	1.1.323	1.1.321	1.1.323	1.1.221
Harpacticus giesbrechti			1.1.223	1.1.221	1.1.323	1.1.321	1.1.323	1.1.221
Harpacticus littoralis			1.1.223	1.1.221	1.1.323	1.1.321	1.1.323	1.1.221
Harpacticus obscurus			1.1.223	1.1.221	1.1.323	1.1.321	1.1.323	1.1.221
Harpacticus septentrionalis			1.1.223	1.2.221	1.1.323	1.1.321	1.1.323	1.1.221
Harpacticus uniremis			1.1.223	1.2.221	1.1.323	1.1.321	1.1.323	1.1.221
Perissocope adiastaltus			0.1.323	0.1.221	0.1.323	1.1.321	0.1.323	1.1.221
Perissocope sp.			0.1.223	0.1.221	0.1.323	1.1.321	0.1.322	1.1.221
Tigriopus brevicornis			1.1.223	1.1.121	1.1.223	1.1.121	1.1.323	1.0.121
Zaus abbreviatus (female)			1.1.223	1.2.221	1.1.323	1.1.321	1.1.323	1.1.221
Zaus caeruleus			1.1.223	1.2.221	1.1.323	1.1.321	1.1.323	1.1.221
Zaus goodsiri			1.1.223	1.1.221	1.1.323	1.1.321	1.1.323	1.1.221
Zaus spinatus (female)			1.1.223	1.2.221	1.1.323	1.1.321	1.1.323	1.1.221
Zaus spinatus (male)			1.1.223	1.1.221	1.1.323	1.1.321	1.1.323	1.1.221

*: inner terminal seta minute.

344

Table 5.

	P1		P2		P3		P4	
TEGASTIDAE P1 with 1-segmented rami not included								
Parategastes sphaericus			1.222	1.2.221	1.322	1.2.321	0.1.222	1.1.021
Tegastes clausi			1.1.222	1.2.221	1.1.322	1.2.321	0.1.322	1.2.221
Tegastes falcatus			1.1.222	1.2.221	1.1.322	1.2.321	0.1.322	1.2.221
Tegastes flavidus			1.1.222	1.2.221	0.1.322	1.2.321	0.1.322	1.2.221
Tegastes grandimanus			1.1.222	1.2.221	1.1.322	1.2.321	0.1.322	1.2.221
Tegastes longimanus			1.1.222	1.2.221	0.1.322	1.2.321	0.1.322	1.2.221
Tegastes nanus			1.1.222	1.2.221	0.1.322	1.2.321	0.1.322	1.2.221
Tegastes satyrus			1.1.222	1.2.221	1.1.322	1.2.221	0.1.322	0.2.121
CLYTEMNESTRIDAE								
Clytemnestra rostrata	021	1.1.220	1.1.222	1.2.221	1.1.323	1.2.321	1.1.323	1.2.221
Clytemnestra scutellata	121	1.1.220	1.1.223	1.2.221	1.1.323	1.2.321	1.1.323	1.2 221
PORCELLIDIIDAE								
Porcellidium spp.	0.0.123	1.2	1.1.223	1.2.121	1.1.323	1.2.221	1.1.323	1.1.121
PELTIDIIDAE								
Alteutha depressa	0.1.5	1.1.221	1.1.223	1.2.221	1.1.323	1.2.321	1.1.323	1.2.221
Alteutha interrupta	0.1.5	1.1.221	1.1.223	1.2.221	1.1.323	1.2.321	1.1.323	1.2.221
Alteutha oblonga	0.1.5	1.0.221	0.1.223	1.2.221	0.1.323	1.2.(2)321	0.1.323	1.2.221
Alteutha roeae	0.1.5	1.1.211	1.1.223	1.1.220	1.1.323	1.1.220	1.1.323	1.1.220
Peltidium purpureum	0.1.4	1.120	1.1.223	1.2.120	1.1.323	1.2.321	1.1.323	1.2.220
Peltidium robustum	0.1.4	1.120	1.1.223	1.2.120	1.1.323	1.1.320	1.1.323	1.2.220
Eupelte sp.	0.1.5	1.121	0.1.223	1.2.221	0.1.323	1.2.221	0.1.323	1.2.221
MIRACIIDAE								
Macrosetella gracilis	0.0.021	1.021	0.1.222	0.2.121	0.1.322	1.1.221	0.1.322	0.1.221

Index of families, genera and species

Valid generic and specific names are printed in *italics*; synonyms in roman type. Figures are <u>underlined</u> and the principal reference to a family or genus is in **bold**. Setal formulae, in the appendix tables, are (in brackets).

Note that the descriptions of families and genera start on p.116. Pages 34 to 42 list the local genera. Pages 43 to 114 contain the ordinal and family keys.

352